MUSIC
BOO

Geoff Tibballs

This is a Parragon Book
First published in 2002

Parragon
Queen Street House
4 Queen Street
Bath BA1 1 HE, UK

Produced by Magpie Books, an imprint of
Constable & Robinson Ltd, London

ISBN 0-75256-948-1

A copy of the British Library Cataloguing-in-Publication Data
is available from the British Library

Printed and bound in the EU

ACKNOWLEDGEMENTS
Illustrations courtesy of Slatter-Anderson, London

Contents

Pot Luck I

Answers on page 8

1. With which group did Belinda Carlisle sing lead vocals before going solo in 1985?

2. Which legendary blues artist was born McKinley Morganfield?

3. Which band's debut single was 'Caught By The Fuzz'?

4. Who played guitar under the name L'Angelo Mysterioso on Cream's 'Badge'?

5. Which 17-year-old unknown replaced guitarist Bernard Butler in Suede?

6. Which duo had a hit with 'Only One Woman' in 1968?

7. Who sang the Crowded House number 'Don't Dream It's Over' at the Nelson Mandela concert at Wembley Stadium in 1988?

8. Which singer did The Nice back in their early days?

9. What was S Club 7's first number one?

10. Which former girlfriend was the subject of Neil Sedaka's 'Oh Carol'?

11. To what did The Farinas change their name in the Sixties?

12. Which band reached number eight in the charts in 1985 with 'Johnny Come Home'?

13. In what year were Radiohead formed?

14. In which city were Super Furry Animals founded?

15. In which band did Dave Stewart and Annie Lennox first enjoy chart success?

16. Who released a 1987 album called 'Document'?

Answers to page 8
EIGHTIES I: **1.** 'True' **2.** Nine **3.** Everything But The Girl **4.** Deborah Harry **5.** Frankie Goes To Hollywood **6.** Chris de Burgh ('Lady In Red') **7.** Forties **8.** Orchestral Manoeuvres In The Dark **9.** 'The Model' **10.** 1981 **11.** 'Morning Train' **12.** 'Don't You Want Me' (Human League) **13.** It was the first new UK number one of the Eighties **14.** Soft Cell **15.** Def Leppard **16.** 1984

R & B 1

Answers on page 9

1. Which group released 'Ghetto Romance'?

2. Which Destiny's Child single was the soundtrack to the Charlie's Angels movie?

3. The album 'Fanmail' was by which band?

4. Sisqo used to be the lead singer of which group?

5. Who had a recent hit with 'Money'?

6. Who made the album 'TP-2.COM'?

7. Who released 'Things I've Seen'?

8. Stargate remixed for Sisqo, but in which country are their studios?

9. What record label are Fierce signed to?

10. What was the title of Shola Ama's first UK single?

11. What was Honeyz first album called?

12. What was Another Level's first UK number one single?

13. Which other solo artist sang on R. Kelly's hit 'I'm Your Angel' in November 1998?

14. Whitney Houston's 'I Will Always Love You' was recorded by which artist in 1974?

15. What is Usher's record label?

16. What was Jennifer Lopez's first single?

Answers to page 9
NAME CHANGES 1: **1.** Blur **2.** Radiohead **3.** The Bay City Rollers **4.** Simon and Garfunkel **5.** Marmalade **6.** Madness **7.** Depeche Mode **8.** Middle Of The Road **9.** The Who **10.** Blondie **11.** Johnny Kidd and The Pirates **12.** The Beach Boys **13.** Talking Heads **14.** Procul Harum **15.** Kajagoogoo **16.** The Byrds

Eighties 1

Answers on page 6

1. What was Spandau Ballet's only number one?

2. How many weeks did Dire Straits' 'Brothers In Arms' spend at the top of the US album charts?

3. Who had a 1988 hit with their version of Danny Whitten's 'I Don't Want To Talk About It'?

4. Whose debut solo album was 'Koo Koo' in 1981?

5. Nasher Nash, Mark O'Toole and Peter Gill were members of which band?

6. Which singer, born Christopher John Davidson, spent three weeks at number one in August 1986 with a song he wrote for his wife?

7. In which decade was Mark Knopfler born?

8. Who reached number three in the UK album charts with 'Architecture And Morality'?

9. Which Kraftwerk number one was officially the B-side of 'Computer Love'?

10. In which year did Bucks Fizz win the Eurovision Song Contest?

11. What was Sheena Easton's '9 To 5' re-titled in the US?

12. What was the biggest-selling UK single of 1981?

13. What was significant about The Pretenders' 'Brass In Pocket'?

14. David Ball was the less flamboyant member of which duo?

15. Who released the 1987 album 'Hysteria'?

16. In which year did Madonna first enter the UK singles charts?

Answers to page 6
POT LUCK 1: **1.** The Go-Go's **2.** Muddy Waters **3.** Supergrass
4. George Harrison **5.** Richard Oakes **6.** Marbles **7.** Paul Young
8. P.P. Arnold **9.** 'Bring It All Back' **10.** Carole King **11.** Family **12.** Fine
Young Cannibals **13.** 1991 **14.** Cardiff **15.** The Tourists **16.** R.E.M.

Name Changes 1

Answers on page 7

1. Which band used to be called Seymour?

2. Who were once known as On A Friday?

3. Which teenybop favourites were formerly called The Saxons?

4. Who changed their name from Tom and Jerry?

5. Who wisely decided to dispense with the name Dean Ford and The Gaylords?

6. Which band were previously called The Invaders?

7. Who were once called Composition Of Sound?

8. To what did Los Caracas change their name?

9. Which Sixties band used to be called The High Numbers?

10. Which American band were once known as The Stilettos?

11. What did Freddie Heath and The Nutters Become?

12. Who were formerly known as Carl and The Passions?

13. Who changed their name from The Artistics?

14. Which Sixties band chose something more Latin than The Paramounts?

15. Who used to be known as Art Nouveau?

16. Who were once called The Beefeaters?

Answers to page 7
R & B 1: **1.** Damage **2.** 'Independent Women' **3.** TLC **4.** Dru Hill
5. Jamelia **6.** R. Kelly **7.** Spooks **8.** Norway **9.** Wildstar **10.** 'You Might Need Somebody' **11.** 'Wonder No. 8' **12.** 'Freak Me' **13.** Celine Dion **14.** Dolly Parton **15.** LaFace **16.** 'If You Had My Love'

Chart Toppers 1

Answers on page 12

1. Which singer reached number one in 1973 with 'Get Down'?

2. In which year did Shakespeares Sister get to number one with 'Stay'?

3. Which group's only number one was 'All Or Nothing'?

4. What was the first reggae record to top the UK charts?

5. For which artist was Kelly Marie's 'Feels Like I'm In Love' originally intended?

6. Which band topped the singles charts in 1999 – 19 years after their previous number one?

7. Which two artists took 'Mary's Boy Child' to number one in the UK?

8. How many number ones did B*Witched have in 1998?

9. With which song did The Bee Gees top the UK charts in October 1967?

10. Which female artist went 'All Around The World' in 1989?

11. Who reached number one in September 1956 with 'Lay Down Your Arms'?

12. What was Christie's only UK number one?

13. From which Boomtown Rats album did 'Rat Trap' come?

14. Who took a Rodgers and Hammerstein song to number one in 1982?

15. Who asked 'Would I Lie To You' in 1992?

16. Which was the first official Stock/Aitken/Waterman production to top the UK charts?

Answers to page 12
BOY BANDS 1: **1.** Blue **2.** RCA **3.** 'Love Me For A Reason' **4.** *North Hollywood High* **5.** Ten **6.** 1995 **7.** *Bean: The Movie* **8.** Mark **9.** 'Do We Rock' **10.** 1996 **11.** Shane Lynch **12.** Two **13.** O-Town **14.** The Moffatts **15.** 'Promises' **16.** 'Relight My Fire'

Albums I

Answers on page 13

1. Which distinctive-looking band released 'Kimono My House'?

2. Which Scottish band topped the UK album charts in 1989 with 'When The World Knows Your Name'?

3. The single 'Pride (In The Name Of Love)' was taken from which U2 album?

4. What was the title of Prince's first number one UK album?

5. Who were 'Nicely Out Of Tune' in 1970?

6. Who had a number one album in 1989 with 'Crossroads'?

7. Which Pulp album spawned 'Common People'?

8. Which Simple Minds album spent a total of 83 weeks in the UK charts?

9. Which two bands made albums called 'Raising Hell'?

10. Which Lou Reed album was re-issued for a second time in 1998?

11. Which Rolling Stones album topped the UK charts in September 1973?

12. Whose second album was titled 'Meat Is Murder'?

13. Which boy band's 1993 number one album reminded them of their home town?

14. Which former soap star's debut album was called 'Ten Good Reasons'?

15. Whose greatest hits album was titled 'Sex Machine'?

16. Whose best-selling album was the 1989 offering 'The Twelve Commandments Of Dance'?

Answers to page 13
SOLO ARTISTS 1: **1.** Harry Chapin **2.** Bill Withers **3.** Eddi Reader
4. Slim Whitman **5.** 'She's The One' **6.** Freda Payne **7.** Dusty Springfield
8. Gary Moore **9.** Gladys Knight **10.** Gene Pitney **11.** 'In The Air Tonight'
12. Cuba **13.** Celine Dion **14.** Randy Crawford **15.** Jacques Brel **16.** 14

Boy Bands 1

Answers on page 10

1. Which group released the single 'All Rise' in 2001?

2. What is Westlife's record label?

3. What was the title of Boyzone's first single?

4. Which Channel 4 TV programme featured 'Bomb Diggy' by Another Level?

5. What number did Five's first single get to in the UK charts?

6. In which year did Backstreet Boys release their first single?

7. From which film was Boyzone's 'Picture Of You'?

8. Which member of a1 played the piano in the performances of 'Everytime'?

9. What was the title of Point Break's first UK single?

10. In which year was 911's first UK single released?

11. Which member of Boyzone was studying an architecture course when he was recruited for the band?

12. What number in the UK charts did the album 'Westlife' reach?

13. Trevor, Ashley and Jacob are members of which boy band?

14. 'Chapter 1: A New Beginning' was which group's debut album?

15. What was the title of Take That's first single?

16. Which Take That single featured Lulu?

Answers to page 10

CHART TOPPERS 1: **1.** Gilbert O'Sullivan **2.** 1992 **3.** The Small Faces **4.** 'Israelites' (Desmond Dekker) **5.** Elvis Presley **6.** Blondie ('Maria') **7.** Harry Belafonte and Boney M **8.** Three – 'C'est La Vie', 'Rollercoaster' and 'To You I Belong' **9.** 'Massachusetts' **10.** Lisa Stansfield **11.** Anne Shelton **12.** 'Yellow River' **13.** 'Tonic For The Troops' **14.** Captain Sensible ('Happy Talk') **15.** Charles & Eddie **16.** 'Respectable' (Mel and Kim)

Solo Artists 1

Answers on page 11

1. Who directed the Oscar-nominated film *Legendary Champions* in 1968 before turning to music?

2. Which American soul singer used to be employed producing toilet seats for Boeing 747s at a Los Angeles aerospace factory?

3. Which former session singer went solo after Fairground Attraction disbanded?

4. Which American artist had 1955 hits with 'Rose Marie' and 'Indian Love Call'?

5. Which Robbie Williams hit was originally recorded by World Party on their 1997 album 'Egyptology'?

6. Whose only number one was 'Band Of Gold'?

7. Which British solo artist was born Mary O'Brien?

8. Which former Thin Lizzy guitarist enjoyed solo success with 'Empty Rooms'?

9. Which Motown artist made her acting debut in the 1976 movie *Pipedream*?

10. 'That Girl Belongs To Yesterday' was a 1964 hit for which American artist?

11. What was Phil Collins's first solo hit?

12. In which country was Gloria Estefan born?

13. Which Canadian chanteuse is the youngest in a family of 12?

14. Who sang with The Crusaders before going solo?

15. Who wrote Terry Jacks's 1974 UK number one 'Seasons In The Sun'?

16. How old was Helen Shapiro when she topped the charts in 1961 with 'You Don't Know'?

Answers to page 11
ALBUMS 1: 1. Sparks 2. Deacon Blue 3. 'The Unforgettable Fire'
4. 'Lovesexy' 5. Lindisfarne 6. Tracy Chapman 7. 'Different Class'
8. 'Once Upon A Time' 9. Fatback Band and Run D.M.C.
10. 'Transformer' 11. 'Goat's Head Soup' 12. The Smiths 13. East 17
('Walthamstow') 14. Jason Donovan 15. James Brown 16. London Boys

— 13 —

Sixties 1

Answers on page 16

1. Which Beatles number gave Peter and Gordon their first hit?

2. Which 17-year-old landed a recording contract after singing to Adam Faith in his dressing-room?

3. Which Sixties singer was famous for his ability to yodel?

4. Art Sharp, John Allen, Pete Shannon, John Hawken, Ray Phillips and Barry Jenkins were the original line-up for which UK band?

5. Which was the last UK number one of the Sixties?

6. Which American singer hit the UK charts with the sinister 'Ode To Billy Joe'?

7. Which Kinks song satirised Carnaby Street narcissism?

8. Athol Guy played the double bass in which Australian band?

9. Which British group – closely modelled on The Rolling Stones – had their only top ten hit with 'Don't Bring Me Down' in 1964?

10. Who were 'Living In The Past' in 1969?

11. Which Manchester band was formed by a merger of The Deltas and The Dolphins?

12. Which complex 1966 number one was recorded over six months during 17 sessions in four studios?

13. Who reached number 12 in the charts with 'Sunny' in September 1966?

14. Who had a hit with 'Three Steps To Heaven' shortly after being killed in a car crash?

15. What was Jimi Hendrix's first UK hit?

16. What was the title of the only hit by the 1910 Fruitgum Co.?

Answers to page 16
POT LUCK 2: 1. George Michael 2. Pete Shelley 3. The Belmonts
4. Chumbawamba 5. Timmy Mallett 6. 'Annie's Song' 7. Nik Kershaw
8. The Netherlands 9. Bobby Goldsboro 10. Mungo Jerry 11. The
Goombay Dance Band 12. 'Calling Occupants Of Interplanetary Craft
(The Recognised Anthem Of World Contact Day)' 13. 'Margate'
14. Rita Coolidge 15. Eighth Wonder 16. Shanks & Bigfoot

Stairway to Heaven I

Answers on page 17

1. Which two members of the same band were killed in separate motorbike crashes in Macon, Georgia, a year and three blocks apart?

2. Whose last words were 'Don't worry, it's not loaded' before shooting himself dead during a 1978 game of Russian roulette?

3. Which former Shadows member was electrocuted by his guitar in 1973?

4. How did Mama Cass Elliot die in 1974?

5. And who died from an accidental drug overdose in the same London flat four years later?

6. In which year was Jim Croce killed in a plane crash?

7. Which singer with Joy Division hanged himself in 1980?

8. Which American singer shot himself dead in his Californian home in 1990?

9. Which legendary soul singer was shot dead by his father during a blazing row in 1984?

10. Which drummer, who tasted chart success with 'Dance With The Devil', was killed in a road smash in 1998?

11. Where was Eddie Cochran killed?

12. How did Graham Bond die in 1974?

13. Who died in a fire at his home in Arkesden, Essex, in 1991?

14. In which year was Otis Redding killed in a plane crash?

15. Which US blues guitarist hanged himself in a prison cell in 1988 following his arrest for drunken behaviour?

16. Which drummer with Booker T and The MGs was shot dead by burglars in 1975?

Pot Luck 2

Answers on page 14

1. Which future international star was sacked from his Saturday job at British Home Stores for not wearing a shirt and tie in the stock-room?

2. Who was lead singer with The Buzzcocks?

3. What was the name of Dion's backing group?

4. Danbert Nobacon was a member of which Nineties band?

5. Which children's TV presenter hid behind the name of Bombalurina?

6. With which John Denver tune did flautist James Galway enjoy his only UK hit?

7. Whose debut single was 'I Won't Let The Sun Go Down On Me'?

8. From which country did Golden Earring originate?

9. Which US singer, who had an international 'weepie' hit in 1968, had first made his name as a guitarist in Roy Orbison's touring band?

10. Ray Dorset was the lead singer with which early Seventies chart band?

11. Who reached number one in 1982 with 'Seven Tears'?

12. Which Carpenters single had 73 letters in its title?

13. Which seaside resort did Chas and Dave sing about in 1982?

14. About whom did Leon Russell supposedly write 'Delta Lady'?

15. What was the name of Patsy Kensit's band?

16. Who reached number one with 'Sweet Like Chocolate' in May 1999?

Answers to page 14
SIXTIES 1: **1.** 'World Without Love' **2.** Sandie Shaw **3.** Frank Ifield **4.** The Nashville Teens **5.** 'Two Little Boys' (Rolf Harris) **6.** Bobbie Gentry **7.** 'Dedicated Follower Of Fashion' **8.** The Seekers **9.** The Pretty Things **10.** Jethro Tull **11.** The Hollies **12.** 'Good Vibrations' **13.** Bobby Hebb **14.** Eddie Cochran **15.** 'Hey Joe' **16.** 'Simon Says'

One-Hit Wonders 1

Answers on page 15

1. Which female American country singer's only hit was a 1968 ditty about a parent teacher association?

2. Which former member of the New Christy Minstrels enjoyed his only hit with the 1965 protest song 'Eve Of Destruction'?

3. With which Beatles song did The Overlanders reach number one in 1966?

4. Which novelty hit famously kept Ultravox's 'Vienna' from the number one spot in 1981?

5. And who sang it?

6. Which 1978 hit was a tribute to painter L.S. Lowry?

7. Whose only UK hit was 'Na Na Hey Hey Kiss Him Goodbye' in 1970?

8. Whose top 50 career began and ended with 'Mickey' in 1982?

9. Whose only hit was the 1985 UK number one 'Move Closer'?

10. Who had a hit with the theme music from the TV detective series *Van Der Valk*?

11. And what was the title of the track?

12. Who reached the top of the American charts in 1968 with 'Green Tambourine'?

13. Which prophetic number one of 1969 brought fleeting fame for Zager and Evans?

14. About which island did Typically Tropical sing in 1975?

15. What was the title of Althia and Donna's only hit?

16. Which American singer's only UK hit was 'Step By Step' in 1973?

Answers to page 15
STAIRWAY TO HEAVEN 1: **1.** Duane Allman and Berry Oakley (Allman Brothers Band) **2.** Terry Kath (Chicago) **3.** John Rostill **4.** Heart attack **5.** Keith Moon **6.** 1973 **7.** Ian Curtis **8.** Del Shannon **9.** Marvin Gaye **10.** Cozy Powell **11.** Chippenham, Wiltshire **12.** He mysteriously fell to his death under a tube train at Finsbury Park Station **13.** Steve Marriott **14.** 1967 **15.** Roy Buchanan **16.** Al Jackson

Punk 1

Answers on page 20

1. Which band started out supporting The Sex Pistols on their 'Anarchy' tour?

2. Which Police single reached number two in the UK charts in July 1979 – nine months after its first entry?

3. Which band named after a TV detective show asked: 'Is Vic There'?

4. Which Sham 69 song revealed the group's geographical origins?

5. Who were banned from appearing at the European Punk Rock Festival in France in August 1976?

6. Who was drummer with The Jam?

7. Whose first album was 'New Boots And Panties!'?

8. What were The Skids working for in 1979?

9. Susan Dallion was working as a waitress in Chislehurst, Kent, when she changed her name to which punk princess?

10. Which was X-Ray Spex's biggest UK hit?

11. Who had a hit in 1979 with 'Back Of My Hand'?

12. Which band were forced to pull out at the last minute of a 1976 interview with Bill Grundy on the *Today* TV show, thereby allowing The Sex Pistols to take their place and make front-page headlines?

13. Which of The Stranglers was once an ice-cream salesman?

14. Which TV presenter was a member of Jet Bronx and The Forbidden?

15. What was Brenda Spencer's role in the history of The Boomtown Rats?

16. 'Oliver's Army' was taken from which album by Elvis Costello and The Attractions?

Answers to page 20
COUNTRY AND WESTERN 1: **1.** Shania Twain **2.** Trisha Yearwood **3.** Dolly Parton **4.** Maurice **5.** Slim Dusty **6.** She had divorced husband George Jones two months before it reached number one in the UK **7.** Loretta Lynn **8.** 30 **9.** England Dan (real name Dan Seals) **10.** Daniel O'Donnell **11.** The Korean War **12.** Roger Miller **13.** Kitty Wells **14.** Crystal Gayle **15.** k.d. lang **16.** Charley Pride

Merseybeat 1

Answers on page 21

1. Ray Ennis, Ralph Ellis, Les Braid and Norman Kuhlke were the original line-up of which Merseybeat group?

2. Which group reached number one in August 1963 with a cover of an old Drifters number?

3. And what was the title of the song?

4. Which group's debut single was 'Hello Little Girl'?

5. Which brothers used to be in a band called The Mars Bars?

6. Which group took their name from the title of a 1956 John Wayne movie?

7. Which Liverpool band did Ringo Starr leave to join The Beatles?

8. Which Merseybeat frontman was born William Ashton?

9. What was inscribed on the drum kit of The Merseybeats' John Banks?

10. Why was Paul McCartney absent when The Quarry Men made their Cavern club debut in August 1957?

11. Which was Billy J. Kramer and The Dakotas' first number one?

12. Which band were voted second behind The Beatles in *Mersey Beat* magazine's first group popularity poll in January 1962?

13. Who reached number three in the UK charts with 'You're No Good' in 1964?

14. Who walked out of The Merseybeats in 1964?

15. Which was The Beatles' fifth consecutive UK number one?

16. Which backing band had an instrumental hit with 'The Cruel Sea' in 1963?

Answers to page 21
NINETIES 1: **1.** Shamen **2.** Mariah Carey **3.** 'Doctor Jones' **4.** Sean Moore **5.** Right Said Fred **6.** Portishead **7.** Massive Attack **8.** 'Dreams' **9.** Four **10.** Kula Shaker ('Hush') **11.** Outhere Brothers **12.** 'Things Can Only Get Better' **13.** Johnny Marr and Bernard Sumner **14.** EMF **15.** Mark Morrison **16.** Canadian

Country and Western 1

Answers on page 18

1. Which Canadian country beauty's father was an Ojibway Indian?

2. Who sang backing vocals on the Garth Brooks album 'No Fences' before becoming a star in her own right?

3. Which voluptuous female artist is one of a family of 12?

4. What was Tex Ritter's real Christian name?

5. Which country star was born David Gordon Kirkpatrick in 1927?

6. What was ironic about Tammy Wynette's 'Stand By Your Man'?

7. Who had a US country number one with the autobiographical 'Coal Miner's Daughter' in 1970?

8. How old was Patsy Cline when she died?

9. Who came from a family of performing Seals?

10. Who released a 1987 album entitled 'The Boy From Donegal'?

11. 'Ruby, Don't Take Your Love To Town' was based on a true incident following which war?

12. Who had a US top ten hit in 1964 with 'Dang Me'?

13. Who was the first female singer to reach number one in the US country charts?

14. Which country singer is a younger sister of Loretta Lynn?

15. Whose debut album was 'A Truly Western Experience'?

16. Who took just 15 minutes to learn and record 'Is Anybody Goin' To San Antone'?

Answers to page 18
PUNK 1: **1.** The Clash **2.** 'Can't Stand Losing You' **3.** Department S **4.** 'Hersham Boys' **5.** The Sex Pistols **6.** Rick Buckler **7.** Ian Dury and The Blockheads **8.** 'Working For The Yankee Dollar' **9.** Siouxsie **10.** 'Germ Free Adolescence' **11.** The Jags **12.** Queen **13.** Jet Black **14.** Loyd Grossman **15.** She shot dead several of her San Diego schoolfriends in 1979, citing as her reason: 'I don't like Mondays' **16.** 'Armed Forces'

Nineties 1

Answers on page 19

1. Who reached number one with 'Ebeneezer Goode' in 1992?

2. Who won 1991 Grammies for Best Female Vocalist and Best New Artist?

3. What was Aqua's second UK number one?

4. Who is the youngest of the Manic Street Preachers?

5. Which band was named after a Bernard Cribbins novelty hit of 1962?

6. Which band were named after the place in south-west England where Geoff Barrow spent his teens?

7. Whose 1998 number one album was titled 'Mezzanine'?

8. Which was The Corrs' first top ten hit in the UK?

9. How many number one singles did Westlife have in 1999?

10. Which band changed their name from The Lovely Lads and hit number two in the UK charts in March 1997 with their version of a Deep Purple song?

11. Who had a 1995 hit with 'Boom Boom Boom'?

12. Which 1994 number one was adopted by the Labour Party as its theme song for the 1997 General Election?

13. Which duo made up Electronic?

14. Whose first hit in 1990 was 'Unbelievable'?

15. Which UK chart topper fell foul of the law again after getting an impostor to do his community service?

16. What nationality is Alanis Morissette?

Answers to page 19
MERSEYBEAT 1: **1.** The Swinging Blue Jeans **2.** The Searchers
3. 'Sweets For My Sweet' **4.** The Fourmost **5.** Gerry and Freddie Marsden **6.** The Searchers **7.** Rory Storm and The Hurricanes **8.** Billy J. Kramer **9.** 'Free Love' **10.** He was away at a scout camp in Derbyshire **11.** 'Bad To Me' **12.** Gerry and The Pacemakers **13.** The Swinging Blue Jeans **14.** Billy Kinsley **15.** 'A Hard Day's Night' **16.** The Dakotas

Beatles 1

Answers on page 24

1. On which regional show did The Beatles make their TV debut in October 1962?
2. Which was the first Beatles song to enter the US charts?
3. Which Lennon and McCartney composition knocked 'Can't Buy Me Love' off the top of the UK chart in April 1964?
4. Who was the first artist to chart in the UK with a cover of a Beatles single?
5. Who did The Beatles meet for the only time on 27 August 1965 in Bel Air, California?
6. Which comedy actor recorded a version of 'A Hard Day's Night' in the guise of Sir Laurence Olivier reciting the song as Richard III?
7. At which Buckinghamshire school did The Beatles appear in April 1963 for £100 at the request of schoolboy Dave Moores?
8. To whom did Paul McCartney become engaged on Christmas Day 1967?
9. Which chart-topping group supported The Beatles on their final UK tour, in December 1965?
10. Which famous photograph was taken at 10am on 8 August 1969?
11. Which track topped the US charts for one week in March 1967?
12. Which venture opened at 94 Baker Street, London, on 7 December 1967?
13. In December 1961, where did The Beatles play their first gig in the south of England?
14. What number did 'Love Me Do' reach in the UK charts?
15. What was the group's last UK number one?
16. For how many weeks did 'From Me To You' remain a UK number one?

Answers to page 24
HEAVY METAL 1: **1.** Megadeth **2.** Israel **3.** His school uniform **4.** 1991 **5.** Metallica **6.** 'Race With The Devil' **7.** Michael Moorcock **8.** Ian Kilmister **9.** Mammoth **10.** Deep Purple **11.** Black Sabbath **12.** The Blackhearts **13.** Jo Jo Gunne **14.** 'Sweet Child O' Mine' **15.** Steppenwolf **16.** Axl Rose

Chart Toppers 2

Answers on page 25

Which artists topped the UK charts with the following tracks?

1. 'Japanese Boy' (1981)

2. 'Beetlebum' (1997)

3. 'Mouldy Old Dough' (1972)

4. 'Tower Of Strength' (1961)

5. 'Ring My Bell' (1979)

6. 'Show Me Heaven' (1990)

7. 'Star Trekkin'' (1987)

8. 'This Is My Song' (1967)

9. 'Son Of My Father' (1972)

10. 'I Don't Wanna Dance' (1982)

11. 'Young At Heart' (1993)

12. 'King Of My Castle' (1999)

13. 'Whole Lotta Woman' (1958)

14. 'Tired Of Waiting For You' (1965)

15. 'Rock Me Amadeus' (1986)

16. 'So You Win Again' (1977)

Answers to page 25
NOVELTY NUMBERS 1: **1.** St Winifred's School Choir **2.** 'Don't Jump Off The Roof Dad' **3.** 51 **4.** 'Gossip Calypso' **5.** 1993 **6.** Brian and Michael **7.** 'Tie Me Kangaroo Down, Sport' **8.** A council flat ('My Old Man's a Dustman') **9.** 'The Fastest Milkman In The West' **10.** Renée and Renato **11.** 1986 **12.** Mike Sarne **13.** The Wombles **14.** Bernard Bresslaw **15.** The Singing Nun **16.** The Singing Dogs

Heavy Metal I

Answers on page 22

1. Which thrash metal quartet was founded in San Francisco in 1983 by guitarist Dave Mustaine?
2. In which country was Gene Simmons of Kiss born?
3. What does AC/DC's Angus Young like to wear on stage?
4. In which year did Nirvana's 'Smells Like Teen Spirit' hit the UK charts?
5. Which band's first demo was titled 'No Life Til' Leather'?
6. Which Adrian Gurvitz number gave Girlschool their first taste of UK chart action?
7. Which science-fiction writer used to be a part-time member of Hawkwind?
8. What is Lemmy's real name?
9. Which UK band of the late Eighties imposed a minimum weight of 20 stone for any potential members?
10. Who entered the *Guinness Book of Records* in 1972 as the loudest band of their time?
11. Who released the 1976 album 'We Sold Our Soul For Rock 'n' Roll'?
12. Ricky Byrd, Gary Ryan and Lee Crystal were which original backing band?
13. Whose debut single, 'Run Run Run', reached number six in the UK charts?
14. Axl Rose's then girlfriend Erin Everly was the subject of which Guns N' Roses track?
15. Who took their name from a novel by cult author Herman Hesse?
16. Who was born William Bailey but changed his name to be an anagram of Oral Sex?

Answers to page 22
BEATLES 1: **1.** *People and Places* **2.** 'I Want To Hold Your Hand'
3. 'World Without Love' (Peter and Gordon) **4.** Ella Fitzgerald ('Can't Buy Me Love') **5.** Elvis Presley **6.** Peter Sellers **7.** Stowe School **8.** Jane Asher **9.** The Moody Blues **10.** The zebra crossing photo for the cover of 'Abbey Road' **11.** 'Penny Lane' **12.** The Apple Boutique **13.** The Palais Ballroom, Aldershot **14.** 17 **15.** 'The Ballad of John and Yoko' **16.** Seven

Novelty Numbers 1

Answers on page 23

1. Who thought there was 'No One Quite Like Grandma' in 1980?

2. What was Tommy Cooper's only UK hit?

3. How old was Clive Dunn when he reached number one with 'Grandad'?

4. What was Bernard Cribbins's third – and final – UK hit of 1962?

5. In which year did Mr Blobby have the Christmas number one?

6. Kevin Parrott and Mick Coleman are better known as which 1978 UK chart toppers?

7. What was Rolf Harris's first UK hit?

8. Where did Lonnie Donegan's old man live in a 1960 UK number one?

9. What was Ernie, to complete the title of Benny Hill's 1971 hit?

10. Hilary Lefter was one half of which supposedly Italian duo of the Eighties?

11. In which year did Cliff Richard team up with The Young Ones for a re-make of 'Living Doll'?

12. Who asked Wendy Richard to 'Come Outside'?

13. Which creatures were Britain's biggest-selling chart act of 1974?

14. Which gormless actor from the TV sitcom *The Army Game* wanted to make 'Mad Passionate Love' in 1958?

15. Who had a hit with 'Dominique' in 1963?

16. Which canine vocal group reached number 13 in the UK charts in 1955 with a medley including 'Three Blind Mice' and 'Jingle Bells'?

Answers to page 23
CHART TOPPERS 2: **1.** Aneka **2.** Blur **3.** Lieutenant Pigeon **4.** Frankie Vaughan **5.** Anita Ward **6.** Maria McKee **7.** The Firm **8.** Petula Clark **9.** Chicory Tip **10.** Eddy Grant **11.** Bluebells **12.** Wamdue Project **13.** Marvin Rainwater **14.** The Kinks **15.** Falco **16.** Hot Chocolate

Pot Luck 3

Answers on page 28

1. Who played guitar on Kate Bush's 'Wuthering Heights'?

2. Which Paul McCartney song was banned by the BBC in 1972 for being too sexual?

3. Who was the subject of Derek and The Dominos' 'Layla'?

4. Who was sacked from her job at New York fast-food restaurant Dunkin' Donuts for squirting jam at a customer?

5. In which country was Neneh Cherry born?

6. Who recorded 'The Trumpton Riots'?

7. Who left The Buzzcocks to form Magazine?

8. Who reached number three in the UK charts with 'Boxerbeat' in 1983?

9. Who was the vocalist with Stiff Little Fingers?

10. Which band consisted solely of Matt Johnson on its formation in 1979?

11. In which year did Robbie Williams leave Take That?

12. What was Squeeze's first UK top twenty hit?

13. Which Canadian band released 'Mmmm Mmmm Mmmm' in 1994?

14. Which Eighties band recorded a song about a *Doctor Who* actor?

15. Which fruit did The Stranglers sing about in 1977?

16. Which district of London featured in a Dave Dee, Dozy, Beaky, Mick and Tich song title of 1968?

Answers to page 28
NAME CHANGES 2: **1.** Rat Scabies **2.** Georgie Fame **3.** Stuart Goddard **4.** Billy Ocean **5.** Dr John **6.** Harold Jenkins **7.** Fish **8.** Del Shannon **9.** Captain Sensible **10.** Alice Cooper **11.** Adam Faith **12.** Meat Loaf **13.** Sandie Shaw **14.** Paul Jones **15.** DJ Jazzy Jeff **16.** Nena

Home Towns 1

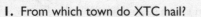

Answers on page 29

1. From which town do XTC hail?

2. Paper Lace came from which English city?

3. Tanita Tikaram was an unlikely product of which Hampshire town?

4. Where did The Jam form?

5. Which city does Joe Cocker come from?

6. Wayne Fontana and The Mindbenders came out of which city?

7. In which town was Tom Jones born?

8. Which Scottish town do Big Country come from?

9. Which Florida town was home to Lynyrd Skynyrd?

10. R.E.M. and The B-52's both come from which town in Georgia?

11. Which pair were the most famous sons of Bushey, Hertfordshire?

12. Which Eighties duo, who had two number one albums, met at school in Bath?

13. Which city was home to The Teardrop Explodes?

14. The Housemartins were based in which northern city?

15. Who is Cheshunt Secondary Modern School's most famous ex-pupil?

16. Which two successful Seventies bands had a strong Hereford influence?

Answers to page 29
GIRL BANDS 1: **1.** The Weatherman **2.** Kerry Katona **3.** Three Little Women **4.** 'I Know Where It's At' **5.** BeBe Winans **6.** 'Stop' **7.** 1992 **8.** 'Right Now' **9.** Spice Girls **10.** 7 **11.** TLC **12.** 'I Quit' **13.** Precious **14.** 12th **15.** Wyclef Jean **16.** Honeyz

Name Changes 2

Answers on page 26

1. Which punk drummer started life as Chris Miller?

2. Who was born Clive Powell?

3. What is Adam Ant's real name?

4. Which soul singer was originally known as Leslie Charles?

5. To what did Malcolm Rebannack change his name?

6. Who decided that it would be a good idea to change his name to Conway Twitty?

7. What moniker did Derek Dick adopt?

8. Which American artist of the Sixties changed his name from Charles Westover?

9. Who is Ray Burns better known as?

10. Whose real name is Vince Furnier?

11. To what did Terry Nelhams change his name?

12. Which American heavyweight used to be known as Marvin Lee Aday?

13. Who started life as Sandra Goodrich?

14. Who decided that Paul Pond was unsuitable for a stage name?

15. Who is Jeffrey Townes better known as?

16. Which German singer changed her name from Gabriela Kerner?

Answers to page 26
POT LUCK 3: **1.** Dave Gilmour **2.** 'Hi Hi Hi' **3.** Patti Boyd **4.** Madonna
5. Sweden **6.** Half Man Half Biscuit **7.** Howard Devoto **8.** Joboxers
9. Jake Burns **10.** The The **11.** 1995 **12.** 'Take Me I'm Yours' **13.** Crash
Test Dummies **14.** Human League ('Tom Baker') **15.** 'Peaches' **16.** Soho
('Last Night In Soho')

Girl Bands 1

Answers on page 27

1. Who did B*Witched blame it on in 1999?

2. Which member of Atomic Kitten left to have Bryan McFadden from Westlife's baby?

3. What does 3LW stand for?

4. What was All Saints' first UK single?

5. Who featured on Eternal's number one single, 'I Wanna Be The Only One'?

6. Which was the first single released by the Spice Girls not to reach number one in the UK?

7. In which year was TLC's first single 'Ain't 2 Proud 2 Beg' released?

8. What was Atomic Kitten's debut UK chart single?

9. Who made history by having their first six releases top the UK chart?

10. What number did All Saints' single 'War Of Nerves' reach in the UK charts in December 1998?

11. Whose album was called 'Crazysexycool'?

12. What was the title of Hepburn's debut single?

13. Which girl band represented the United Kingdom in the 1999 Eurovision Song Contest?

14. And where did they finish?

15. Who featured on Destiny's Child's debut single 'No No No'?

16. 'Finally Found', 'Love Of A Lifetime' and 'End Of The Line' were top ten singles for which group?

Answers to page 27
HOME TOWNS 1: 1. Swindon 2. Nottingham 3. Basingstoke
4. Woking 5. Sheffield 6. Manchester 7. Pontypridd 8. Dunfermline
9. Jacksonville 10. Athens 11. Wham! 12. Tears For Fears
13. Liverpool 14. Hull 15. Cliff Richard 16. Mott The Hoople and The Pretenders

Seventies 1

Answers on page 32

1. Which *Opportunity Knocks* winners reached number one in the UK in 1974?
2. Russell Thompkins Jnr was the lead singer with which Philly band?
3. Which two girls had barely left school in Jamaica when they topped the UK charts in February 1978?
4. Which former journalist on the *Colchester Gazette* fronted a band that had their first hit with 'Judy Teen' in 1974?
5. Which Scottish band were exposed by the *News of the World* in 1972 for backstage shenanigans involving female fans?
6. Which American band released the 1970 album 'Cosmo's Factory'?
7. Which American crooner did Mud support on a 1973 tour?
8. Which group did Olivia Newton-John join in 1970?
9. The Eagles were originally hired as the backing band to which singer?
10. Which was Barry Manilow's first UK hit?
11. Dan McCafferty was lead singer with which Seventies band?
12. Which 10cc track was named Best Beat Song at the 1974 Ivor Novello Awards?
13. Which 1972 UK number one was inspired by babysitting his manager's daughter?
14. Which Ruby and The Romantics cover gave The Carpenters a US number two in February 1972?
15. Who was the frontman of Tubeway Army?
16. Which Dusty Springfield classic gave the Bay City Rollers their last UK top ten hit?

Answers to page 32
LYRICS 1: 1. 'Careless Whisper' (George Michael) 2. 'Angels' (Robbie Williams) 3. 'Especially For You' (Kylie and Jason) 4. 'I'm A Believer' (The Monkees) 5. 'I Will Survive' (Gloria Gaynor) 6. 'I Say A Little Prayer' (Dionne Warwick) 7. 'Hot Stuff' (Donna Summer) 8. 'Lyin' Eyes' (The Eagles) 9. 'Losing My Religion' (R.E.M.) 10. 'House Of Fun' (Madness) 11. 'Heaven Is A Place On Earth' (Belinda Carlisle) 12. 'Chain Reaction' (Diana Ross) 13. 'A New England' (Kirsty MacColl) 14. 'You Don't Have To Say You Love Me' (Dusty Springfield) 15. 'China In Your Hand' (T'Pau) 16. 'I'm Still Standing' (Elton John)

Jazz 1

Answers on page 33

1. In which year did Dizzy Gillespie die?

2. With which title track of a musical did Louis Armstrong reach number four in the UK chart in 1964?

3. Who was known as 'The First Lady of Song'?

4. What was Milt Jackson's nickname?

5. In which year did Dave Brubeck chart in the UK with 'Take Five'?

6. With which instrument is Sonny Rollins usually associated?

7. Who wrote 'Dream Of Life' for Billie Holliday before finally being recognised as an outstanding jazz singer herself?

8. Which Blossom is a noted jazz singer/pianist?

9. Who began playing the trumpet when he was eight after being inspired by seeing a Louis Armstrong concert in Stockholm?

10. Which trumpet great died in a Pennsylvania car crash in 1956?

11. With which song did Billy Eckstine and Sarah Vaughan achieve their only UK chart success as a duo?

12. Which song did Billy Eckstine take to number three as a soloist in 1954?

13. In which instrument did Marian McPartland specialise?

14. George Auld, Buddy Rich and Helen Forrest were all members of whose Big Band in 1939?

15. Which big band leader formed his own experimental Innovations Orchestra?

16. In 1968 at the age of 69, which jazz icon became the oldest artist ever to top the UK charts?

Answers to page 33
ALBUMS 2: **1.** Big Country **2.** Swing Out Sister **3.** Manic Street Preachers **4.** Led Zeppelin **5.** Queen **6.** The Moody Blues **7.** Rush **8.** Electric Light Orchestra **9.** Shania Twain **10.** Curiosity Killed The Cat **11.** Chris Rea **12.** Simon and Garfunkel **13.** Paul Young **14.** Elton John **15.** Paul Weller **16.** Simple Minds

Lyrics 1

Answers on page 30

From which songs are the following lyrics taken?

1. 'I'm never gonna dance again, guilty feet have got no rhythm'
2. 'And through it all she offers me protection, a lot of love and affection'
3. 'No more dreaming about tomorrow, forget the loneliness and the sorrow'
4. 'I thought love was only true in fairytales, meant for someone else but not for me'
5. 'At first I was afraid, I was petrified'
6. 'From the moment I wake up, before I put on my make-up'
7. 'Dialled about a thousand numbers lately, almost rang the phone off the wall'
8. 'City girls just seem to find out early how to open doors with just a smile'
9. 'Every whisper of every waking hour I'm choosing my confessions'
10. 'Welcome to the lion's den, temptation's on its way'
11. 'In this world we're just beginning to understand the miracle of living'
12. 'You took a mystery and made me want it, you got a pedestal and put me on it'
13. 'I loved you then and I love you still, I put you on a pedestal, you put me on the Pill'
14. 'You don't have to stay forever, I will understand'
15. 'It was a flight on the wings of a young girl's dreams'
16. 'Looking like a true survivor, feeling like a little kid'

Answers to page 30
SEVENTIES 1: **1.** Paper Lace ('Billy Don't Be A Hero') **2.** The Stylistics **3.** Althia and Donna **4.** Steve Harley (and Cockney Rebel) **5.** Marmalade **6.** Creedence Clearwater Revival **7.** Jack Jones **8.** Toomorrow **9.** Linda Ronstadt **10.** 'Mandy' **11.** Nazareth **12.** 'Rubber Bullets' **13.** 'Clair' by Gilbert O'Sullivan **14.** 'Hurting Each Other' **15.** Gary Numan **16.** 'I Only Wanna Be With You'

Albums 2

Answers on page 31

Who released the following albums?

1. 'The Crossing' (1983)

2. 'It's Better To Travel' (1987)

3. 'This Is My Truth Tell Me Yours' (1998)

4. 'Houses Of The Holy' (1973)

5. 'A Day At The Races' (1977)

6. 'Days Of Future Passed' (1968)

7. 'Moving Pictures' (1981)

8. 'Discovery' (1979)

9. 'Come On Over' (1998)

10. 'Keep Your Distance' (1987)

11. 'Auberge' (1991)

12. 'Bookends' (1968)

13. 'No Parlez' (1984)

14. 'Caribou' (1974)

15. 'Stanley Road' (1995)

16. 'Street Fighting Years' (1989)

Answers to page 31
JAZZ 1: **1.** 1993 **2.** 'Hello Dolly' **3.** Ella Fitzgerald **4.** 'Bags' **5.** 1961
6. Tenor saxophone **7.** Carmen McRae **8.** Blossom Dearie **9.** Rolf
Ericson **10.** Clifford Brown **11.** 'Passing Strangers' **12.** 'No One But You'
13. Piano **14.** Artie Shaw **15.** Stan Kenton **16.** Louis Armstrong

Indie 1

Answers on page 36

1. In which city were Oasis playing when Creation boss Alan McGee spotted their potential and signed them on the spot?

2. Which Pulp single was accompanied by a short film in which celebrities were quizzed on the loss of their virginity?

3. Which band's compilation album was called 'Like You Do'?

4. In which year were Radiohead formed?

5. Whose biggest-selling album was titled 'Expecting To Fly'?

6. Rick McMurray, Tim Wheeler, Mark Hamilton and Charlotte Hatherley make up which band?

7. Tim Booth is lead singer with which band?

8. Which band's first UK chart single was 'U 16 Girls'?

9. What was Blur's first number one single in the UK?

10. Who vanished into thin air on 1 February 1995?

11. Which band split up in August 1995, only to re-form two years later and enjoy a number one album?

12. Which bassist left The La's to form Cast?

13. Which was Catatonia's first UK number one album?

14. With which Birmingham goth band did Dodgy's Nigel Clarke and Matthew Priest play in the early Eighties?

15. As which lead singer is Simon Rowbottom better known?

16. Which band took their name from a character in the novel 'To Kill A Mockingbird'?

Answers to page 36
ELVIS 1: **1.** 'All Shook Up' **2.** *The Ed Sullivan Show* **3.** 'I Need Your Love Tonight' **4.** 'All Shook Up' **5.** 'Jailhouse Rock' **6.** They were his last live performances for nearly three years because of his army call-up **7.** *GI Blues* **8.** 'Surrender' **9.** Aaron Schroeder and Wally Gold **10.** Joe Esposito **11.** 'Are You Lonesome Tonight?' **12.** The International **13.** The Jordanaires **14.** *Playboy* magazine's **15.** Bruce Springsteen **16.** 'Way Down'

Pot Luck 4

Answers on page 37

1. In the Seventies, which half of a famous duo saw his first two UK solo hits both go to number one, albeit at four year intervals?

2. Which B-side of Jasper Carrott's 'Funky Moped' was banned by the BBC for sexual innuendo?

3. Who played synthesiser on David Bowie's 'Space Oddity'?

4. Who had a 1954 hit with 'Gilly Gilly Ossenfeffer Katzenellen Bogen By The Sea'?

5. Which Pink Floyd track was dedicated to their erstwhile member, the reclusive Syd Barrett?

6. Which two TV shows were the subject of hits for The Firm in the Eighties?

7. Which was the best-selling UK single of 1981?

8. Which 1998 hit for All Saints was the 800th UK number one single?

9. Justin Currie and Iain Harvie formed which Scottish band in 1983?

10. Who was The Searchers' original drummer?

11. Which group were originally going to be called Daddy before deciding to take their name from the title of a 1910 book by W.H. Davies?

12. What is Roachford's Christian name?

13. What was Simple Minds' first UK number one single?

14. Who released the 1995 album 'Zeitgeist'?

15. Which backing singer on Don Henley's 1989 album 'The End Of The Innocence' has since gone on to enjoy a successful career herself?

16. Which convent-educated Sixties pop star is the daughter of an Austrian baroness?

Answers to page 37
COVER VERSIONS 1: **1.** The Bangles **2.** 'The Loco-Motion' **3.** Cleopatra **4.** 'I Have A Dream' **5.** 1985 **6.** 'Tragedy' **7.** Billy Ocean **8.** Geri Halliwell **9.** Bananarama **10.** 2 **11.** Kim Wilde **12.** Don Lang and His Frantic Five **13.** Labelle **14.** 'Hazy Shade Of Winter' **15.** 'Jackie' **16.** Bern Elliott and The Fenmen

Elvis 1

Answers on page 34

1. What was Elvis's first UK number one?

2. On which TV show was Elvis filmed from the waist up only?

3. Which track formed a double A-side with 'A Fool Such As I'?

4. Which was the only UK number one on which Elvis had a writing credit?

5. Which Elvis number achieved the distinction of being the first song to enter the UK charts at number one?

6. What was significant about Elvis's two concerts at Russwood Park, Memphis, on 15 March 1958?

7. From which Elvis film was 'Wooden Heart' taken?

8. Which Elvis hit was a revamping of an old Italian song, 'Return To Sorrento'?

9. Who wrote 'Good Luck Charm'?

10. Who was Elvis's best man at his wedding to Patricia Beaulieu in 1967?

11. What was Elvis's first UK number one of 1961?

12. At which Las Vegas hotel was 'The Wonder of You' recorded live?

13. What was the name of Elvis's regular backing singers?

14. Into which Hall of Fame was Elvis inducted in January 1968?

15. Which rock star tried to get to see Elvis on 29 April 1976 by climbing the fence at Graceland, only to be escorted off the premises by security guards?

16. Which song was a posthumous UK number one for Elvis?

Answers to page 34
INDIE 1: **1.** Glasgow **2.** 'Do You Remember The First Time?' **3.** Lightning Seeds **4.** 1991 **5.** The Bluetones **6.** Ash **7.** James **8.** Travis **9.** 'Country House' **10.** Richey Edwards (Manic Street Preachers) **11.** The Verve **12.** John Power **13.** International Velvet **14.** Three Cheers For Tokyo **15.** Sice (Boo Radleys) **16.** Boo Radleys

Cover Versions 1

Answers on page 35

1. Atomic Kitten's 2001 UK number one, 'Eternal Flame', was a 1989 hit for which other girl band?

2. Which Little Eva song did Kylie Minogue cover in 1988?

3. Which band covered The Jackson Five hit 'I Want You Back' in 1998?

4. Which cover of an Abba song did Westlife take to number one in 1999?

5. In which year did a-ha release the original version of a1's 'Take On Me'?

6. Which song was a number one for both The Bee Gees and Steps?

7. Who originally recorded Boyzone's 'When The Going Gets Tough, The Tough Get Going'?

8. 'It's Raining Men' was a number two hit for The Weathergirls in 1984, but who topped the charts with it in 2001?

9. 'Last Thing On My Mind' was an early hit for Steps, but who originally recorded it in 1992?

10. What UK chart position did Robbie Williams reach with his 1996 cover of George Michael's 'Freedom'?

11. 'You Keep Me Hangin' On' was a hit for The Supremes in 1966. Who covered it 20 years later?

12. Who recorded The Cartoons' 1999 hit 'Witch Doctor' 41 years earlier?

13. All Saints' 1998 number one 'Lady Marmalade' was a hit for which group in 1975?

14. Which Simon and Garfunkel song did The Bangles cover in 1988?

15. Scott Walker and Marc Almond both had hits with which song?

16. The Flying Lizards' 'Money' was a hit for which band in 1963?

Answers to page 35
POT LUCK 4: 1. Art Garfunkel ('I Only Have Eyes For You' (1975) and 'Bright Eyes' (1979)) 2. 'Magic Roundabout' 3. Rick Wakeman 4. Max Bygraves 5. 'Shine On You Crazy Diamond' 6. *Minder* ('Arthur Daley ('E's Alright)' and *Star Trek* ('Star Trekkin'')) 7. 'Don't You Want Me' (Human League) 8. 'Bootie Call' 9. Del Amitri 10. Chris Curtis 11. Supertramp 12. Andrew 13. 'Belfast Child' 14. The Levellers 15. Sheryl Crow 16. Marianne Faithfull

One-Hit Wonders 2

Answers on page 40

1. Whose moment of glory was a UK number one with 'Woodstock' in 1970?

2. Who had her only hit with 'One Day At A Time' in 1979?

3. 'Together We Are Beautiful' was a hit for which singer in 1980?

4. What was Norman Greenbaum's only hit?

5. Who got to number one in 1962 with 'Nut Rocker'?

6. Who were 'Up Town Top Ranking' in 1978?

7. What was the title of Charlene's 1982 UK number one?

8. With which number did M/A/R/R/S reach the top of the UK chart in 1987?

9. Whose finest hour was 'Float On' in 1977?

10. Who failed to set the world alight after hitting number one with 'Fire' in 1968?

11. Which cartoon characters had a UK number one hit in 1969?

12. Who insisted that there was 'No Charge' in 1976?

13. Which backing singers on 'Matchstalk Men and Matchstalk Cats And Dogs' themselves became one-hit wonders two years later?

14. Who had a hit with 'Turtle Power' in 1990?

15. With which song did John Fred and His Playboy Band trouble the charts for the only time?

16. Which curious creature gave Sheb Wooley his only hit?

Answers to page 40

SINGER/SONGWRITERS 1: **1.** 'Cold Spring Harbor' **2.** Have a UK number one single ('Don't Go Breaking My Heart') **3.** k.d. lang **4.** Carole King **5.** Michael Jackson **6.** Alanis Morissette **7.** Nick Lowe **8.** 'Big Yellow Taxi' **9.** Neil Sedaka **10.** 'Only The Lonely' **11.** John Denver **12.** Pincus **13.** David Parton **14.** 'I Just Called To Say I Love You' **15.** David Gray **16.** Peter Skellern

Glam Rock 1

Answers on page 41

1. Which Sixties band did Sweet's Brian Connolly and Mick Tucker used to be with?

2. Who rejected the names Terry Tinsel, Stanley Sparkle and Vicky Vomit before choosing his stage name?

3. Which one-time T. Rex bassist co-wrote 'Grandad' for Clive Dunn?

4. Which group consisted of Alan Williams, Tony Thorpe, Bill Hurd, Mick Clarke and John Richardson?

5. What was Kenny's first UK hit?

6. Which other future star was studying at Bromley Technical High School with a young David Bowie?

7. What was the title of David Bowie's second UK number one album?

8. In which year did T. Rex get to number one with 'Metal Guru'?

9. What was Sweet's first UK hit?

10. Which famous inventor was the subject of a Sweet track?

11. What was Gary Glitter's last UK number one?

12. With which song did The Glitter Band obtain their highest UK chart position of number two?

13. On which show did Sweet make their UK TV debut in January 1971?

14. What was David Bowie's first US top twenty hit?

15. Who was Marc Bolan's other half in T. Rex?

16. In which English city did the final live T. Rex gig take place, on 20 March 1977?

Answers to page 41
DANCE 1: 1. 'Blue' 2. Four 3. Darude 4. Cassandra 5. Kernkraft
6. 'Chocolate' 7. Eiffel 65 8. 2 9. Manifesto 10. 'Start The Commotion'
11. 'Dominoid' 12. 'Don't Stop' 13. Basement Jaxx 14. Groove Armada
15. Seven 16. 'Astral America'

Singer/Songwriters 1

Answers on page 38

1. What was the title of Billy Joel's 1971 album?
2. What did Elton John manage with Kiki Dee that he had previously been unable to do by himself?
3. Which Canadian singer/songwriter's first names are Kathryn Dawn?
4. Whose biggest-selling album was 'Tapestry'?
5. The experience of backing which artist on his world tour is retold in Sheryl Crow's 'What I Can Do For You'?
6. Who had hits with 'Head Over Feet' and 'Thank U'?
7. Which singer/songwriter started out as bass player and vocalist with Kippington Lodge?
8. What was Joni Mitchell's only UK hit?
9. 'Stupid Cupid' was whose first major hit?
10. Which song did Roy Orbison decided to record himself after it had been rejected by both Elvis Presley and The Everly Brothers?
11. Which singer/songwriter was killed in 1997 when his private plane plunged into the Pacific?
12. What is Barry Manilow's real surname?
13. Which 'unknown' had a UK hit with Stevie Wonder's 'Isn't She Lovely'?
14. What was Stevie Wonder's only solo UK number one?
15. Who had a hit with 'Babylon' in 2000?
16. Which singer/songwriter, who charted with 'You're A Lady' and 'Hold On To Love', formed a short-lived 1984 band called Oasis with Julian Lloyd Webber and Mary Hopkin?

Answers to page 38
ONE-HIT WONDERS 2: 1. Matthews' Southern Comfort 2. Lena Martell 3. Fern Kinney 4. 'Spirit In The Sky' 5. B Bumble and The Stingers 6. Althia and Donna 7. 'I've Never Been To Me' 8. 'Pump Up The Volume' 9. The Floaters 10. The Crazy World Of Arthur Brown 11. The Archies ('Sugar Sugar') 12. J. J. Barrie 13. St Winifred's School Choir ('There's No One Quite Like Grandma') 14. Partners In Kryme 15. 'Judy In Disguise (With Glasses)' 16. 'The Purple People Eater'

Dance 1

Answers on page 39

1. Which colour was the title of an Eiffel 65 single?

2. How many members were in Vengaboys?

3. Who released 'Heart Of Asia'?

4. Who featured on Rui Da Silva's single 'Touch Me'?

5. Which German dance group released 'Zombienation'?

6. Shanks and Bigfoot had a number one hit with 'Sweet Like' what?

7. 'Europop' was an album by which dance band?

8. What number did DJ Jean's 'The Launch' reach in the UK singles charts in 1999?

9. What record label were Yomanda signed to when they released 'Synth & Strings'?

10. What was the follow-up to The Wiseguys' single 'Ooh La La'?

11. What was Moloko's first UK single?

12. What was the title of ATB's second single?

13. Whose 1999 album was titled 'Remedy'?

14. Who reached number 19 in the UK singles charts with 'At The River' in August 1999?

15. How many weeks did 'King Of My Castle' by Wamdue Project spend in the UK singles chart?

16. What was Apollo Four Forty's first UK chart single called?

Answers to page 39
GLAM ROCK 1: **1.** Wainwright's Gentlemen **2.** Gary Glitter **3.** Herbie Flowers **4.** The Rubettes **5.** 'The Bump' **6.** Peter Frampton **7.** 'Pin-Ups' **8.** 1972 **9.** 'Funny, Funny' **10.** 'Alexander Graham Bell' **11.** 'Always Yours' **12.** 'Goodbye My Love' **13.** *Lift Off* **14.** 'Space Oddity' **15.** Mickey Finn **16.** Portsmouth

Fifties 1

Answers on page 44

1. Adrian Hill worked as a fitter in a Leeds engineering works before changing his name to become which successful recording artist?

2. Which Fifties crooner once worked as a prizefighter under the name Kid Crochet?

3. Which pianist had a 1959 chart topper with 'Roulette'?

4. In which year did 'Rock Around The Clock' first enter the UK charts for Bill Haley and The Comets?

5. Who had a 1956 UK number one with 'Sixteen Tons'?

6. What was the title of Ruby Murray's first hit?

7. Concetta Franconero was better known as which Fifties singer?

8. Who had a 28-year wait between her first UK hit, 'Under The Bridges of Paris', in 1955 and her second, 'Where Is My Man', in 1983?

9. Which tune did Perez Prado and Eddie Calvert each take to number one in the UK charts in 1955?

10. Which session band became one-hit wonders in 1956 with 'It's Almost Tomorrow'?

11. What was the title of Cliff Richard's second UK number one?

12. In 1957, who became the first Liverpool act to top the UK charts?

13. What was Lonnie Donegan's real Christian name?

14. Which 1958 chart topper shot himself dead five years later?

15. Which two artists had UK number one hits with 'Singing The Blues'?

16. Which excerpt from 'The Threepenny Opera', translated into English, became a 1959 UK number one for Bobby Darin?

Answers to page 44
STAIRWAY TO HEAVEN 2: 1. Brian Jones 2. Sandy Denny 3. Dennis Wilson 4. Patsy Cline 5. Joe Meek 6. Clarence White 7. Marc Bolan 8. Jimi Hendrix 9. Dave Prater 10. She died in a 1985 suicide pact with her female companion, Annie Pescher 11. Badfinger (Pete Ham in 1975 and Tom Evans in 1983) 12. Johnny Ace 13. Keith Relf 14. Lynyrd Skynyrd 15. 1985 16. Michael Hutchence

Chart Toppers 3

Answers on page 45

In which years did the following tracks reach number one in the UK singles chart?

1. 'Can The Can' (Suzi Quatro)

2. 'Doop' (Doop)

3. 'The Sun Ain't Gonna Shine Anymore' (Walker Brothers)

4. 'I Hear You Knocking' (Dave Edmunds Rockpile)

5. 'It's A Sin' (Pet Shop Boys)

6. 'Rose Marie' (Slim Whitman)

7. 'Cars' (Gary Numan)

8. 'Girlfriend' (Billie)

9. 'Some Might Say' (Oasis)

10. 'I Owe You Nothing' (Bros)

11. 'Sailing' (Rod Stewart)

12. 'Atomic' (Blondie)

13. 'Do It Again' (The Beach Boys)

14. 'Without You' (Nilsson)

15. 'Men In Black' (Will Smith)

16. 'Do You Love Me' (Brian Poole and The Tremeloes)

Answers to page 45
POT LUCK 5: 1. Chris Curtis, the ex-Searchers drummer, was one of the founders of Deep Purple but left after a few days 2. The Cranberries 3. Leitch 4. The Lovin' Spoonful 5. Modern Romance 6. Hank Wangford 7. Humble Pie 8. Alison Moyet 9. The Humblebums 10. It is short for Refugees (two of the three were expatriate Haitians) 11. 'He's So Fine' 12. Clannad 13. Eddy Grant 14. Heather Small 15. Mike Rutherford 16. Rolf Harris

Stairway to Heaven 2

Answers on page 42

1. Who drowned in the swimming pool of his Sussex home in 1969?

2. Which lead singer with Fairport Convention died in 1978 after falling down stairs?

3. Which Beach Boy drowned in a boating accident off the coast of California in 1983?

4. Which female country singer died in a Tennessee plane crash in 1963?

5. Which legendary producer shot himself on 3 February 1967, the anniversary of the death of his hero, Buddy Holly?

6. Which member of The Byrds was killed by a drunk driver in 1973?

7. Who was killed near Putney on 16 September 1977?

8. Who died in a basement bedroom at the Samarkand Hotel, Notting Hill Gate, on 18 September 1970?

9. Which of Sam and Dave was killed in a 1988 road smash?

10. How did The Singing Nun die?

11. Which Seventies band lost both guiding lights to suicide?

12. Which American R & B star shot himself dead in 1954 while playing Russian roulette backstage?

13. Which former singer with The Yardbirds was electrocuted in 1976 while tuning his guitar?

14. Three members of which band were wiped out in a Mississippi plane crash in 1977?

15. In which year did Ricky Nelson die in a plane crash?

16. Who was found hanging in a Sydney hotel room in 1997?

Answers to page 42
FIFTIES 1: **1.** Ronnie Hilton **2.** Dean Martin **3.** Russ Conway **4.** 1955 **5.** Tennessee Ernie Ford **6.** 'Heartbeat' **7.** Connie Francis **8.** Eartha Kitt **9.** 'Cherry Pink And Apple Blossom Wine' **10.** The Dreamweavers **11.** 'Travellin' Light' **12.** Frankie Vaughan **13.** Anthony **14.** Michael Holliday **15.** Guy Mitchell and Tommy Steele **16.** 'Mack The Knife'

Pot Luck 5

Answers on page 43

1. Who linked The Searchers and Deep Purple?

2. Dolores O'Riordan is the singer with which Irish band?

3. What is Donovan's surname?

4. John Sebastian, Zal Yanovsky, Steve Boone and Joe Butler were the original members of which Sixties band?

5. Who had a 1981 hit with 'Ay Ay Ay Ay Moosey'?

6. Which country music star is a qualified gynaecologist?

7. Peter Frampton and Steve Marriott formed which supergroup in 1969?

8. Who released a 1987 album 'Raindancing'?

9. Gerry Rafferty and Billy Connolly played together as which duo?

10. How did The Fugees get their name?

11. 'My Sweet Lord' was accused of being too similar to which Chiffons hit?

12. Enya used to play the piano with which Irish band?

13. Which member of The Equals enjoyed solo success over a decade later?

14. Who was the vocalist with M People?

15. Who was the Mike of Mike and The Mechanics?

16. Which entertainer broke down in tears on breakfast TV when hearing Mike and The Mechanics' 'The Living Years'?

Answers to page 43
CHART TOPPERS 3: **1.** 1973 **2.** 1994 **3.** 1966 **4.** 1970 **5.** 1987 **6.** 1955 **7.** 1979 **8.** 1998 **9.** 1995 **10.** 1988 **11.** 1975 **12.** 1980 **13.** 1968 **14.** 1972 **15.** 1997 **16.** 1963

Name Changes 3

Answers on page 48

1. Which Eighties band changed their name from Caviar?

2. Which rap artist was born Tracy Marrow?

3. Which band were previously called Kippington Lodge?

4. Which punk rocker started life as William Broad?

5. What were Idle Race once known as?

6. Which guitar legend was born Brian Rankin?

7. Which band were formerly known as The Spectres?

8. Caesar and Cleo found fame as which duo?

9. Which band changed their name from The New Yardbirds?

10. Who came up with a better name than The Golliwogs?

11. Which Liverpool group were originally known as The Mavericks?

12. What was Dr Feelgood's real name?

13. Which Sixties girl band used to be called The Primettes?

14. Which band started out as Angel and The Snakes?

15. To what did The New Journeymen change their name in the Sixties?

16. Which girl band sensibly decided to dispense with their name of The Bangs?

Answers to page 48
CHRISTMAS HITS 1: 1. 'Christmas Alphabet' 2. Dickie Valentine
3. Greg Lake 4. 'Long Haired Lover From Liverpool' 5. The Goodies
6. 1973 7. Twiggy 8. 'Lonely This Christmas' 9. 4 10. 'Bohemian
Rhapsody' 11. The Flying Pickets ('Only You') 12. Shakin' Stevens
13. 'Earth Song' 14. 'Mull Of Kintyre' 15. Johnny Mathis 16. Johnny
Hammer

Eighties 2

Answers on page 49

1. Which chart-topping duo were the Appleby sisters better known as?

2. Which was the biggest-selling UK single of 1984?

3. Which three posthumous UK number one hits did John Lennon have?

4. Who wrote 'Chain Reaction' for Diana Ross?

5. Which was the first R.E.M. single to chart in the UK?

6. Who produced Feargal Sharkey's 'A Good Heart'?

7. Which 1981 chart topper was a cover version of a 1954 Rosemary Clooney hit?

8. Which duo with a combined age of 80 reached number one in the UK charts in September 1985 with a cover version of a Sixties classic?

9. Who sang lead vocal on The Cars' 'Drive'?

10. Who won Best British Group at the 1983 Brit Awards?

11. Which re-release that featured in a TV commercial for Miller Lite lager gave The Hollies an unexpected number one in 1988?

12. What was Depeche Mode's first UK top ten hit?

13. What nationality were a-ha?

14. Which ex-Clash member fronted Big Audio Dynamite?

15. Who had a 1987 hit with a cover of Bread's 'Everything I Own'?

16. Which 1989 hit was Cliff Richard's 100th single?

Answers to page 49
FILM TRACKS 1: **1.** 'When You Say Nothing At All' **2.** *The Full Monty*
3. 'Turn Back Time' **4.** *Dirty Dancing* **5.** Diana King **6.** *Top Gun* **7.** *When Harry Met Sally* **8.** The Foundations **9.** *Up Close and Personal*
10. Christopher Cross **11.** *Pulp Fiction* **12.** Boy Meets Girl
13. 'Unchained Melody' **14.** *Godzilla* **15.** *Mermaids* **16.** The Cardigans

— 47 —

Christmas Hits 1

Answers on page 46

1. Which 1955 song was the first record made specifically for the Christmas market to reach number one in the UK charts?

2. And who sang it?

3. Who reached number two in 1975 with 'I Believe In Father Christmas'?

4. What was the 1972 Christmas number one?

5. Who released 'Father Christmas Do Not Touch Me' in 1974?

6. In which year was 'Merry Xmas Everybody' a monster hit for Slade?

7. Which former model originally recorded Cliff Richard's 'Mistletoe And Wine'?

8. What was Mud's Christmas offering for 1974?

9. What number did Wizzard's 'I Wish It Could Be Christmas Everyday' reach in the UK charts in 1973?

10. Which song was the UK Christmas number one in both 1975 and 1991?

11. Red Stripe was a member of which band that had the 1983 Christmas number one?

12. Which artist formerly known as Michael Barrett enjoyed a 1985 yuletide chart topper, 'Merry Christmas Everyone'?

13. What was the 1995 UK Christmas number one?

14. Which Christmas number one was composed out of a perceived need to give Scotland a contemporary anthem?

15. Who had a 1976 Christmas hit with 'When A Child Is Born'?

16. According to Scaffold's 1968 Christmas number one, 'Lily The Pink', who had a terrible s-s-s-s-stammer?

Answers to page 46
NAME CHANGES 3: **1.** Bros **2.** Ice-T **3.** Brinsley Schwarz **4.** Billy Idol **5.** The Nightriders **6.** Hank Marvin **7.** Status Quo **8.** Sonny and Cher **9.** Led Zeppelin **10.** Creedence Clearwater Revival **11.** The Merseybeats **12.** Lee Brilleaux **13.** The Supremes **14.** Blondie **15.** The Mamas and The Papas **16.** The Bangles

Film Tracks 1

Answers on page 47

1. Which Ronan Keating song was used in the 1999 film *Notting Hill*?

2. Which film featured 'You Sexy Thing' by Hot Chocolate?

3. Which Aqua hit was heard in the 1998 film *Sliding Doors*?

4. Which film featured '(I've Had) The Time Of My Life' by Bill Medley and Jennifer Warnes?

5. Who performed 'I Say A Little Prayer' for *My Best Friend's Wedding*?

6. Berlin's 'Take My Breath Away' came from which Tom Cruise film?

7. 'It Had To Be You' by Harry Connick Jnr featured in which Meg Ryan film?

8. Which Sixties band recorded 'Build Me Up Buttercup' which was used in the 1998 comedy *There's Something About Mary* starring Cameron Diaz?

9. Which film featured Celine Dion's 'Because You Loved Me'?

10. Who sang 'Arthur's Theme (Best That You Can Do)' from the 1981 film *Arthur*?

11. 'Son Of A Preacher Man' by Dusty Springfield was used in which film directed by Quentin Tarantino?

12. Who performed 'Waiting For A Star To Fall' from the film *Three Men and a Little Lady*?

13. Which song by The Righteous Brothers was used in the 1990 film *Ghost*?

14. 'Deeper Underground' by Jamiroquai featured in which 1998 film?

15. Cher's 'The Shoop Shoop Song (It's In His Kiss)' was used in which film?

16. Who performed 'Lovefool' in *Romeo and Juliet*, starring Leonardo DiCaprio?

Answers to page 47
EIGHTIES 2: 1. Mel and Kim 2. 'Do They Know It's Christmas'?
3. '(Just Like) Starting Over', 'Imagine' and 'Woman' 4. The Bee Gees
5. 'The One I Love' 6. Dave Stewart 7. 'This Ole House' (Shakin'
Stevens) 8. David Bowie and Mick Jagger ('Dancing In The Street')
9. Benjamin Orr 10. Dire Straits 11. 'He Ain't Heavy, He's My Brother'
12. 'Just Can't Get Enough' 13. Norwegian 14. Mick Jones 15. Boy
George 16. 'The Best Of Me'

Albums 3

Answers on page 52

1. Which track from Dire Straits' 'Brothers In Arms' featured vocals by Sting?

2. Which was the biggest-selling UK album of 1992?

3. Whose best-selling album was titled 'The Lexicon Of Love'?

4. Who released the album 'Arrival' in 1976?

5. Which former husband of Kirsty MacColl produced U2's debut album, 'Boy'?

6. Whose albums have included 'The Lion And The Cobra' and 'Universal Mother'?

7. Which Phil Collins album was the UK best-seller of 1990?

8. Which was the first Led Zeppelin album to be given a proper title instead of merely a number?

9. What was the title of Elton John's second album?

10. In 1996, which album had the shortest title ever to top the UK chart?

11. Which was Roxy Music's first UK number one album?

12. Who were in 'Cloudcuckooland' in 1990?

13. Which band's albums have included 'Black Sea', 'English Settlement' and 'Mummer'?

14. Whose debut album in 1987 was titled 'Raintown'?

15. Which album spent a total of 303 weeks in the UK album charts from 1970?

16. What was Rod Stewart's first UK number one album?

Answers to page 52
SOLO ARTISTS 2: **1.** 'Dizzy' **2.** Maria Muldaur **3.** Chris Rea **4.** 'Reach Out And Touch (Somebody's Hand)' **5.** Dusty Springfield **6.** 1979 **7.** Kylie Minogue **8.** Chaka Khan **9.** Robert **10.** Toni Braxton **11.** Neil Sedaka **12.** His then girlfriend, Christie Brinkley **13.** Because he is related to Herman Melville, author of *Moby Dick* **14.** David Essex **15.** Peter Frampton ('Frampton Comes Alive') **16.** 'An Englishman In New York'

Pot Luck 6

Answers on page 53

1. What was significant about The Johnston Brothers' 1955 number one 'Hernando's Hideaway'?

2. Which Annie Lennox number was the first hit single in the CD age not to be available on vinyl?

3. Which 1972 Paul McCartney track was banned by the BBC for being too political?

4. Which Eighties band were named after Mr Spock's Vulcan friend in *Star Trek*?

5. Who was the female member of New Order?

6. What is Seal's full name?

7. Which film track kept Squeeze's 'Cool For Cats' from number one in 1979?

8. Steve Winwood, Dave Mason, Chris Wood and Jim Capaldi were the original line-up for which Sixties band?

9. As a 15-year-old, which musical giant was jailed for three months in 1960 for stealing 300 tyres from a Los Angeles car dealer?

10. Which female rocker left school in Detroit in 1964 and formed The Pleasure Seekers with her three sisters?

11. Who played harmonica and guitar on Bill Wyman's album 'Stone Alone'?

12. How many Red Balloons did Nena have?

13. Who duetted with Paul McCartney on the 1982 hit 'The Girl Is Mine'?

14. With which band did Midge Ure have his first UK number one?

15. Which Jamaican group reached the charts with 'Black And White' in 1971?

16. Where was Roger Whittaker leaving in 1969?

Answers to page 53
EUROVISION 1: **1.** 'La La La' (1968) **2.** Spain **3.** The Allisons **4.** Nicki French **5.** Co-Co **6.** 1969 **7.** Sweden **8.** 1997 **9.** 'Love Games' **10.** 1956 **11.** 'Knock Knock Who's There' **12.** Johnny Logan **13.** 13 **14.** The construction of a hydro-electric power station **15.** He received *nul points* for Norway in 1978 with 'Mil Etter Mil' **16.** Gina G

Solo Artists 2

Answers on page 50

1. Which song links Tommy Roe with Vic Reeves?

2. Who spent 'Midnight At The Oasis' in 1974?

3. Which Middlesbrough-born artist saved up to buy his first guitar by working in his family's ice-cream parlour?

4. Which was Diana Ross's debut solo single?

5. Which British girl singer was deported from South Africa in December 1964 for singing to a multi-racial audience at a cinema near Cape Town?

6. In which year did Joe Jackson record 'Is She Really Going Out With Him'?

7. Which singer once played Charlotte Kernow in the TV series *The Hendersons*?

8. What did Yvette Stevens change her name to?

9. What does the R. stand for in R. Kelly?

10. Who reached number two in the UK charts in 1994 with 'Breathe Again'?

11. Which singer/songwriter contributed the whistling to the 1957 Pat Boone hit 'Love Letters In The Sand'?

12. About whom did Billy Joel write 'Uptown Girl'?

13. Why did Richard Melville Hall decide to call himself Moby?

14. Whose 1975 album was called 'All The Fun Of The Fair'?

15. Whose is the biggest-selling live album of all time?

16. Which Sting single was written about Quentin Crisp?

Answers to page 50
ALBUMS 3: 1. 'Money For Nothing' 2. 'Stars' by Simply Red 3. ABC
4. Abba 5. Steve Lillywhite 6. Sinead O'Connor 7. '...But Seriously'
8. 'Houses Of The Holy' 9. 'Elton John' 10. 'K' by Kula Shaker
11. 'Stranded' 12. Lightning Seeds 13. XTC 14. Deacon Blue
15. 'Bridge Over Troubled Water' (Simon and Garfunkel) 16. 'Every Picture Tells A Story'

Eurovision 1

Answers on page 51

1. Which Eurovision Song Contest winner had no fewer than 138 la's?

2. And which country was responsible for it?

3. Which male duo came second for the UK in the 1961 contest with 'Are You Sure'?

4. 'Don't Play That Song Again' prophetically came a lowly 16th for the UK in 2000 for which singer?

5. With which group had Cheryl Baker of Bucks Fizz previously represented the UK in the Eurovision?

6. Which year's contest ended in a four-way tie?

7. Which country won in 1984 with 'Diggy Loo Diggy Ley'?

8. In which year were Katrina and The Waves triumphant with 'Love Shine A Light'?

9. Which 1984 UK entry by Belle and The Devotions was booed after newspaper stories in Holland claimed the song was similar to an old Supremes number?

10. In which year was the first Eurovision Song Contest?

11. With which song did Mary Hopkin come second in 1970?

12. Who was the first singer to win the Eurovision twice?

13. How old was Belgium's 1986 Eurovision winner, Sandra Kim?

14. What was the subject of Norway's 1980 entry?

15. What is Jahn Teigen's claim to Eurovision fame?

16. Who came eighth for the UK in 1996 with 'Ooh Aah…Just A Little Bit'?

Answers to page 51
POT LUCK 6: **1.** They were the first set of unrelated brothers to top the UK chart **2.** 'Cold' **3.** 'Give Ireland Back To The Irish' **4.** T'Pau **5.** Gillian Gilbert **6.** Sealhenry Samuel **7.** 'Bright Eyes' (Art Garfunkel) **8.** Traffic **9.** Barry White **10.** Suzi Quatro **11.** Van Morrison **12.** 99 **13.** Michael Jackson **14.** Slik **15.** Greyhound **16.** 'Durham Town'

Rolling Stones 1

Answers on page 56

1. Which number did the Stones perform on the very first edition of *Top of the Pops*?
2. Charlie Watts's book, 'Ode To A High Flying Bird', was a tribute to which jazz great?
3. Which Stones single of 1963 had previously been recorded by The Beatles?
4. Which was the only Stones number one on which Mick Taylor played?
5. On which Stones double A-side did Lennon and McCartney provide backing vocals?
6. Which was the first number one to be written by Jagger and Richard?
7. Who designed the sleeve of 'Sticky Fingers'?
8. Which live album was recorded at New York's Madison Square Garden in November 1969?
9. What was the B-side to 'Honky Tonk Women'?
10. Who was the first Stone to release a solo album?
11. Which was the Stones' last top ten UK single?
12. On which Stones track was Jagger portrayed as the Boston Strangler?
13. Which Stone was once part of a school choir that sang Handel's *Messiah* at Westminster Abbey in the presence of the Queen?
14. In which year did 'Get Off of My Cloud' reach number one in the UK?
15. Who joined Jagger on stage in Tokyo in March 1988, duetting with him on 'Brown Sugar' and 'It's Only Rock 'n' Roll'?
16. Which Stone accidentally set himself on fire after falling asleep in his room at the Londonderry House Hotel, Hyde Park, in 1973?

Answers to page 56
SEVENTIES 2: 1. Clodagh Rodgers 2. C.W. McCall 3. Gloria Gaynor 4. The Pretenders 5. Status Quo 6. Gerry Monroe 7. Guys and Dolls 8. Don Williams 9. Sham 69 10. Demis Roussos 11. Isley Brothers 12. Dr Hook 13. Jethro Tull 14. Peter Gabriel 15. Three Degrees 16. John Paul Young

— 54 —

Classical Gas 1

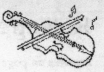

Answers on page 57

1. In which German city was Beethoven born?

2. Who wrote *The Barber of Seville*?

3. What nationality was Haydn?

4. How old was Mozart when he died?

5. Who composed the 'Brandenburg Concertos'?

6. Which Puccini opera of 1926 was never finished?

7. What nationality was Sibelius?

8. Who composed 'A German Requiem'?

9. In which year did Tchaikovsky compose *The Nutcracker*?

10. At what age did Chopin make his debut as a pianist?

11. Which German composer claimed that his best ideas came from two imaginary companions, Florestan and Eusebius?

12. Which composer was paid an annual allowance by wealthy widow Nadezhda von Meck on condition that they never met?

13. What was Debussy's Christian name?

14. Who wrote the music for *The Firebird*?

15. Who composed *Tales From The Vienna Woods*?

16. Which composer died at Bayreuth in Germany in 1886?

Answers to page 57
POT LUCK 6: **1.** Joe Cocker **2.** 'Memory' **3.** Shirley Manson **4.** 'Spirit In The Sky' (Norman Greenbaum and Dr and The Medics) **5.** The Gap Band **6.** Whigfield **7.** 'Saturday Night' **8.** 'Just What I Always Wanted' **9.** 'Enola Gay' (Orchestral Manoeuvres In The Dark) **10.** Cher **11.** Patrick Macnee and Honor Blackman ('Kinky Boots') **12.** 'Call Me' **13.** 'Hey Child' **14.** David Bowie **15.** Mel Smith and Kim Wilde **16.** Manic Street Preachers

Seventies 2

Answers on page 54

Which artists had hits with the following tracks in the Seventies?

1. 'Jack In The Box' (1971)

2. 'Convoy' (1976)

3. 'Never Can Say Goodbye' (1974)

4. 'Stop Your Sobbing' (1979)

5. 'Mystery Song' (1976)

6. 'Sally' (1970)

7. 'There's A Whole Lot Of Loving' (1975)

8. 'I Recall A Gypsy Woman' (1976)

9. 'If The Kids Are United' (1978)

10. 'Happy To Be On An Island In The Sun' (1975)

11. 'Harvest For The World' (1976)

12. 'Sylvia's Mother' (1972)

13. 'The Witch's Promise' (1970)

14. 'Solsbury Hill' (1977)

15. 'Take Good Care Of Yourself' (1975)

16. 'Love Is In The Air' (1978)

Answers to page 54
ROLLING STONES 1: 1. 'I Wanna Be Your Man' 2. Charlie Parker
3. 'I Wanna Be Your Man' 4. 'Honky Tonk Women' 5. 'We Love You'/
'Dandelion' 6. 'The Last Time' 7. Andy Warhol 8. 'Get Yer Ya-Ya's Out'
9. 'You Can't Always Get What You Want' 10. Bill Wyman 11. 'Start Me
Up' 12. 'Midnight Rambler' 13. Keith Richards 14. 1965 15. Tina Turner
16. Keith Richards

Pot Luck 6

Answers on page 55

1. Which singer worked as an apprentice fitter with the East Midlands Gas Board in Sheffield in 1960?

2. Which song from the musical *Cats* gave Elaine Paige a UK top ten hit in 1981?

3. Who once said that the Spice Girls should be 'tarred and feathered'?

4. Which song was a UK number one hit for different artists in 1970 and 1986?

5. Which Eighties band took their name from the initials of three streets in their home town of Tulsa, Oklahoma?

6. Who was the first new artist to go straight in at number one on the UK singles chart?

7. And what was the title of the song?

8. Which was Mari Wilson's most successful single?

9. Which 1980 hit was named after the plane that dropped the atomic bomb on Hiroshima?

10. Which female singer did uncredited vocals on Meat Loaf's 'Dead Ringer For Love'?

11. Which duo's combined age totalled 132 when they charted in 1990?

12. Which Blondie hit was taken from the film *An American Gigolo*?

13. Which East 17 single was written for Tony Mortimer's daughters Atlanta and Ocean?

14. Who did backing vocals on Mott The Hoople's 'All The Young Dudes'?

15. Who were Mel and Kim for Comic Relief in 1987?

16. Whose 1992 album was called 'Generation Terrorists'?

Answers to page 55
CLASSICAL GAS 1: **1.** Bonn **2.** Rossini **3.** Austrian **4.** 35 **5.** Bach
6. *Turandot* **7.** Finnish **8.** Brahms **9.** 1892 **10.** Eight **11.** Schumann
12. Tchaikovsky **13.** Claude **14.** Stravinsky **15.** Johann Strauss the Younger **16.** Liszt

Backstreet Boys 1

Answers on page 60

1. Who is the oldest member of Backstreet Boys?

2. What was the title of the band's first UK number one single?

3. What was the first single released off the 'Black And Blue' album?

4. Which two members are cousins?

5. What is A.J.'s full name?

6. Which member used to be a ventriloquist?

7. In which state was Nick Carter born?

8. Who has a younger brother called Aaron?

9. Which band member helped to write 'Larger Than Life'?

10. In which year did Backstreet Boys have their first UK top ten hit?

11. And what was the title of the single?

12. What was the title of the band's second album?

13. What is the band's record label?

14. Which Backstreet Boy had a role in *Edward Scissorhands*?

15. What number did 'Millennium' reach in the UK album charts?

16. What was the band's only UK single release of 1998?

Answers to page 60
COUNTRY AND WESTERN 2: **1.** The Scottsville Squirrel Barkers (Chris Hillman and Bernie Leadon) **2.** Earl Scruggs **3.** Mel Tillis **4.** Otis Dewey Whitman Jnr **5.** The First Edition **6.** Jimmie Rodgers **7.** The Mavericks **8.** Mutt Lange **9.** He stuck pins in a map and paired a town in Arkansas with one in Texas **10.** Bill Monroe **11.** Hank Mizell **12.** Emmylou Harris **13.** 'I Can't Help It If I'm Still in Love With You' **14.** Merle Haggard **15.** The Flying Burrito Brothers **16.** Patsy Cline

Duos 1

Answers on page 61

1. On the platform of which English railway station did Paul Simon write 'Homeward Bound'?

2. Daryl Dragon is the male half of which duo?

3. Which Seventies middle-of-the-road duo achieved fame via the TV talent show *Opportunity Knocks*?

4. What was the title of Windsor Davies and Don Estelle's hit album of 1976?

5. Which Beatles cover version was The Carpenters' debut single?

6. What nationality were Nina and Frederick?

7. And which children's favourite did they take to number three in the UK charts in 1960?

8. Who recorded the original version of Soft Cell's 'Tainted Love'?

9. Where did Soft Cell play their first gig?

10. Which duo comprised Alison Moyet and Vince Clarke?

11. Which duo first met when she waited on his table at Pippins restaurant in Hampstead?

12. Which pair won the Best British Group category at the 1989 Brit Awards?

13. What was the title of Daryl Hall and John Oates's first UK top ten single?

14. Which Simon and Garfunkel classic was the first disc played by Capital Radio?

15. Which song kept The Eurythmics' 'Sweet Dreams (Are Made Of This)' off the top of the UK charts in March 1983?

16. Which duo evolved from a Californian group called The Paramours?

Answers to page 61
CHART TOPPERS 4: **1.** Middle Of The Road **2.** 'Kung Fu Fighting'
3. 'The Power Of Love' (Frankie Goes To Hollywood and Jennifer Rush)
4. 'Parallel Lines' **5.** Jimmy Nail **6.** 'Killing Me Softly' (The Fugees)
7. Steve and Muff Winwood **8.** John Leyton ('Johnny Remember Me')
9. Brotherhood Of Man ('Angelo') **10.** Sweet Sensation **11.** Falco
12. 'Rock Me Amadeus' **13.** Chrissie Hynde **14.** Herman's Hermits
15. 'I'm Into Something Good' **16.** Pussycat ('Mississippi')

Country and Western 2

Answers on page 58

1. Which bluegrass band – also known as The Kentucky Mountain Boys – had a future Byrd and a future Eagle among its members?

2. Which country artist recorded the 1972 album 'I Saw The Light With Some Help From My Friends'?

3. Which country singer/songwriter, who penned 'Ruby, Don't Take Your Love To Town', was left with a permanent stutter after contracting malaria at the age of three?

4. What is Slim Whitman's real name?

5. Which group backed Kenny Rogers on his first two UK hits?

6. Who was known as 'The Singing Brakeman'?

7. Raul Malo is the lead singer with which country rock band?

8. To which successful record producer is Shania Twain married?

9. How did Conway Twitty come by his stage name?

10. Who was generally regarded as the 'father of bluegrass music'?

11. Who had a 1976 UK hit with 'Jungle Rock' – 19 years after the track was recorded?

12. Whose debut album was 'Gliding Bird'?

13. Which 'Heart Like A Wheel' track won Linda Ronstadt a Grammy Award for Best Female Country Vocal?

14. Who did President Nixon say was his favourite country singer?

15. Ex-Byrds Gram Parsons and Chris Hillman were instrumental in forming which country rock band in 1968?

16. Which country star was born Virginia Patterson Hensley?

Answers to page 58
BACKSTREET BOYS 1: **1.** Kevin Richardson **2.** 'I Want It That Way' **3.** 'Shape Of My Heart' **4.** Brian and Kevin **5.** Alexander James McLean **6.** A.J. **7.** New York State **8.** Nick **9.** Brian Littrell **10.** 1996 **11.** 'We've Got It Goin' On' **12.** 'Backstreet's Back' **13.** Jive **14.** Nick Carter **15.** 2 **16.** 'All I Have To Give'

Chart Toppers 4

Answers on page 59

1. Sally Carr was lead singer with which 1971 UK chart toppers?

2. Which 1974 hit about martial arts was recorded in ten minutes and went on to sell 10 million copies worldwide?

3. Which title made UK number one twice in the space of a year in the mid-Eighties, but with completely different songs?

4. From which Blondie album was the 1979 hit 'Sunday Girl' taken?

5. Which actor/singer reached number one in July 1992 with 'Ain't No Doubt'?

6. Which cover of a Roberta Flack song became the biggest-selling single of 1996?

7. Which two brothers were members of The Spencer Davis Group?

8. Which 1961 UK chart topper was best known for playing Biggles on TV?

9. Who took a sad song about a Mexican shepherd boy to the top of the UK charts in 1977?

10. Which *New Faces* winners had a 1974 number one with 'Sad Sweet Dreamer'?

11. Which 1986 chart topper was born in Vienna as Johann Holzel?

12. And with which song about a famous composer did he taste fame?

13. Who was guest vocalist on UB40's 'I Got You Babe'?

14. Which Manchester-based Sixties group had one number one in the UK but two in America?

15. And what was their British success?

16. Which were the first Dutch group to have a UK number one?

Answers to page 59

DUOS 1: 1. Widnes 2. Captain and Tennille 3. Peters and Lee 4. 'Sing Lofty' 5. 'Ticket To Ride' 6. Danish 7. 'Little Donkey' 8. Gloria Jones 9. Leeds Polytechnic 10. Yazoo 11. The Eurythmics (Annie Lennox and Dave Stewart) 12. Erasure 13. 'I Can't Go For That (No Can Do)' 14. 'Bridge Over Troubled Water' 15. 'Total Eclipse Of The Heart' (Bonnie Tyler) 16. The Righteous Brothers

Reggae 1

Answers on page 64

1. Which reggae artist, who charted in 1986 with 'Hello Darling', also teamed up with Arsenal FC for their 1993 Cup Final song?

2. With which song did Desmond Dekker get to number two in the UK in 1970?

3. Frederick 'Toots' Hibbert was leader of which band?

4. What does Everton Brown prefer to call himself?

5. Which British reggae band named themselves after the form issued to unemployed people so that they can claim benefit?

6. What was Bob Marley's only UK hit of 1983?

7. Why were Alex Hughes's records never heard on radio?

8. Who had a 1974 hit with his version of 'Help Me Make It Through The Night'?

9. Who topped the UK charts in 1974 with a cover of a Bread song?

10. Which Bob Marley track reached number five in the UK in 1992?

11. Who had a 1979 hit with 'Reggae For It Now'?

12. Which infamous Max Romeo track managed to reach the UK top ten despite a total radio ban?

13. Who is Orville Richard Burrell better known as?

14. Who sang about 'Ram Goat Liver' in 1976?

15. Which reggae band reached number five in the UK singles chart in 1969 with 'Return Of Django'?

16. With which song did Shaggy top the charts in 1993?

Answers to page 64
MADONNA 1: **1.** The Breakfast Club **2.** 'Into The Groove' **3.** 'Crazy For You' and 'Gambler' **4.** 'The Virgin Tour' **5.** Bette Midler **6.** 1987 **7.** Michael Jackson **8.** 1991 **9.** 'Frozen' **10.** 'Erotica' **11.** 'Bedtime Story' **12.** *Top of the Pops* **13.** Gothenburg **14.** 'True Blue' **15.** Babyface **16.** 'Like A Prayer'

Sixties 2

Answers on page 65

1. Which band did Peter Frampton join as a 16-year-old?
2. In which year were Fleetwood Mac formed?
3. Who had a hit with the ethereal 'Kites'?
4. What was The Move's first single?
5. Which supergroup started out in the Sixties as The Architectural Abdabs?
6. Which Troggs single was banned in Australia on account of its suggestive lyrics?
7. What was Screaming Lord Sutch's backing band?
8. Which Monkees hit was originally called 'Randy Scouse Git'?
9. Which Dusty Springfield song was the first-ever to be played on *Top of the Pops*?
10. Who played piano on The Hollies' 1969 hit 'He Ain't Heavy...He's My Brother'?
11. Whose hits included 'I Love My Dog' and 'I'm Gonna Get Me A Gun'?
12. Who had a 1968 hit with 'Everything I Am'?
13. What did Brian Poole become for a while after splitting from The Tremeloes?
14. Which group changed their name from Bag Of Blues?
15. Who was the driving force behind Family Dogg?
16. Which Australian band of the Sixties, who had a hit with 'Friday On My Mind', were the forerunners of AC/DC?

Answers to page 65
LYRICS 2: **1.** 'Maneater' (Hall and Oates) **2.** 'The Air That I Breathe' (The Hollies) **3.** 'Rave On' (Buddy Holly) **4.** 'Against All Odds (Take A Look At Me Now)' (Phil Collins) **5.** 'Dancing Girls' (Nik Kershaw) **6.** 'Everything I Do (I Do It For You)' (Bryan Adams) **7.** 'Delilah' (Tom Jones) **8.** 'From Me To You' (The Beatles) **9.** 'Can't Stand Losing You' (The Police) **10.** 'Invisible Touch' (Genesis) **11.** 'Country House' (Blur) **12.** 'Song For Whoever' (The Beautiful South) **13.** 'Heart Of Glass' (Blondie) **14.** 'Peaceful Easy Feeling' (The Eagles) **15.** 'Summer Holiday' (Cliff Richard) **16.** 'I Can't Control Myself' (The Troggs)

Madonna 1

Answers on page 62

1. Which band did Madonna form with then boyfriend Dan Gilroy?

2. What was Madonna's first UK number one?

3. Which two singles were taken from the film *Vision Quest*?

4. Which tour did Madonna begin in April 1985?

5. Who said that Madonna is 'a woman who pulled herself up by her bra straps'?

6. In which year did Madonna tour Britain for the first time?

7. Who was Madonna's escort for the 1991 Oscars?

8. In which year did *In Bed With Madonna* premiere in London?

9. Which 1998 hit was Madonna's first UK number one for eight years?

10. Which single sampled 'Jungle Boogie' by Kool and The Gang?

11. Which 1995 release ended Madonna's run of 32 consecutive US top forty singles hits?

12. On 2 November 1995 Madonna made her first appearance for 11 years on which show?

13. In which city did Madonna begin the European leg of her 'Blonde Ambition' tour in 1990?

14. What was the title of Madonna's second UK number one album?

15. Who did backing vocals on 'Take A Bow'?

16. Which Madonna video was banned by the Vatican on grounds of blasphemy?

Lyrics 2

Answers on page 63

From which songs are the following lyrics taken?

1. '(Oh-oh here she comes) Watch out boy, she'll chew you up'

2. 'Peace came upon me and it leaves me weak'

3. 'The way you dance and hold me tight, the way you kiss and say goodnight'

4. 'And there's nothing left here to remind me, just the memory of your face'

5. 'Take off the twilight and the skies so grey'

6. 'You can't tell me it's not worth dying for'

7. 'I saw the flickering shadows of her love on her blind'

8. 'I've got everything that you want, like a heart that is oh-so true'

9. 'I guess you'd call it cowardice, but I'm not prepared to go on like this'

10. 'She reaches in and grabs right hold of your heart'

11. 'I'm paying the price of living life at the legal limit'

12. 'I love you from the bottom of my pencil case'

13. 'Once I had a love and it was divine'

14. 'I like the way your sparkling earrings lay against your skin, so brown'

15. 'We're going where the sun shines brightly'

16. 'Your slacks are low and your hips are showing'

Answers to page 63
SIXTIES 2: **1.** The Herd **2.** 1967 **3.** Simon Dupree and The Big Sound **4.** 'Night Of Fear' **5.** Pink Floyd **6.** 'I Can't Control Myself' **7.** The Savages **8.** 'Alternate Title' **9.** 'I Only Want To Be With You' **10.** Elton John **11.** Cat Stevens **12.** Plastic Penny **13.** A butcher **14.** Jethro Tull **15.** Steve Rowland **16.** The Easybeats

Pot Luck 7

Answers on page 68

1. Which Angie was the subject of the Rolling Stones' track of the same name?

2. Which band took their name from the villain in Jane Fonda's 1968 film *Barbarella* since many of their early gigs were played at Barbarella's club in Birmingham?

3. Who were the first American group to top the UK charts?

4. What were the Christian names of The Everly Brothers?

5. Which Celine Dion track was the theme to *Sleepless in Seattle*?

6. Who was sacked from East 17 in 1997 after his comments about Ecstasy?

7. Which saxophonist was the Johnny of Johnny and The Hurricanes?

8. Which music paper did Chrissie Hynde used to write for?

9. Which ska prince was born Cecil Bustamante Campbell?

10. Roger Hodgson, Bob Benberg and John Helliwell were members of which Seventies band?

11. Who was lead singer with The Waterboys?

12. Which singer was an apprentice at Vauxhall Motors in Luton before leaving in 1978?

13. Which Supremes hit did Kim Wilde cover in 1986?

14. Who performed with the jazz-funk outfit Fusion before going solo?

15. Which Sixties group had what was then considered the novelty of a female drummer?

16. And what was her name?

Answers to page 68
SOUL 1: **1.** 'Papa's Got A Brand New Bag' **2.** Charles and Eddie **3.** The Chi-Lites **4.** The Bar-Kays **5.** Arthur Conley **6.** Lee Dorsey **7.** The Isley Brothers **8.** Philadelphia **9.** Archie Bell and The Drells **10.** Sam and Dave **11.** Johnny Nash **12.** (Detroit) Spinners **13.** Eddie Holman **14.** Bob Marley **15.** The Stylistics **16.** '(Sittin' On) The Dock Of The Bay'

One-Hit Wonders 3

Answers on page 69

1. Which band's only hit was the 1976 offering 'Afternoon Delight'?

2. Which twins had a UK number one with 'When' in 1958?

3. Who begged: 'Tell Laura I Love Her' in 1962?

4. Which *Neighbours* actor reached the UK top fifty just once – with 'Don't It Make You Feel Good'?

5. What was the title of Shorty Long's only UK hit?

6. 'They're Coming To Take Me Away, Ha-Haaa!' was a 1966 hit for which emperor?

7. Carly Simon provided backing vocals on 'Kissing With Confidence', a 1983 recording by which one-hit wonder?

8. Which 1969 one-hit wonders had their record banned by the BBC?

9. Which UK number one provided Kitty Kallen's moment of glory in 1954?

10. Which group's cover version of The Beatles' 'Ob-La-Di, Ob-La-Da' gave them their only hit?

11. Who had a 1969 UK top twenty hit with a medley of 'Sing A Rainbow' and 'Love Is Blue'?

12. Which instrumental got to number seven for East Of Eden in 1971?

13. Whose only UK hit was 'Gonna Make You An Offer You Can't Refuse' in 1973?

14. Who sang 'Let's Go To San Francisco' in 1967?

15. George Harrison played bass guitar on which 1974 hit for Splinter?

16. Which Australian band tasted sweet success with 'Howzat' in 1976?

Answers to page 69
COVER VERSIONS 2: 1. 'How Deep Is Your Love' 2. Wheatus
3. Bananarama 4. 'Blame It On The Boogie' 5. The Four Preps 6. Nicki French 7. Little Anthony and The Imperials 8. 'Speaking In Tongues'
9. The Velvelettes 10. 'Going Down To Liverpool' 11. The Corrs
12. The Four Seasons 13. 'Don't Tell My Heart' 14. Denise and Johnny
15. 'Killing Me Softly With His Song' 16. Betty Hutton

Soul 1

Answers on page 66

1. What was James Brown's first US top ten hit?

2. Which duo who had a worldwide hit with 'Would I Lie To You' first met on a subway train?

3. Which group had a US number one with 'Oh Girl' in 1972?

4. Four members of which band were killed along with Otis Redding in a 1967 plane crash?

5. Who had a 1967 hit with 'Sweet Soul Music'?

6. Who was 'Working In The Coalmine' in 1966?

7. O'Kelly, Rudolph and Ronald were which band of brothers?

8. In which US city were The Stylistics formed?

9. Who went on a 'Soul City Walk' in 1976?

10. Which duo had a 1969 hit with 'Soul Sister Brown Sugar'?

11. Who had hits with 'You Got Soul' and 'I Can See Clearly Now'?

12. Which US group were given the prefix 'Detroit' to distinguish them from a British folk group of the same name?

13. Whose only UK hit was the 1974 single '(Hey There) Lonely Girl'?

14. Who wrote 'Stir It Up' for Johnny Nash?

15. 'Betcha By Golly, Wow' was the first UK hit for which band?

16. Which was Otis Redding's biggest-selling single?

Answers to page 66
POT LUCK 7: **1.** Angie Bowie **2.** Duran Duran **3.** Bill Haley and The Comets **4.** Don and Phil **5.** 'When I Fall In Love' **6.** Brian Harvey **7.** Johnny Paris **8.** *New Musical Express* **9.** Prince Buster **10.** Supertramp **11.** Mike Scott **12.** Paul Young **13.** 'You Keep Me Hangin' On' **14.** Nik Kershaw **15.** The Honeycombs **16.** Anne 'Honey' Lantree

Cover Versions 2

Answers on page 67

1. Which Bee Gees song did Take That cover in 1996?

2. Which band covered Erasure's 'A Little Respect' in 2001?

3. Which girl band covered The Beatles' 'Help!' in 1989

4. Which song links The Jacksons and Big Fun?

5. Who originally recorded Paul Young's 'Love Of The Common People'?

6. Who covered Bonnie Tyler's 'Total Eclipse Of The Heart' in 1995?

7. Who recorded the original version of 'Tears On My Pillow', released by Kylie Minogue in 1990?

8. 'Burning Down The House' was a 1999 hit for Tom Jones and The Cardigans, but on which Talking Heads album did it originally appear?

9. Bananarama and Fun Boy Three had a hit in 1982 with 'Really Saying Something (He Was Really Sayin' Somethin')', but who originally recorded it?

10. Which song links Katrina and The Waves with The Bangles?

11. Who covered 'Dreams' by Fleetwood Mac in 1998?

12. Who originally recorded 'Bye Bye Baby', a hit for The Bay City Rollers in 1975?

13. Billy Ray Cyrus's 'Achy Breaky Heart' was originally recorded by The Marci Brothers under a different title. What was it?

14. Who covered Kylie and Jason's hit 'Especially For You' in 1998?

15. Lori Leiberman was the first to record which Roberta Flack classic?

16. Who originally recorded 'It's Oh So Quiet', a hit for Bjork in 1995?

Answers to page 67
ONE-HIT WONDERS 3: 1. Starland Vocal Band 2. The Kalin Twins
3. Ricky Valance 4. Stefan Dennis 5. 'Here Comes The Judge'
6. Napoleon XIV 7. Will Powers 8. Jane Birkin and Serge Gainsbourg ('Je T'Aime…Moi Non Plus') 9. 'Little Things Mean A Lot' 10. The Bedrocks
11. The Dells 12. 'Jig-A-Jig' 13. Jimmy Helms 14. The Flowerpot Men
15. 'Costafine Town' 16. Sherbet

Folk 1

Answers on page 72

1. As whom was Hudson Leadbetter more usually known?

2. Who released the 1975 album 'Diamonds And Rust'?

3. Who spent six months as a singer with The Strawbs before joining Fairport Convention in 1968?

4. What is Melanie's surname?

5. Whose debut album was 'The Sophisticated Beggar'?

6. Which folk group gave Paul Simon his first UK chart success with 'Someday One Day' in 1966?

7. Which group took their name from a Lincolnshire waggoner celebrated in song?

8. Craig and Charlie Reid are better known as which duo?

9. What nationality is Gordon Lightfoot?

10. Who popularised the song 'Little Boxes'?

11. Which 1968 UK top five hit by a London busker was recorded for just £8?

12. Whose second album was titled 'Ramblin' Boy'?

13. Who wrote 'If I Were A Carpenter'?

14. The million-selling single 'Amazing Grace' was taken from which Judy Collins album?

15. With whom did The Chieftains collaborate for their 1988 album 'Irish Heartbeat'?

16. Which two artists had UK hits with 'Elusive Butterfly' in 1966?

Answers to page 72
NINETIES 2: 1. 'Firestarter' 2. EMF 3. 'The Chronic' 4. Elastica
5. 'Genie In A Bottle' 6. Shirley Manson 7. Texas 8. DJ Shadow
9. 'Hangin' Tough' by New Kids On The Block 10. Hannon (aka Divine Comedy) wrote the theme music for *Father Ted* 11. 'Renaissance'
12. Teddy Pendergrass 13. Mark Knopfler 14. Weeks 15. 'Automatic For The People' 16. 'I Should Coco'

Steps I

Answers on page 73

1. What is H's real name?

2. What was the title of Steps' first UK hit?

3. And what form of dancing did it feature?

4. Which two members of Steps are Welsh?

5. What was Steps' first UK number one?

6. Which TV talent show did Steps present?

7. Which Kylie Minogue single did Steps cover?

8. What Had A Hold On Steps' Heart?

9. Which single had an Oriental theme to the video?

10. What was the title of the other song on the double A-side with 'When I Said Goodbye'?

11. What was the title of Steps' first album?

12. Which girl band originally recorded 'Last Thing On My Mind'?

13. On which 1999 charity single in aid of the Brit Trust did Steps take part?

14. Which Steps single of March 1999 reached number two in the UK charts?

15. What was the title of Steps' second album?

16. What is Lisa's surname?

Answers to page 73
EAGLES 1: **1.** Jackson Browne **2.** 'Desperado' **3.** 'Tequila Sunrise'
4. London **5.** Don Felder **6.** James Dean **7.** 'The Best Of My Love'
8. 'I Wish You Peace' (Patti Reagan Davis) **9.** Timothy B. Schmit
10. 'Hotel California' **11.** 'The Carpenters 1969–1973' **12.** Elton John
13. Randy Meisner **14.** 'New Kid In Town' **15.** Don Felder **16.** Bruce
Hornsby

Nineties 2

Answers on page 70

1. Which 1996 UK number one prompted complaints that it encouraged young people to commit arson?

2. Which band's original line-up consisted of James Atkin, Ian Dench, Zak Foley, Derry Brownson and Mark Decloedt?

3. Which Dr Dre album title is slang for marijuana?

4. Justine Frischmann left Suede to front which Indie band?

5. What was Christina Aguilera's first UK hit?

6. Who is the lead singer of Garbage?

7. Whose biggest-selling album was 'White On Blonde'?

8. What does hip hop artist Josh Davis call himself?

9. What was the first new UK number one of the Nineties?

10. What links Neil Hannon with Father Dougal?

11. Which M People single from 1994 was the theme from the BBC2 series *The Living Soap*?

12. Which soul singer was featured on the K.W.S. single 'The More I Get, The More I Want'?

13. Who played guitar on Jimmy Nail's 1995 hit 'Big River'?

14. What is Des'ree's surname?

15. From which R.E.M. album did 'Everybody Hurts' come?

16. What was the title of Supergrass's debut album?

Answers to page 70
FOLK 1: **1.** Leadbelly **2.** Joan Baez **3.** Sandy Denny **4.** Safka **5.** Roy Harper **6.** The Seekers **7.** Steeleye Span **8.** The Proclaimers **9.** Canadian **10.** Pete Seeger **11.** 'Rosie' by Don Partridge **12.** Tom Paxton **13.** Tim Hardin **14.** 'Whales And Nightingales' **15.** Van Morrison **16.** Bob Lind and Val Doonican

Eagles 1

Answers on page 71

1. Who co-wrote 'Take It Easy' with Glenn Frey?

2. Which Eagles album has a cowboy theme?

3. Which was the first single to be written by Don Henley and Glenn Frey?

4. In which city were the band's first two albums recorded?

5. Which guitarist joined The Eagles in 1974?

6. The 'On The Border' album features a track about which legendary US movie star and youth icon?

7. Which was the band's first million-selling single?

8. Which track from 'One Of These Nights' was co-written by a future US President's daughter?

9. Who replaced Randy Meisner in 1977?

10. Which single was The Eagles' only top ten UK hit?

11. Which 'Best of' album kept 'Hotel California' from the top spot in the UK?

12. Who played piano for an encore of Chuck Berry's 'Carol' when The Eagles toured Europe in 1977?

13. Who sang lead vocal on 'Take It To The Limit'?

14. Which was the first single to be released from 'Hotel California'?

15. Which Eagle played in a band with Stephen Stills at the age of 13?

16. Who played piano on Don Henley's 1989 single 'The End Of The Innocence'?

Answers to page 71
STEPS 1: 1. Ian Watkins 2. '5, 6, 7, 8' 3. Line dancing 4. H and Lisa
5. 'Heartbeat/Tragedy' 6. *Steps to the Stars* 7. 'Better The Devil You Know' 8. Love 9. 'After The Love Has Gone' 10. 'Summer Of Love'
11. 'Step One' 12. Bananarama 13. 'Thank Abba For The Music'
14. 'Better Best Forgotten' 15. 'Steptacular' 16. Scott-Lee

Rock 'n' Roll 1

Answers on page 76

1. The phrase 'That'll Be The Day' was used by which actor in the 1956 Western classic *The Searchers*?

2. From which town in Texas did The Crickets hail?

3. Whose career nearly came to an end when it emerged that he had married his 14-year-old cousin?

4. Which 1955 movie featured 'Rock Around The Clock'?

5. Who wrote 'Jailhouse Rock'?

6. What was Buddy Holly's only solo UK number one single?

7. Which was the only number one on which Cliff Richard was backed by The Drifters before they changed their name to The Shadows?

8. In which year did Adam Faith have his first UK number one?

9. And what was the title?

10. Who changed his name from Reg Smith and had a 1958 hit with 'Endless Sleep'?

11. What was Eddie Cochran's 'C'mon Everybody' originally titled?

12. Which American singer, who would resurface in the Seventies, recorded the original version of the Billy Fury hit 'Halfway To Paradise'?

13. Who wrote 'It Doesn't Matter Anymore'?

14. What was the name of Marty Wilde's backing group?

15. From which film was 'Great Balls Of Fire' taken?

16. What did The Big Bopper like in 1958?

Answers to page 76
HEAVY METAL 2: 1. Paul Di'Anno 2. Mötley Crüe 3. Brian Robertson
4. Kiss 5. Jon Bon Jovi 6. Ozzy Osbourne 7. Saxon 8. Steven Adler
9. Sheffield 10. Rick Allen 11. Deep Purple 12. Mountain 13. 1980
14. Black Sabbath 15. AC/DC 16. Frank Beard

Film Tracks 2

Answers on page 77

1. Which Shania Twain hit was used in the 1999 film *Notting Hill*?

2. From which film was Wet Wet Wet's 'Love Is All Around'?

3. Who sang 'Up Where We Belong' from the film *An Officer and a Gentleman*?

4. Which Mama Cass song was used in the film *French Kiss* starring Meg Ryan?

5. Who sang 'Show Me Heaven' from the Tom Cruise film *Days Of Thunder*?

6. 'Brown-Eyed Girl' by Van Morrison featured in which film?

7. Who sang 'Footloose' from the film of the same name?

8. Which 1994 film featured 'Maneater' 12 years after it had been a hit for Daryl Hall and John Oates?

9. Which song by The Wannadies was used in the 1996 film *Romeo and Juliet*?

10. In which film was Kylie Minogue's hit 'Tears On My Pillow' used?

11. Which group sang the theme for the Bond movie *The Living Daylights*?

12. Who performed 'Stay (I Missed You)' from the 1994 film *Reality Bites*?

13. Who had a hit with the song 'A Life Less Ordinary' from the film of the same name starring Ewan McGregor?

14. Which film featured The Bangles' hit 'Hazy Shade Of Winter'?

15. Which Beach Boys song was used in the film *Cocktail*?

16. Blondie's 'Call Me' featured in which Richard Gere film?

Answers to page 77
POT LUCK 8: **1.** King Crimson **2.** The line which mentioned Coca-Cola had to be changed to cherry cola **3.** 'Galveston' **4.** Phil Collins **5.** Tab Hunter (1957) and Donny Osmond (1973) **6.** Don McLean **7.** 'Do You Know The Way To San Jose?' **8.** Five Star **9.** Bev Bevan **10.** Two **11.** George Harrison **12.** The Hooters **13.** Berlin ('Take My Breath Away') **14.** Les McKeown **15.** Village People **16.** Sir Douglas Quintet

Heavy Metal 2

Answers on page 74

1. Who did Bruce Dickinson replace as singer with Iron Maiden?

2. Which US heavy metal band was formed by Nikki Sixx in 1980?

3. Which ex-Thin Lizzy guitarist joined Motorhead in 1982?

4. Which band released a 1976 album titled 'Destroyer'?

5. As a teenager, which heavy metal frontman used to be employed making Christmas decorations?

6. And which rocker used to work as a labourer in a slaughterhouse?

7. Which English band were formerly known as Son Of A Bitch?

8. Which Guns N' Roses drummer had to be replaced temporarily after breaking his hand in a brawl?

9. Def Leppard come from which English city?

10. Which Def Leppard drummer lost his left arm in a car crash in 1984?

11. Which band were originally called Roundabout?

12. Leslie West and Felix Pappalardi were founder members of which band?

13. In which year did Motorhead release 'Ace Of Spades'?

14. Whose 1980 album was titled 'Heaven And Hell'?

15. 'Rock 'n' Roll Damnation' was which band's first UK hit?

16. Which is the only member of ZZ Top not to have a long beard?

Answers to page 74
ROCK 'N' ROLL 1: **1.** John Wayne **2.** Lubbock **3.** Jerry Lee Lewis **4.** *Blackboard Jungle* **5.** Jerry Leiber and Mike Stoller **6.** 'It Doesn't Matter Anymore' **7.** 'Living Doll' **8.** 1959 **9.** 'What Do You Want?' **10.** Marty Wilde **11.** 'Let's Get Together' **12.** Tony Orlando **13.** Paul Anka **14.** The Wildcats **15.** *Jamboree* **16.** 'Chantilly Lace'

Pot Luck 8

Answers on page 75

1. Robert Fripp, Mike Giles, Ian McDonald and Greg Lake were the original line-up of which band?

2. What did the BBC force The Kinks to change when they sang 'Lola' on *Top of the Pops*?

3. Which Texas town did Glen Campbell sing about in 1969?

4. Who played drums on Adam Ant's 'Puss 'n Boots'?

5. Which two artists took 'Young Love' to number one in the UK charts?

6. A performance by which singer inspired 'Killing Me Softly With His Song'?

7. Which cover of a Dionne Warwick song featured on the Frankie Goes To Hollywood album 'Welcome To The Pleasuredome'?

8. The Pearson family formed which troubled Eighties band?

9. Who was the drummer with The Move?

10. How many Martha's were there in Martha and The Muffins?

11. Who was the youngest Beatle?

12. Rob Hyman and Eric Bazilian led which American band of the Eighties?

13. Terri Nunn was the lead singer with which band who enjoyed a number one in 1986?

14. Which Bay City Roller was charged with reckless driving after killing a 75-year-old woman?

15. Which colourful Seventies group were assembled by record producer Jacques Morali?

16. Which aristocratic band's only hit was the 1965 single 'She's About A Mover'?

Answers to page 75
FILM TRACKS 2: 1. 'You've Got A Way' 2. *Four Weddings And A Funeral* 3. Joe Cocker and Jennifer Warnes 4. 'Dream A Little Dream Of Me' 5. Maria McKee 6. *Sleeping with the Enemy* 7. Kenny Loggins 8. *Runaway Bride* 9. 'You & Me Song' 10. *The Delinquents* 11. a-ha 12. Lisa Loeb and Nine Stories 13. Ash 14. *Less Than Zero* 15. 'Kokomo' 16. *American Gigolo*

Name Changes 4

Answers on page 80

1. Which British rocker changed his name from Ronald Wycherley?

2. Who was born James Jewel Osterburg?

3. Which Irish band used to be known as The Incomparable Benzini Brothers?

4. What did the ill-fated Jiles Perry Richardson change his name to?

5. Which country star was born Brenda Gail Webb?

6. Which soul singer who had a comeback hit with 'Ain't Gonna Bump No More (With No Big Fat Woman)' changed his name from Joseph Arrington Jnr?

7. Which Welsh singer with a throaty voice was born Gaynor Hopkins?

8. Who changed his name from Steven Georgiou to notch up a succession of hits in the Sixties and Seventies?

9. Which Seventies singer was previously both Bernard Jewry and Shane Fenton?

10. Which rap artist's real name is Calvin Broadus?

11. Which heavy metal band were formerly known as Atomic Mass?

12. Which reggae artist changed his name from James Chambers?

13. What is Captain Beefheart's real name?

14. What were The Box Tops previously known as?

15. Which punk band were originally called The Nightlife Thugs?

16. Which outrageous US star of the Sixties changed his name from James Smith?

Answers to page 80
SIXTIES 3: **1.** Jonathan King **2.** Brian Hyland **3.** Manfred Mann **4.** Gene Pitney **5.** The Hollies **6.** Dusty Springfield **7.** Sandie Shaw **8.** The Foundations **9.** The Herd **10.** The Casuals **11.** Billy Fury **12.** Joe Dolan **13.** The Ivy League **14.** Engelbert Humperdinck **15.** The McCoys **16.** R. Dean Taylor

Motown 1

Answers on page 81

1. Who had a 1973 hit with 'Papa Was A Rollin' Stone'?

2. Who originally recorded Diana Ross and The Supremes' 1969 hit 'Someday We'll Be Together'?

3. Which Motown group were originally called The Del-Phis?

4. Who recorded romantic duets with, in turn, Mary Wells, Kim Weston and Tammi Terrell?

5. With which Moody Blues number did The Four Tops have a top three UK hit in 1971?

6. What is Smokey Robinson's real Christian name?

7. In which year did Smokey Robinson leave The Miracles?

8. What was Gladys Knight and The Pips' last UK hit for Tamla Motown?

9. What was The Jackson Five's first UK hit?

10. Which other Jackson originally recorded The Jacksons' 'Doctor My Eyes'?

11. What was Diana Ross's first solo UK number one?

12. Which Motown classic enjoyed a new lease of life in 1986 after being featured in a TV commercial for Levi's 501 jeans?

13. Which fellow Motown band rejected 'Where Did Our Love Go', thus allowing it to become the Supremes' first major hit?

14. What was Diana Ross's last new UK hit with The Supremes?

15. And which 1970 number gave The Supremes their first UK hit without Diana Ross?

16. Who replaced Eldridge Bryant in The Temptations in 1963?

Answers to page 81
R & B 2: **1.** Three **2.** French **3.** Lisa 'Left Eye' Lopes **4.** Another Level
5. R. Kelly **6.** 'U Know What's Up' **7.** Sisqo **8.** 'Wonderful Tonight'
9. 2001 **10.** Whitney Houston **11.** Jennifer Lopez **12.** Monica **13.** Ireland
14. Kelis **15.** Mel B **16.** Annie Lennox

Sixties 3

Answers on page 78

Which artists had UK hits with the following Sixties songs?

1. 'Everyone's Gone To The Moon'

2. 'Ginny Come Lately'

3. 'Oh No Not My Baby'

4. 'That Girl Belongs To Yesterday'

5. 'Bus Stop'

6. 'I Close My Eyes And Count To Ten'

7. 'Girl Don't Come'

8. 'Baby, Now That I've Found You'

9. 'From The Underworld'

10. 'Jesamine'

11. 'Jealousy'

12. 'Make Me An Island'

13. 'Tossing And Turning'

14. 'Winter World Of Love'

15. 'Hang On Sloopy'

16. 'Gotta See Jane'

Answers to page 78
NAME CHANGES 4: 1. Billy Fury 2. Iggy Pop 3. Hothouse Flowers
4. Big Bopper 5. Crystal Gayle 6. Joe Tex 7. Bonnie Tyler 8. Cat Stevens
9. Alvin Stardust 10. Snoop Doggy Dog 11. Def Leppard 12. Jimmy Cliff
13. Don Van Vliet 14. Ronnie & The Devilles 15. The Boomtown Rats
16. P.J. Proby

R & B 2

Answers on page 79

1. How many members are there in Destiny's Child?

2. What nationality is Naima of Honeyz?

3. Which member of TLC featured on Mel C's single 'Never Be The Same Again'?

4. Dane Bowers was associated with which group?

5. Which R & B solo artist released 'If I Could Turn Back The Hands Of Time'?

6. Lisa 'Left Eye' Lopes featured on which of Donell Jones's singles?

7. 'Thong Song' and 'Incomplete' are singles by which artist?

8. Which Eric Clapton song was successfully covered by Damage in 1997?

9. In which year did Usher release 'Pop Ya Collar'?

10. Which female artist got to number two in the UK charts in 1999 with 'My Love Is Your Love'?

11. Which R & B/Latino artist was voted the world's sexiest female in 2001?

12. Who did Brandy team up with on the single 'The Boy Is Mine'?

13. Which country is Samantha Mumba from?

14. Who was 'Caught Out There'?

15. Which Spice Girl released 'Feels So Good'?

16. Who provided backing vocals on Whitney Houston's 1996 single 'Step By Step'?

Answers to page 79
MOTOWN 1: 1. The Temptations 2. Johnny Bristol 3. Martha and The Vandellas 4. Marvin Gaye 5. 'Simple Game' 6. William 7. 1972
8. 'Neither One Of Us (Wants To Be The First To Say Goodbye)'
9. 'I Want You Back' 10. Jackson Browne 11. 'I'm Still Waiting'
12. 'I Heard It Through The Grapevine' 13. The Marvelettes
14. 'Someday We'll Be Together' 15. 'Up The Ladder To The Roof'
16. David Ruffin

Punk 2

Answers on page 84

1. Why was The Stranglers' performance at a February 1977 gig at London's Rainbow Theatre cut short?

2. What was The Clash's debut single?

3. Who were the first UK punk band to play in the US?

4. Which band undertook a covert 1977 tour as Spots?

5. Who were 'Top Of The Pops' in 1978?

6. Jimmy Pursey was lead singer with which band?

7. Whose first UK top ten hit was 'Into The Valley'?

8. Johnnie Fingers, Pete Briquette and Simon Crowe were members of which punk band?

9. Which Kinks track did The Jam cover in 1978?

10. Who was singer with Generation X before branching out into a successful solo career?

11. Which band released a 1976 album called 'Teenage Depression'?

12. Which band enjoyed their only UK number one in 1991 as the result of a TV commercial for Levi's jeans?

13. Which Sex Pistols track was recorded with Great Train Robber Ronnie Biggs in Rio de Janeiro?

14. Which band stripped a heckler at Swindon in 1982 and used his bare buttocks as tom-toms during 'Golden Brown'?

15. Whose 1978 album was titled 'Another Music In A Different Kitchen'?

16. Which Barry Ryan cover gave The Damned their biggest hit?

Answers to page 84
BLUES 1: **1.** U2 **2.** B.B. – Albert King was born Albert Nelson and Freddie King was born Billy Myles **3.** Van Morrison **4.** Rufus Thomas **5.** 'Babyface' **6.** Willie Mae Thornton **7.** 43 **8.** Muddy Waters **9.** Roy Gaines **10.** The Bluesbreakers **11.** Alexis Korner's Blues Incorporated **12.** John Lee Hooker **13.** Howlin' Wolf **14.** 'Peg Leg' **15.** Peter Green **16.** Chris Farlowe

Home Towns 2

Answers on page 85

1. Which was the home city of Dave Dee, Dozy, Beaky, Mick and Tich?

2. In which city did The Spencer Davis Group start out?

3. Showaddywaddy and Engelbert Humperdinck come from which city?

4. Where is home to The Chieftains?

5. In which Merseyside town were China Crisis formed?

6. Where do Echo and The Bunnymen come from?

7. Which Nineties band are the most famous sons of Cinderford in Gloucestershire?

8. From which city do Human League hail?

9. Three-quarters of Level 42 were brought up on which island?

10. What do Ritchie Blackmore and John Cleese have in common?

11. Which punk band were formed in Chiddingford, Surrey?

12. In which Sussex town did Brett Anderson form the prototype of Suede?

13. Which city do Duran Duran come from?

14. Which Sixties group pioneered the Tottenham Sound?

15. Which new wave band sounded French but had its roots in Basildon, Essex?

16. Which London suburb is home to The Bluetones?

Answers to page 85
U2 1: **1.** Bono Vox **2.** A Miss Wet T-shirt contest **3.** 'October' **4.** 'War' **5.** 'Pride (In The Name Of Love)' **6.** 'Under A Blood Red Sky' **7.** 'Angel Of Harlem' **8.** The ballroom at Slane Castle **9.** 'A Sort Of Homecoming' **10.** 1987 **11.** Dave Evans **12.** 'Rattle And Hum' **13.** 'Desire' **14.** 'Hold Me, Thrill Me, Kiss Me, Kill Me' **15.** The Zoo Tour **16.** 'Where The Streets Have No Name'

Blues 1

Answers on page 82

1. With which band did B.B. King team up for the 1989 hit 'When Love Comes To Town'?

2. Which of the triumvirate of Kings who ruled the blues in the Sixties was the only genuine King?

3. Who released the 1968 album 'Astral Weeks'?

4. Who was 'Walking The Dog' in 1963?

5. What was Jesse Thomas's nickname?

6. Which blues singer was known as 'Big Mama'?

7. How old was Bessie Smith when she died?

8. Which blues legend was born McKinley Morganfield?

9. What was the name of Grady Gaines's guitar-playing brother?

10. What was John Mayall's famous band?

11. Charlie Watts, Long John Baldry and Jack Bruce all played with which blues band in the early Sixties?

12. Whose albums include 'Mad Man's Blues', 'Free Beer And Chicken' and 'Chill Out'?

13. To what did Chester Arthur Burnett change his name?

14. What was Joshua Howell's nickname?

15. Which future Fleetwood Mac guitarist joined John Mayall's Bluebreakers in 1965 as a temporary substitute for Eric Clapton?

16. Which British blues singer had hits with 'Out Of Time' and 'Handbags And Gladrags'?

Answers to page 82
PUNK 2: **1.** The organisers turned off the power because they objected to the four-letter word on Hugh Cornwell's T-shirt **2.** 'White Riot' **3.** The Damned **4.** The Sex Pistols (Spots = Sex Pistols On Tour Secretly) **5.** Rezillos **6.** Sham 69 **7.** The Skids **8.** The Boomtown Rats **9.** 'David Watts' **10.** Billy Idol **11.** Eddie and The Hot Rods **12.** The Clash ('Should I Stay Or Should I Go)' **13.** 'No One Is Innocent (A Punk Prayer By Ronald Biggs)' **14.** The Stranglers **15.** The Buzzcocks **16.** 'Eloise'

U2 1

Answers on page 83

1. Which Dublin hearing-aid shop inspired Paul Hewson in his choice of stage name?

2. What did U2 find themselves supporting in Dallas during their 1981 US tour?

3. What was the title of U2's second album?

4. From which album was 'New Year's Day' taken?

5. Which U2 track was dedicated to Martin Luther King Jnr?

6. Which was U2's first live album?

7. Which U2 single was a tribute to Billie Holliday?

8. In which unusual setting was the album 'The Unforgettable Fire' recorded?

9. What was the first track on 'The Unforgettable Fire'?

10. In which year was 'The Joshua Tree' released?

11. What is The Edge's real name?

12. Which was U2's fourth UK number one album?

13. Which was U2's first UK number one single?

14. Which U2 single was taken from the film *Batman Forever*?

15. Which mammoth U2 tour began in 1992?

16. The video for which single was filmed on the roof of a Los Angeles building?

Pot Luck 9

Answers on page 88

1. Which one-time drummer with The Farm is a scriptwriter for *Brookside*?

2. Which band's albums included 'Pictures At An Exhibition', 'Tarkus' and 'Brain Salad Surgery'?

3. What was the name of Dion's backing group?

4. Jake Hooker, Alan Merrill and Paul Varley made up which Seventies teenybop group that had their own TV series?

5. Which American country singer who enjoyed widespread chart success in the late Sixties used to be backed by a band known as The Western Wranglers?

6. What were the names of the two Bellamy Brothers?

7. Which singer was the subject of Don McLean's 'American Pie'?

8. Which band named themselves after an unpopular gym teacher at their school?

9. Which Beatle was previously paid £2 10s a week as a messenger for British Railways?

10. Gwen Stefani led which chart-topping band of the Nineties?

11. Who was the vocalist with Sad Café before going solo?

12. Which successful American singer/songwriter of the Seventies once worked as a computer specialist at a Los Angeles bank?

13. Which four-piece band lost two of its members to drug deaths in successive years – 1982 and 1983?

14. Which UK Sixties band were previously known as The Ravens?

15. In which year did Roy Orbison die?

16. How many UK number ones has Engelbert Humperdinck had?

Answers to page 88
ABBA 1: **1.** The Hep Stars **2.** 'Ring Ring' **3.** 'S.O.S.' **4.** 'Mamma Mia'
5. Five **6.** 'Money, Money, Money' (it only reached no. 3) **7.** 'Fernando'
8. 1978 **9.** 1978 **10.** 'Voulez-Vous' **11.** Because of statements they made on TV supporting Polish Solidarity **12.** 1981 **13.** 'Super Trouper'
14. It is the only case of a palindromic artist and title **15.** 'Knowing Me, Knowing You' **16.** 'Thank You For The Music'

Albums 4

Answers on page 89

1. Which band released the 1996 album 'Moseley Shoals'?

2. Who had a number one album called 'Very' in 1993?

3. Which 1983 UK number one album was inspired by the teachings of therapist Arthur Janov?

4. Which Michael Jackson album spent 173 weeks in the UK charts?

5. What was the biggest-selling UK album of 1989?

6. Which Irish band released a 1994 album titled 'Everybody Else Is Doing It, So Why Can't We?'

7. Which is the best-selling album of all time in the UK?

8. 'Pet Sounds' was a ground-breaking 1966 album for which American band?

9. What was the eagerly awaited follow-up to Oasis's '(What's The Story) Morning Glory'?

10. Which 1978 album went on to spend 395 weeks in the UK charts?

11. Which Michael Jackson album was the UK best-seller of 1987?

12. Whose number one album was 'Back To Front' in 1992?

13. Which band released 'A Question Of Balance' in 1970?

14. 'Electric Warrior' was a number one album for which band in 1972?

15. Who reckoned 'Blondes Have More Fun' in 1978?

16. Who released the double album 'Tusk' in 1979?

Answers to page 89
COVER VERSIONS 3: **1.** Saragossa Band **2.** 'I Still Believe' **3.** Westlife **4.** 'It Only Takes A Minute' **5.** Randy and The Rainbows **6.** 'I Shot The Sheriff' **7.** 'Indian Love Call' **8.** Mariah Carey **9.** Sunny Dae and The Knights **10.** Undercover **11.** 'Could It Be Magic' **12.** Harold Melvin and The Bluenotes **13.** Fine Young Cannibals **14.** 'Reach Out I'll Be There' **15.** Doris Troy **16.** 'Can't Take My Eyes Off You'

Abba I

Answers on page 86

1. With which top Swedish band was Benny Andersson the pianist before forming Abba?

2. The year before *Waterloo*, which other Abba composition had failed to be chosen as Sweden's Eurovision Song Contest entry?

3. Which Abba single had previously been recorded by Agnetha on her solo album 'Eleven Women In One Building'?

4. Which Abba song ended the nine-week reign of Queen's 'Bohemian Rhapsody' at the top of the UK singles chart?

5. How many singles did Abba have in Australia's top 30 at one time in 1976?

6. Six out of seven successive Abba singles reached number one in the UK. Which was the one to miss out?

7. Which single had already been recorded by Frida on her album 'Frida Alone'?

8. Which year saw the premier of *Abba – The Movie*?

9. In which year did Benny and Frida marry and Bjorn and Agnetha file for divorce?

10. Which was the first album recorded at Abba's Polar Studios in Stockholm?

11. Why were Abba banned from the Soviet Union in 1982?

12. When did Benny and Frida split up?

13. Which was Abba's last UK number one single?

14. What is unique about 'S.O.S.' by Abba?

15. Which Abba track was the title of a Steve Coogan comedy series?

16. What was Abba's last single before the break-up of the group?

Answers to page 86
POT LUCK 9: **1.** Roy Boulter **2.** Emerson, Lake and Palmer **3.** The Belmonts **4.** Arrows **5.** Glen Campbell **6.** Howard and David **7.** Buddy Holly **8.** Lynyrd Skynyrd (Leonard Skinner) **9.** Ringo Starr **10.** No Doubt **11.** Paul Young **12.** Harry Nilsson **13.** The Pretenders **14.** The Kinks **15.** 1988 **16.** Two – 'Release Me' and 'The Last Waltz'

Cover Versions 3

Answers on page 87

1. Who originally recorded 'Agadoo', covered by Black Lace in 1984?

2. Which song links Brenda K. Starr and Mariah Carey?

3. Who covered Billy Joel's 'Uptown Girl' in 2001?

4. One Hundred Ton and A Feather, Tavares and Take That have all recorded which song?

5. Who originally recorded Blondie's 1978 hit 'Denis'?

6. Which Eric Clapton hit did Warren G cover in 1997?

7. Which song was recorded by Slim Whitman, Karl Denver and Ray Stevens in three different decades?

8. Who recently covered 'Against All Odds (Take A Look At Me Now)', a hit for Phil Collins in 1984?

9. Who recorded the original version of 'Rock Around The Clock' in 1952?

10. Who covered Gerry Rafferty's 'Baker Street' in 1992?

11. Donna Summer, Barry Manilow and Take That have all recorded which song?

12. Who originally recorded 'Don't Leave Me This Way', a 1986 hit for The Communards?

13. Who covered Elvis Presley's 'Suspicious Minds' in 1986?

14. Which song links The Four Tops, Gloria Gaynor and Michael Bolton?

15. Who was the first artist to record The Hollies' 'Just One Look'?

16. Frankie Valli, Andy Williams and Boystown Gang have all recorded which song?

Answers to page 87
ALBUMS 4: **1.** Ocean Colour Scene **2.** The Pet Shop Boys **3.** 'The Hurting' (Tears For Fears) **4.** 'Thriller' **5.** 'Ten Good Reasons' (Jason Donovan) **6.** The Cranberries **7.** 'Sgt. Pepper's Lonely Hearts Club Band' **8.** The Beach Boys **9.** 'Be Here Now' **10.** 'Bat Out Of Hell' (Meat Loaf) **11.** 'Bad' **12.** Lionel Richie **13.** The Moody Blues **14.** T. Rex **15.** Rod Stewart **16.** Fleetwood Mac

Singer/Songwriters 2

Answers on page 92

1. How old was Kate Bush when she wrote the lyrics to 'The Man With The Child In His Eyes'?

2. What was the title of Tracy Chapman's biggest-selling single?

3. What was Neil Diamond's first UK hit?

4. Which Neil Diamond song was autobiographical?

5. About whom did Elton John write 'Someone Saved My Life Tonight'?

6. And which Elton John song was a tribute to tennis player Billie Jean King?

7. Which song did Billy Joel write about his first wife and manager, Elizabeth?

8. What is Prince's full name?

9. What was the title of Prince's debut album?

10. Which Neil Sedaka song was banned by several US radio stations?

11. Which Neil Sedaka hit was subsequently covered by The Partridge Family?

12. As what was Stevie Wonder known on his early releases?

13. Who cut his first solo record under the name True Taylor?

14. Who provided falsetto backing on Elton John's 'Nikita'?

15. What was George Michael's second solo UK number one?

16. Who received 461 Valentine's Day cards after indicating that she never received any in the lyrics of her 1975 song 'At Seventeen'?

Answers to page 92
DANCE 2: 1. Bryan Adams 2. Fragma 3. Ibiza 4. Fatboy Slim 5. 'Move Your Body' 6. Des Mitchell 7. Taka Boom 8. Germany 9. 9pm 10. Alice Deejay 11. Moloko 12. Antoine Clamaran 13. Shout 14. Gram'ma Funk 15. Spiller 16. French

Chart Toppers 5

Answers on page 93

1. Who were the first father and son to have topped the UK charts?

2. Who were the first father and daughter to top the UK charts?

3. Which soul artist was the subject of 'Geno' by Dexy's Midnight Runners?

4. What nationality is Johnny Logan?

5. Which TV theme reached number one in the UK in 1980?

6. Who sang on Adamski's 1990 number one 'Killer'?

7. Who was the first black female artist to reach number one in the UK?

8. Who were the first female duo to top the UK singles chart?

9. Which 1972 number one was a tribute to a 19th-century artist?

10. Who had a number one in 1999 with 'Flat Beat'?

11. What was the best-selling UK single of 1976?

12. Who was the lead singer of Union Gap who had a 1968 number one with 'Young Girl'?

13. Which 1969 chart topper was born Roberta Lee Streeter before taking her stage surname from a film?

14. Which Eurovision Song Contest winner topped the UK charts in 1982?

15. Who had a 1959 number one with 'Here Comes Summer'?

16. Who were the first mother and son to reach number one in the UK?

Answers to page 93
BOB DYLAN 1: **1.** Robert Zimmerman **2.** Dylan Thomas **3.** 1962 **4.** His girlfriend Suze Rotolo **5.** 'The Times They Are A-Changin' **6.** 'Bringing It All Back Home' **7.** Newport Folk Festival **8.** 'Mr Tambourine Man' **9.** 'Like A Rolling Stone' **10.** Manfred Mann **11.** *Pat Garrett and Billy the Kid* **12.** 1991 **13.** Al Kooper **14.** His then wife Sarah Lowndes **15.** The Grateful Dead **16.** 'Tarantula'

Dance 2

Answers on page 90

1. Which male solo artist sang with Chicane on the single 'Don't Give Up'?

2. Which dance group had a number one hit with 'Toca's Miracle'?

3. Where were Vengaboys going to in the title of their 1999 single?

4. Who is Norman Cook better known as?

5. What was Eiffel 65's follow-up to 'Blue'?

6. Who Welcomed You To The Dance?

7. Who featured with Joey Negro on the single 'Must Be The Music'?

8. Which country does the DJ Sash come from?

9. At what time did ATB say they would come in the title of their 1999 single?

10. Who released the single 'Better Off Alone'?

11. Who wanted you to 'Sing It Back'?

12. Who had a single titled 'We Come To Party'?

13. Basement Jaxx wanted everyone to 'Jump 'n''…what?

14. Who did Groove Armada feature in their single 'I See You Baby'?

15. Who had a number one in 2000 with 'Groovejet'?

16. What nationality are Modjo?

Answers to page 90

SINGER/SONGWRITERS 2: **1.** 14 **2.** 'Fast Car' **3.** 'Crackling Rosie'
4. 'I Am…I Said' **5.** Long John Baldry **6.** 'Philadelphia Freedom' **7.** 'Just The Way You Are' **8.** Prince Rogers Nelson **9.** 'For You' **10.** 'I Go Ape'
11. 'Breaking Up Is Hard To Do' **12.** Little Stevie Wonder **13.** Paul Simon
14. George Michael **15.** 'A Different Corner' **16.** Janis Ian

Bob Dylan 1

Answers on page 91

1. What is Bob Dylan's real name?

2. After which poet did he reputedly name himself?

3. In which year did Dylan make his first appearance in the UK?

4. Who was pictured on the cover of his second album, 'The Freewheelin' Bob Dylan'?

5. Which was Dylan's first UK single?

6. Which Dylan album features 'Subterranean Homesick Blues'?

7. At which 1965 festival did folk purists in the audience try to boo Dylan off stage?

8. Which Dylan song was a US number one for The Byrds in 1965?

9. Which six-minute track became Dylan's first million-selling single?

10. Which UK band had a 1966 hit with a cover version of Dylan's 'Just Like A Woman'?

11. In which Sam Peckinpah film did Dylan play an outlaw named Alias?

12. In which year did Dylan receive a Lifetime Achievement Award at the Grammys?

13. Which member of Blood Sweat and Tears played the organ on 'Like A Rolling Stone'?

14. For whom did Dylan write 'Lay Lady Lay'?

15. Which band collaborated with Dylan on the 1989 album 'Dylan And The Dead'?

16. Which Dylan novel was published in 1970?

Answers to page 91
CHART TOPPERS 5: **1.** Ringo Starr (Beatles) and Zak Starkey (who sang with The Crowd on the charity record 'You'll Never Walk Alone' in 1985) **2.** Frank and Nancy Sinatra ('Something Stupid') **3.** Geno Washington **4.** Australian **5.** 'Theme From M*A*S*H (Suicide Is Painless)' **6.** Seal **7.** Winifred Atwell **8.** Baccara **9.** 'Vincent' (Van Gogh) by Don McLean **10.** Mr Oizo **11.** 'Save Your Kisses For Me' **12.** Gary Puckett **13.** Bobbie Gentry **14.** 'A Little Peace' by Nicole **15.** Jerry Keller **16.** Hilda and Rob Woodward of Lieutenant Pigeon

Eighties 3

Answers on page 96

Who had UK hits with the following tracks in the Eighties?

1. 'Driving In My Car'

2. 'The Riddle'

3. 'Sweet Dreams (Are Made Of This)'

4. 'Suburbia'

5. 'Happy Hour'

6. 'The Cutter'

7. 'Da Da Da'

8. 'Ghostdancing'

9. 'Hard Habit To Break'

10. 'Truly'

11. 'Mystify'

12. 'Somewhere In My Heart'

13. 'A View To A Kill'

14. 'Only When You Leave'

15. 'Fields Of Fire (400 Miles)'

16. 'Is That Love?'

Answers to page 96
POT LUCK 10: **1.** Charles Manson **2.** The Clash **3.** 1970 **4.** Girlschool **5.** Kid Creole and The Coconuts **6.** Dusty Springfield **7.** Olivia Newton-John **8.** They used to ban any song about death **9.** Eric Bazilian **10.** Howard Greenfield **11.** James Taylor **12.** Showaddywaddy **13.** The Dreamers **14.** 'Red Red Wine' **15.** Peter Gabriel **16.** Jimmy Page

Lyrics 3

Answers on page 97

From which songs are the following lyrics taken?

1. 'You gave away the things you loved, and one of them was me'

2. 'Good or bad, like it or not, it's the only one we've got'

3. 'Oh yeah, I'll tell you something, I think you'll understand'

4. 'Since you've been gone I've been lost'

5. 'All I want is a photo in my wallet, a small remembrance of something more solid'

6. 'Street's like a jungle so call the police, following the herd down to Greece'

7. 'We don't talk about love, we only want to get drunk'

8. 'I never thought it would happen with me and a girl from Clapham'

9. 'These are my salad days slowly being eaten away'

10. 'Well, I'm standing on a corner in Winslow, Arizona'

11. 'You've found the secret code I use to wash away my lonely blues'

12. 'My hands are shaky and my knees are weak, I can't seem to stand on my own two feet'

13. 'You got beautiful eyes, you got beautiful thighs, you've got a lot without a doubt'

14. 'She calls out to the man on the street, he can see she's been crying'

15. 'You're my sun, my moon, my guiding star'

16. 'Once I get you up there I'll be holding you so near'

Answers to page 97
GIRL BANDS 2: **1.** Vicki and Debbi Peterson **2.** Siobhan Fahey **3.** Jean Terrell **4.** The Shangri-Las **5.** Martha and The Vandellas **6.** 'Too Much' **7.** Prince **8.** Christopher **9.** 'Venus' **10.** Fun Boy Three **11.** Lois **12.** It was his motorbike that was revved on 'Leader Of The Pack' **13.** The Supremes **14.** 'Walk Like An Egyptian' **15.** 1989 **16.** The Shirelles

Pot Luck 10

Answers on page 94

1. Which notorious killer was among those who auditioned unsuccessfully for The Monkees?

2. 'Topper' Headon was drummer with which punk band?

3. In which year was the Glastonbury Festival first held?

4. Enid Williams and Kim McAuliffe founded which all-female heavy metal band?

5. Which band had seven UK hits between 1981 and 1983, including three in the top ten, but never once entered the US top 100?

6. Which Sixties singer had been sacked from her sales job at Bentalls department store in Kingston, Surrey, after blowing all the fuses?

7. Which Australian singer's grandfather won the 1954 Nobel Prize for physics?

8. Why did the BBC ban 'Tell Laura I Love Her', Ricky Valance's 1960 hit?

9. Who wrote Joan Osborne's 1996 hit 'One Of Us'?

10. With which lyricist did Neil Sedaka team up in the early Fifties?

11. To whom was Carly Simon married from 1972 to 1983?

12. Dave Bartram was lead singer with which rock 'n' roll revival band?

13. What was the name of Freddie Garrity's backing band?

14. Which Neil Diamond song did UB40 take to number one in 1983?

15. Who played flute on Cat Stevens's 'Lady D'Arbanville'?

16. Which legendary rock guitarist played on Donovan's 'Sunshine Superman'?

Answers to page 94
EIGHTIES 3: **1.** Madness **2.** Nik Kershaw **3.** The Eurythmics **4.** Pet Shop Boys **5.** The Housemartins **6.** Echo and The Bunnymen **7.** Trio **8.** Simple Minds **9.** Chicago **10.** Lionel Richie **11.** INXS **12.** Aztec Camera **13.** Duran Duran **14.** Spandau Ballet **15.** Big Country **16.** Squeeze

Girl Bands 2

Answers on page 95

1. Which two sisters were members of The Bangles?
2. Which member of Bananarama used to work in the press office at Decca Records?
3. Who replaced Diana Ross in The Supremes?
4. Which Sixties band were composed of two pairs of sisters?
5. Which girl band had a 1965 hit with 'Nowhere To Run'?
6. Which single enabled the Spice Girls to become the first act to have their first six releases reach number one in the UK charts?
7. Who wrote The Bangles' 'Manic Monday'?
8. Under what pseudonym did he write it?
9. Which cover of a Shocking Blue hit from 1970 did Bananarama take to number eight in the UK charts in 1986?
10. With whom did Bananarama team up for the 1982 hit 'It Ain't What You Do, It's The Way That You Do It'?
11. Which sister of Martha Reeves joined the Vandellas in 1968?
12. What important role did Joey Veneri play in the history of The Shangri-Las?
13. Which girl group appeared as nuns in a 1968 episode of the TV series *Tarzan*?
14. Which Bangles hit had previously been rejected by Toni Basil?
15. In which year did The Bangles split up?
16. Shirley Owens, 'Micki' Harris, Doris Coley and Beverly Lee were the original members of which girl group?

Answers to page 95
LYRICS 3: **1.** 'You're So Vain' (Carly Simon) **2.** 'I Won't Let The Sun Go Down On Me' (Nik Kershaw) **3.** 'I Want To Hold Your Hand' (The Beatles) **4.** 'Every Breath You Take' (The Police) **5.** 'Picture This' (Blondie) **6.** 'Girls And Boys' (Blur) **7.** 'A Design For Life' (Manic Street Preachers) **8.** 'Up The Junction' (Squeeze) **9.** 'Gold' (Spandau Ballet) **10.** 'Take It Easy' (The Eagles) **11.** 'Sex Bomb' (Tom Jones) **12.** 'All Shook Up' (Elvis Presley) **13.** 'Rabbit' (Chas and Dave) **14.** 'Another Day In Paradise' (Phil Collins) **15.** 'You're The First, The Last, My Everything' (Barry White) **16.** 'Come Fly With Me' (Frank Sinatra)

Led Zeppelin 1

Answers on page 100

1. Whose remark about a disastrous gig 'going down like a lead zeppelin' resulted in the band acquiring their new name?

2. Which headliners at a 1969 Boston gig refused to take the stage after support act Led Zeppelin had gone down so well?

3. In which year was the 'Led Zeppelin' album released?

4. In which year did Led Zeppelin release their first single in the UK?

5. Which track earned the band their only US gold disc single?

6. Why did the band play a 1970 gig in Copenhagen as The Nobs?

7. 'Stairway To Heaven' first appeared on which album?

8. What is the playing time of 'Stairway To Heaven'?

9. On which island was Robert Plant badly injured in a 1975 car crash?

10. In which year did John Bonham die?

11. Who replaced Bonham when Led Zeppelin reformed in 1988?

12. What was the name of Led Zeppelin's own record label, first used in 1974?

13. Which band did Jimmy Page join in 1960?

14. With which band was Robert Plant performing when Jimmy Page first saw him?

15. The keys to which American city were Led Zeppelin given in April 1970?

16. Which album featured 'Immigrant Song'?

Answers to page 100
FILM TRACKS 3: 1. 'Blaze Of Glory' 2. *Bean: The Movie* 3. Stealers Wheel
4. 'She' 5. 'A View To A Kill' 6. 'Silver Dream Machine' 7. *Wild Wild West*
8. Huey Lewis and The News 9. 'The King Of Wishful Thinking'
10. *Trainspotting* 11. *The Graduate* 12. 'I Still Haven't Found What I'm Looking For' 13. *Footloose* 14. 'Raindrops Keep Falling On My Head'
15. 'It Must Have Been Love' 16. Barbra Streisand

Novelty Numbers 2

Answers on page 101

1. Who was strongly advised not to look in the lyrics of Ray Stevens's 'The Streak'?

2. Which midget did Ray Stevens take to number two in the UK charts in 1971?

3. Which TV soldiers had a number one with an old Inkspots song in 1975?

4. And what was the title of the song?

5. Which long-deceased comedians had a number two hit in 1975?

6. Which song did the 1970 England World Cup Squad take to number one?

7. Which footballer was the subject of The Cockerel Chorus's 1973 hit?

8. Which star of a TV docusoap covered a Madness hit in 1997?

9. Who had a hit with 'Vindaloo' in 1998?

10. Who were 'Doctorin' The Tardis' in 1988?

11. Which doll did Aqua take to number one for four weeks in 1997?

12. Which Indie band teamed up with Frank Skinner and David Baddiel for 'Three Lions' in 1996?

13. What did Baz Luhrmann say everybody was free to wear in 1999?

14. Which comedian charted in 1962 using his catchphrase in a version of 'Singin' In The Rain'?

15. Which old Traffic number was a hit for one of *The Young Ones* in 1984?

16. Which TV policeman had a number two hit with the theme from his series in 1992?

Answers to page 101
SEVENTIES 3: **1.** C.W. McCall ('Convoy') **2.** 'Love Grows (Where My Rosemary Goes)' by Edison Lighthouse **3.** Chicory Tip **4.** Chas Chandler **5.** David Cassidy **6.** The Bay City Rollers **7.** Curved Air **8.** He often wore a bee-like, black and yellow striped top **9.** The Rolling Stones **10.** Genesis **11.** 'Tie A Yellow Ribbon Round The Old Oak Tree' **12.** Slade **13.** The Rubettes **14.** David Essex **15.** Mott The Hoople **16.** Grace Slick (Jefferson Airplane)

Film Tracks 3

Answers on page 98

1. Which Bon Jovi song was used in the film *Young Guns II*?

2. Which film featured Boyzone's 'Picture Of You'?

3. Who recorded 'Stuck In The Middle With You' which was heard in the Quentin Tarantino film *Reservoir Dogs*?

4. Which Elvis Costello song was used in *Notting Hill*?

5. Which Duran Duran song was the theme to a Bond movie?

6. Which David Essex hit was taken from *Silver Dream Racer*?

7. Which 1999 film featured 'Balaimos' by Enrique Iglesias?

8. Whose recording of 'Power Of Love' was heard in *Back To The Future*?

9. Which Go West song was used in the film *Pretty Woman*?

10. Which film included Iggy Pop's 'Lust For Life'?

11. Simon and Garfunkel's 'Mrs Robinson' was taken from which film?

12. Which U2 hit was used in *Runaway Bride*?

13. Bonnie Tyler's 'Holding Out For A Hero' was taken from which film?

14. Sacha Distel had a hit with which track from *Butch Cassidy and the Sundance Kid*?

15. Which Roxette hit was taken from *Pretty Woman*?

16. Who had a 1977 hit with the theme from *A Star Is Born*?

Answers to page 98
LED ZEPPELIN 1: 1. Keith Moon 2. Iron Butterfly 3. 1969 4. 1997
5. 'Whole Lotta Love' 6. Eva von Zeppelin, relative of the airship
designer, had threatened to sue if the family name was used in Denmark
7. 'Led Zeppelin IV' 8. 8min 1 sec 9. Rhodes 10. 1980 11. His son Jason
12. Swan Song 13. Neil Christian and The Crusaders
14. Hobbstweedle 15. Memphis 16. 'Led Zeppelin III'

Seventies 3

Answers on page 99

1. Which one-hit wonder of 1976 went on to become mayor of Ouray, Colorado?

2. Which 1970 UK number one was recorded by a group of session musicians?

3. Peter Hewson was the singer with which 1972 UK chart toppers?

4. Which Animal managed Slade?

5. Who was featured bare-chested on the cover of *Rolling Stone* in January 1972?

6. Which teenybop group had their own TV series called *Shang-A-Lang*?

7. With which progressive rockers was Stewart Copeland the drummer before forming The Police?

8. How did Gordon Sumner acquire his nickname of 'Sting'?

9. Which band's equipment van was dynamited during a 1972 tour of Canada?

10. Which band recorded the album 'Selling England By The Pound'?

11. Which 1973 hit told the story of an ex-con returning home to his loved one after serving a three-year jail sentence?

12. Which band were pilloried by teachers in the belief that their phonetic spelling of titles set a bad example to children?

13. Who had a 1974 hit with 'Juke Box Jive'?

14. 'Gonna Make You A Star' was the first number one for which artist?

15. Overend Watts, 'Buffin' and Ariel Bender were members of which Seventies band?

16. Which singer with an American band wanted to name her daughter God before settling for China?

Answers to page 99
NOVELTY NUMBERS 2: **1.** Ethel **2.** Bridget **3.** Windsor Davies and Don Estelle **4.** 'Whispering Grass' **5.** Laurel and Hardy **6.** 'Back Home'
7. Cyril Knowles ('Nice One Cyril') **8.** Maureen Rees ('Driving In My Car') **9.** Fat Les **10.** The Timelords **11.** Barbie **12.** The Lightning Seeds **13.** Sunscreen **14.** Norman Vaughan ('Swinging In The Rain') **15.** 'Hole In My Shoe' (Neil) **16.** Nick Berry ('Heartbeat')

Folk 2

Answers on page 104

1. Which dead-pan Yorkshire folk singer told the story of 'Sister Josephine'?

2. Who was born Janis Fink?

3. Which trio originally comprised Bob Shane, Nick Reynolds and Dave Guard?

4. George, Finbar, Eddie and Paul made up which Irish family band?

5. What was Peter, Paul and Mary's first UK chart success?

6. Who had a lovely time on a 1979 day trip to North Wales?

7. With which song did Steeleye Span have a top five hit in 1975?

8. Whose debut album was 'If You Saw Through My Eyes'?

9. Which dead comedy genius was the subject of Al Stewart's 1977 hit 'Year Of The Cat'?

10. From which country do Runrig hail?

11. Which of The Spinners has an actor son who has appeared in *Soldier, Soldier* and *Brookside*?

12. Which Lancashire group were originally known as The Wednesday Folks?

13. Which band were formed in 1962 in the back of O'Donoghue's bar in Dublin?

14. What nationality were The Bushwackers?

15. Mike Heron, Robin Williamson and Clive Palmer formed which folk band in Glasgow in 1965?

16. Which band had a 1966 UK hit with 'Three Wheels On My Wagon'?

Answers to page 104
POT LUCK 11: 1. 'When Irish Eyes Are Smiling' 2. Love Affair
3. 'A Hard Rain's A-Gonna Fall' 4. 'Gypsies, Tramps And White Trash'
5. 'Speedy Gonzales' 6. Keith Richard 7. 'What's The New Mary Jane'
8. Bread 9. Rochdale 10. 'It's Good News Week' 11. Tina Turner
12. Annie Lennox 13. David Bowie 14. Eddie Miller 15. 'Saturday Night Fever' 16. Marty Wilde

Beach Boys 1

Answers on page 105

1. Which Beach Boys' single put new lyrics to Chuck Berry's 'Sweet Little Sixteen'?

2. Which guest artist played lead guitar on 'Good Vibrations'?

3. Which group originally recorded 'Barbara Ann'?

4. Which B-side of 'I Get Around' had been written for The Ronettes but had been rejected by Phil Spector?

5. Who joined the band as a temporary replacement for Brian Wilson in 1965?

6. Who became a full-time Beach Boy in 1965?

7. Which half of a surfing duo sang backing vocals on 'Barbara Ann'?

8. Which Beach Boys single was a traditional Caribbean tune dating back to 1927?

9. Which song beat 'Good Vibrations' to win a 1967 Grammy Award?

10. Which Beach Boy was acquitted of draft evasion in 1967?

11. In which year was 'Darlin'' released?

12. From which album was 'Cottonfields' taken?

13. What was The Beach Boys' second UK number one single?

14. Who joined The Beach Boys for 'Fun Fun Fun' in 1996?

15. What relation was Mike Love to the Wilson brothers?

16. Who suffered a mental breakdown after *Pet Sounds*?

Answers to page 105
ALBUMS 5: 1. Slade 2. The Bee Gees 3. Cher 4. Squeeze 5. Paul Simon 6. Carly Simon 7. Paul McCartney 8. Catatonia 9. The Eagles 10. Roxy Music 11. Elton John 12. Madonna 13. Neil Young 14. Mariah Carey 15. Bread 16. Billy Joel

Pot Luck 11

Answers on page 102

1. Which traditional Irish song was written by George Graff, a German who never set foot in Ireland in his life?

2. Steve Ellis was lead singer with which Sixties band?

3. Which Bob Dylan song gave Bryan Ferry his first solo hit?

4. What was the original title of Cher's hit 'Gypsies, Tramps And Thieves'?

5. Which Pat Boone song was banned in the US for being offensive to Mexicans?

6. Which member of The Rolling Stones was jailed in 1967 for allowing his house to be used for the illegal smoking of cannabis?

7. What would have been the next Beatles single had the band not split?

8. Which band came up with their name after being stuck in traffic behind a Wonder Bread lorry?

9. Where did Mike Harding's Cowboy come from?

10. What was the only hit of Hedgehoppers Anonymous?

11. Which glamorous granny was born Annie Mae Bullock?

12. Which female singer used to work in an Aberdeen fish factory?

13. Bing Crosby and Marc Bolan both died within weeks of recording TV shows with which singer?

14. Who originally recorded the Engelbert Humperdinck number one 'Release Me'?

15. Which was the biggest-selling album of 1978?

16. Which rock 'n' roller wrote the Status Quo hit 'Ice In The Sun'?

Answers to page 102
FOLK 2: **1.** Jake Thackray **2.** Janis Ian **3.** The Kingston Trio **4.** The Fureys **5.** 'Blowing In The Wind' **6.** Fiddler's Dram ('Day Trip To Bangor (Didn't We Have A Lovely Time)') **7.** 'All Around My Hat' **8.** Iain Matthews **9.** Tony Hancock **10.** Scotland **11.** Mick Groves (father of David Groves) **12.** Fivepenny Piece **13.** The Dubliners **14.** Australian **15.** Incredible String Band **16.** The New Christy Minstrels

Albums 5

Answers on page 103

Which artists released the following albums?

1. 'Slayed?' (1973)

2. 'Spirits Having Flown' (1979)

3. 'Love Hurts' (1991)

4. 'East Side Story' (1981)

5. 'Graceland' (1987)

6. 'No Secrets' (1973)

7. 'Flowers In The Dirt' (1989)

8. 'Equally Cursed And Blessed' (1999)

9. 'The Long Run' (1979)

10. 'Manifesto' (1979)

11. 'Don't Shoot Me I'm Only The Piano Player' (1973)

12. 'True Blue' (1986)

13. 'After The Goldrush' (1970)

14. 'Daydream' (1995)

15. 'On The Waters' (1970)

16. 'An Innocent Man' (1983)

Answers to page 103
BEACH BOYS 1: **1.** 'Surfin' USA' **2.** Glen Campbell **3.** The Regents
4. 'Don't Worry Baby' **5.** Glen Campbell **6.** Bruce Johnston **7.** Dean
Torrence of Jan and Dean **8.** 'Sloop John B' **9.** 'Winchester Cathedral' by
The New Vaudeville Band **10.** Carl Wilson **11.** 1967 **12.** '20/20'
13. 'Do It Again' **14.** Status Quo **15.** Cousin **16.** Brian Wilson

Indie 2

Answers on page 108

1. Who found their way to 'Hope Street' in 1995?

2. Which was the first Lightning Seeds single to make the UK top twenty?

3. Which lead singer with The Verve has been concentrating on a solo career?

4. Which impersonator appeared on the Manic Street Preachers' album 'Everything Must Go'?

5. Who did Jarvis Cocker walk home from school in 'Disco 2000'?

6. Brothers Mark and Scott Morriss are members of which band?

7. Which actor did the narration on the Blur single 'Parklife'?

8. Which characters from *The X Files* gave Catatonia their first chart success?

9. Who had a hit with 'Trouble' in 2000?

10. Who asked: 'Why Does It Always Rain On Me'?

11. 'Supersonic' was which band's first UK hit?

12. Which band were named Best Newcomers at the 1995 Brit Awards?

13. Which band released the album 'Jollification'?

14. Martin Carr is the creative influence behind which band?

15. Danny Goffey, Gary Coombes and Mickey Quinn were the original members of which band?

16. Which Manic Street Preachers' single was dedicated to a photographer friend of the band who had committed suicide?

Answers to page 108
GARAGE 1: **1.** Romina Johnson **2.** DJ Luck and MC Neat
3. Truesteppers **4.** Misteeq **5.** Victoria Beckham **6.** Melanie Blatt
7. Craig David **8.** Bomfunk MCs **9.** 'Woman Trouble' **10.** Donell Jones and Brian Harvey **11.** Finland **12.** 'Fill Me In' **13.** DJ Luck and MC Neat
14. Oxide and Neutrino **15.** Break dancing **16.** 2

Eurovision 2

Answers on page 109

1. Which country's 1960 entry, 'Voi-Voi', was an arrangement of a traditional Lapp reindeer-herding call?

2. Which country boycotted the 1981 contest, saying that it was too old-fashioned?

3. Which country blacked out Israel's victorious 1978 entry?

4. Who was 'A Man Without Love' for the UK in the 1966 contest?

5. Which country called their 1977 entry 'Boom Boom Boomerang' in protest at inane Eurovision song titles?

6. Which blonde actress came tenth for the UK in 1991?

7. In which year did the UK win the Eurovision for the first time?

8. Who won for Monaco in 1971 with 'Un Banc, Un Arbre, Une Rue'?

9. Which country gained their first win in the contest in 2001?

10. Which transsexual won for Israel in 1998?

11. Where did Lynsey De Paul and Mike Moran finish with 'Rock Bottom' in 1977?

12. Which nation achieved an unprecedented hat-trick of wins between 1992 and 1994?

13. In 1973, which country became the first to retain the Eurovision crown?

14. What was the UK entry when Abba won in 1974?

15. Which country's 1985 entrant was Vikki, followed two years later by Rikki?

16. In 1987, which country's group were referred to by BBC presenter Ray Moore as 'an ugly crowd', thereby sparking a diplomatic row?

Answers to page 109
DISCO 1: 1. 'How Deep Is Your Love' 2. Donna Summer 3. Baccara 4. 'Night fever' 5. 'Stayin' Alive' 6. John Travolta and Olivia Newton-John 7. Disco Tex 8. 'Love To Love You Baby' 9. Biddu 10. 'I Love To Love (But My Baby Loves To Dance)' 11. Baccara 12. 'I Feel Love' 13. 'Down Deep Inside' 14. Seven 15. 'Sorry I'm A Lady' 16. The Electric Dolls

Garage 1

Answers on page 106

1. Who featured on Artful Dodger's single 'Movin' Too Fast'?

2. Who had a hit with 'A Little Bit Of Luck'?

3. Dane Bowers sang with which Garage band?

4. Which group released 'All I Want'?

5. Which Spice Girl sang with Truesteppers?

6. Which member of All Saints sang on Artful Dodger's 2001 single 'TwentyFourSeven'?

7. Who had hits with '7 Days' and 'Walking Away'?

8. Which band had a hit with 'Freestyler'?

9. Robbie Craig and Craig David sang on which Artful Dodger single?

10. Which two male artists sang on 'True Step Tonight'?

11. Bomfunk MCs are from which country?

12. What was Craig David's first solo single?

13. Who released 'Piano Loco'?

14. Who sampled the *Casualty* theme tune in one of their singles?

15. What type of dancing do Bomfunk MCs feature in their performances?

16. What number did 'Out Of Your Mind', Victoria Beckham's single with Truesteppers, reach in the UK charts?

Answers to page 106
INDIE 2: **1.** The Levellers **2.** 'Pure' **3.** Richard Ashcroft **4.** 'Elvis Impersonator' **5.** Deborah **6.** The Bluetones **7.** Phil Daniels **8.** 'Mulder And Scully' **9.** Coldplay **10.** Travis **11.** Oasis **12.** Oasis **13.** The Lightning Seeds **14.** Boo Radleys **15.** Supergrass **16.** 'Kevin Carter'

Disco 1

Answers on page 107

1. Which was the first Bee Gees single to be released from *Saturday Night Fever*?

2. Which disco queen was born LaDonna Andrea Gaines?

3. Maria Mendiola and Mayte Mateus were better known as which duo?

4. Which disco record did The Bee Gees take to number one in April 1978?

5. Which Bee Gees hit did N-Trance take into the charts 17 years later?

6. Which Seventies duo's first two singles reached number one in the UK?

7. Who sang with The Sex-O-Lettes?

8. Which Donna Summer hit was inspired by a re-issue of 'Je T'Aime...Moi Non Plus'?

9. Which Indian producer worked with Tina Charles?

10. Which song did Tina Charles take to number one in 1976?

11. Who became the first Spanish act to hit number one in the UK?

12. Which Donna Summer record was at number one when Elvis Presley died?

13. Which Donna Summer hit was taken from the film *The Deep*?

14. How many Bee Gees songs were on the 'Saturday Night Fever' album?

15. What was Baccara's follow-up to 'Yes, Sir, I Can Boogie'?

16. Who originally recorded 'Dr Love', a disco hit for Tina Charles in 1976?

Answers to page 107
EUROVISION 2: 1. Norway 2. Italy 3. Jordan 4. Kenneth McKellar
5. Austria 6. Samantha Janus 7. 1967 8. Severine 9. Estonia 10. Dana International 11. Second 12. Ireland 13. Luxembourg 14. 'Long Live Love' (Olivia Newton-John) 15. United Kingdom 16. Turkey

One-Hit Wonders 4

Answers on page 112

1. Whose only UK hit was the 1975 single 'Eighteen With A Bullet'?

2. In 1957, which song gave The Southlanders their only UK top twenty hit?

3. Which 1968 song gave The Paper Dolls their only chart success?

4. Which Sixties namesakes of a Nineties heavy rock band had their only hit with 'Rainbow Chaser' in 1968?

5. Which song from *Paint Your Wagon* gave actor Lee Marvin an unexpected number one?

6. Who insisted: 'I'm Gonna Run Away From You' in 1971?

7. Which two disc jockeys parodied 'Convoy' as Laurie Lingo and The Dipsticks in 1976?

8. Whose only chart success was with the 1960 Eurovision Song Contest entry 'Looking High, High, High'?

9. Who was 'Swinging On A Star' in 1963?

10. Which forerunners of 10cc got to number two with 'Neanderthal Man' in 1970?

11. Who sang about 'Johnny Reggae' in 1971?

12. Who begged: 'Gimme Dat Ding' in 1970?

13. With which song did The Fantastics chart in 1971?

14. Who covered The Honeycombs' 'Have I The Right' in 1977?

15. Whose only chart action was with 'Mr Bass Man' in 1963?

16. Who reached number 14 in the UK charts with 'That's Nice' in 1966?

Answers to page 112
CHART TOPPERS 6: **1.** 1966 **2.** 1974 **3.** 1984 **4.** 1986 **5.** 1957 **6.** 1998 **7.** 1995 **8.** 1977 **9.** 1966 **10.** 1972 **11.** 1980 **12.** 1984 **13.** 1993 **14.** 1959 **15.** 1967 **16.** 1964

Lyrics 4

Answers on page 113

From which songs are the following lyrics taken?

1. 'Once upon a time I was falling in love, now I'm only falling apart'

2. 'I'm on the hunt down after you'

3. 'When they said you was high-classed, well that was just a lie'

4. 'How many heartaches must I stand before I find the love to let me live again'

5. 'Her eyes were making silent demands as her hair came undone in my hands'

6. 'Bittersweet memories, that is all I'm taking with me'

7. 'Every night I'm lying in bed holding you close in my dreams'

8. 'Some people live with the fear of a touch and the anger of having been a fool'

9. ''Cause the boy with the cold hard cash is always Mr Right'

10. 'Maybe I will never be all the things that I want to be'

11. 'But he's a liar and I'm not sure about you'

12. 'The young dreams should be dreamed together'

13. 'The Sweeney's doing ninety cos they've got the word to go and get a gang of villains in a shed up at Heathrow'

14. 'All the leaves are brown and the sky is grey'

15. 'Every morning I would see her waiting at the stop, sometimes she'd shop and she would show me what she'd bought'

16. 'Some girls like to run around, like to handle everything they see'

Answers to page 113
ROBBIE WILLIAMS 1: **1.** 'Freedom' **2.** 'Life Thru A Lens' **3.** Guy Chambers **4.** Tom Jones **5.** 1997 **6.** 'Life Thru A Lens' **7.** Barry Davies **8.** 'Millennium' **9.** 'No Regrets' **10.** 'I've Been Expecting You' **11.** Liam Gallagher **12.** Double-glazing **13.** Cutest Rush **14.** 'Back For Good' **15.** 3 **16.** Port Vale

Chart Toppers 6

Answers on page 110

In which years did the following tracks reach number one in the UK charts?

1. 'Pretty Flamingo' (Manfred Mann)

2. 'Jealous Mind' (Alvin Stardust)

3. 'Freedom' (Wham!)

4. 'Papa Don't Preach' (Madonna)

5. 'Diana' (Paul Anka)

6. 'Millennium' (Robbie Williams)

7. 'Back For Good' (Take That)

8. 'So You Win Again' (Hot Chocolate)

9. 'Strangers In The Night' (Frank Sinatra)

10. 'School's Out' (Alice Cooper)

11. 'Crying' (Don McLean)

12. 'The Reflex' (Duran Duran)

13. 'No Limit' (2 Unlimited)

14. 'Dream Lover' (Bobby Darin)

15. 'A Whiter Shade Of Pale' (Procul Harum)

16. 'The House Of The Rising Sun' (The Animals)

Answers to page 110
ONE-HIT WONDERS 4: **1.** Pete Wingfield **2.** 'Alone' **3.** 'Something Here In My Heart (Keeps A Tellin' Me No)' **4.** Nirvana **5.** 'Wand'rin' Star' **6.** Tami Lynn **7.** Paul Burnett and Dave Lee Travis **8.** Bryan Johnson **9.** Big Dee Irwin **10.** Hotlegs **11.** The Piglets **12.** Pipkins **13.** 'Something Old, Something New' **14.** The Dead End Kids **15.** Johnny Cymbal **16.** Neil Christian

Robbie Williams 1

Answers on page 111

1. Which cover of a George Michael song gave Robbie Williams his first solo hit?

2. What was the autobiographical title of his first solo album?

3. Who is Robbie's usual co-writer?

4. With whom did Robbie duet at the 1998 Brit Awards?

5. In which year was 'Angels' released?

6. From which album was 'Angels' taken?

7. Which sports commentator spoke on the video for 'She's The One'?

8. Which single sampled the theme from the James Bond movie *You Only Live Twice*?

9. Neil Tennant and Neil Hannon did guest vocals on which single?

10. Which was Robbie's number one album of 1998?

11. Which rival band member has Robbie publicly challenged to a fight?

12. What did Robbie used to sell for a living before joining Take That?

13. In which band did Robbie play with Gary Barlow and Howard Donald prior to Take That?

14. What was Robbie's last single with Take That?

15. What was the highest UK chart position of 'Let Me Entertain You'?

16. Which football team does Robbie support?

Answers to page 111
LYRICS 4: **1.** 'Total Eclipse Of The Heart' (Bonnie Tyler) **2.** 'Hungry Like The Wolf' (Duran Duran) **3.** 'Hound Dog' (Elvis Presley) **4.** 'You Can't Hurry Love' (The Supremes) **5.** 'Oh Yeah' (Ash) **6.** 'I Will Always Love You' (Whitney Houston) **7.** 'The Best Of My Love' (The Eagles) **8.** 'An Innocent Man' (Billy Joel) **9.** 'Material Girl' (Madonna) **10.** 'Live Forever' (Oasis) **11.** 'There's A Guy Works Down The Chip Shop Swears He's Elvis (Kirsty MacColl) **12.** 'The Young Ones' (Cliff Richard) **13.** 'Cool For Cats' (Squeeze) **14.** 'California Dreamin' (Mamas and The Papas) **15.** 'Bus Stop' (The Hollies) **16.** 'She'd Rather Be With Me' (The Turtles)

Cover Versions 4

Answers on page 116

1. Who had a 1979 hit with K.W.S.'s 1992 chart topper 'Please Don't Go'?

2. Which Congregation hit did Paul Young cover in 1990?

3. Which song, previously a hit for Bobby Day in 1958 and Michael Jackson in 1972, was covered by Lolly in 1999?

4. Who recorded the original version of The Commitments' 'Mustang Sally'?

5. Which *EastEnders* re-hashed a Chris Montez hit in 1999?

6. Who had a 1983 hit with a version of Ricky Nelson's 'It's Late'?

7. Who originally recorded 'Freak Me', a 1998 number one for Another Level?

8. Which David Bowie hit did Glamma Kid cover in 1998?

9. Which Kinks song was covered by Kirsty MacColl in 1989?

10. Which Mamas and The Papas song did Bitty McLean take to number six in the UK charts in 1994?

11. Which song links The Ronettes, Dave Edmunds and The Ramones?

12. Which song, a hit for both David Whitfield and Frankie Laine in 1953, also proved successful for Barbara Dickson in 1976?

13. Which Nilsson hit was covered by The Beautiful South?

14. Before The Rolling Stones, who had a hit in the Sixties with 'Harlem Shuffle'?

15. Which sentiment was shared by Stephen Stills in 1971 and Luther Vandross in 1994?

16. Who originally had a UK hit with 'Red Red Wine', a 1983 number one for UB40?

Answers to page 116
NINETIES 3: **1.** Martine McCutcheon **2.** 'Talk On Corners' (The Corrs) **3.** The Beautiful South **4.** 'Say What You Want' **5.** Sharleen Spiteri **6.** Shirley Manson (Garbage) **7.** 'I Believe I Can Fly' **8.** 'Ice Ice Baby' **9.** Run-DMC vs. Jason Nevins **10.** Erasure **11.** 'Australia' **12.** Deep Blue Something **13.** 'Sunchyme' **14.** 'A Red Letter Day' **15.** 'Cotton Eye Joe' **16.** Tina Turner

Pot Luck 12

Answers on page 117

1. Which eccentric singer from Jethro Tull was often witnessed wandering around Luton with a lampshade on his head?

2. Which airport did Cats U.K. sing about in 1979?

3. And which Hampshire city was the subject of a Mike Oldfield instrumental?

4. Which band chose their name from an old newspaper story about Frankie Vaughan moving into films?

5. Which American singer, who had a UK number one in 1976, was once ranked joint 85th in the world for the high jump?

6. Which actor is generally thought to be the subject of Carly Simon's 'You're So Vain'?

7. Which folk singer once gave the kiss of life to a sheep?

8. Which district of London did Suggs sing about in 1995?

9. What was the name of Wayne Fontana's backing group?

10. Who originally recorded Madness's 'One Step Beyond...'?

11. Who was the leader of The Bonzo Dog Doo-Dah Band?

12. What happened while Calgary's KFSM radio station played Carole King's 'I Feel The Earth Move' in 1971?

13. Which female artist helped out with the vocals on Peter Gabriel's 'Games Without Frontiers'?

14. Who recorded the album 'Oxygene'?

15. What is Dave Dee's surname?

16. Which enigmatic frontman of the Eighties started his career as a music reviewer with *Record Mirror*?

Answers to page 117
NEW ROMANTICS 1: **1.** Bow Wow Wow **2.** Adam and The Ants
3. Reformation **4.** Modern Romance (Geoff Deane) **5.** 'Planet Earth'
6. John Foxx **7.** 'No Regrets' **8.** Steve Strange **9.** 'Rio' **10.** 'Is There Something I Should Know' **11.** Tony Hadley **12.** Martin Kemp
13. Modern Romance **14.** 'Goody Two Shoes' **15.** 'Fade To Grey'
16. 1983

Nineties 3

Answers on page 114

1. Which ex-*EastEnder* enjoyed a 'Perfect Moment' in 1999?

2. Which was the biggest-selling UK album of 1998?

3. Whose 1998 album was titled 'Quench'?

4. What was Texas's first UK top ten hit of the 1990s?

5. Who is the lead singer with Texas?

6. Which Scottish singer with a band used to work in Miss Selfridge before joining Goodbye Mr Mackenzie and then Angelfish?

7. What was R. Kelly's first UK number one?

8. Which 1990 chart topper sampled Queen and David Bowie's 'Under Pressure'?

9. Who had a number one with 'It's Like That' in 1998?

10. Who had a 1994 album called 'I Say I Say I Say'?

11. Which continent did Manic Street Preachers sing about in 1996?

12. Who had 'Breakfast At Tiffany's' in 1996?

13. Which Dario G single sampled Dream Academy's 'Life In A Northern Town'?

14. Which Pet Shop Boys hit of 1997 features the Choral Academy of Moscow?

15. Bob Wills and his Texas Playboys recorded the original version of which 1994 line-dancing number one?

16. Who did Rod Stewart join in a 1990 duet for 'It Takes Two'?

Answers to page 114

New Romantics I

Answers on page 115

1. Which act did Malcolm McLaren form from Adam Ant's original backing group?

2. Which band's debut album was titled 'Dirk Wears White Sox'?

3. On which music label did Spandau Ballet record until 1988?

4. One of the lead singers with which band of New Romantics went on to write the sitcom *Babes in the Wood*?

5. What was the title of Duran Duran's first single?

6. Who did Midge Ure replace as singer with Ultravox?

7. Which Walker Brothers' hit did Midge Ure cover in 1982?

8. Who fronted Visage?

9. From which Duran Duran album was 'Hungry Like The Wolf' taken?

10. Which Duran Duran single went straight into the UK charts at number one in March 1983?

11. Which member of Spandau Ballet once featured in a photo-love story in *My Guy* magazine?

12. Which member of Spandau Ballet had been a promising footballer and had trained with Arsenal in 1975?

13. 'Everybody Salsa' was the first UK hit for which band?

14. Which song gave Adam Ant his first solo number one?

15. Which was Visage's biggest-selling single in the UK?

16. In which year did Spandau Ballet release the album 'True'?

Answers to page 115
POT LUCK 12: **1.** Ian Anderson **2.** 'Luton Airport' **3.** Portsmouth
4. Frankie Goes To Hollywood **5.** Johnny Mathis **6.** Warren Beatty
7. Roy Harper **8.** 'Camden Town' **9.** The Mindbenders **10.** Prince Buster
and The All-Stars **11.** Viv Stanshall **12.** The studio collapsed **13.** Kate
Bush **14.** Jean-Michel Jarre **15.** Harman **16.** Morrissey

Name Changes 5

Answers on page 120

1. Which rap pioneer changed his name from Joseph Saddler?

2. Which New Romantics were previously known as The Makers?

3. Stanley Kirk Burrell is the real name of which rap artist?

4. Which colourful American band used to be known as Wicked Lester?

5. Which Sixties duo were originally known as The Paramours?

6. The Zips, The Innocents and Fire of London were previous names of which band that had a powerful hit about a European city in 1981?

7. Which rap performer changed his name from Rexton Fernando Gordon?

8. Which frontman of an Eighties band was formerly known as Steve Harrington?

9. What was Ricky Nelson's real Christian name?

10. Which Seventies band were previously known as The Shakedown Sound and Silence before taking their new name from a 1967 novel by Willard Manus?

11. Which US singer of the Sixties was born Thomas Gregory Jackson?

12. Who changed his name from Richard Starkey?

13. Which band used to be known as Café Racers before finding a name which reflected their financial plight?

14. Which singer/songwriter was born Henry John Deutschendorf?

15. Which American singer of the Fifties and Sixties changed his name from Walden Robert Cassotto?

16. Whose full name is Robert Thomas Velline?

Answers to page 120
CLASSICAL GAS 2: **1.** Hungarian **2.** Mendelssohn **3.** Saint-Saëns
4. Richard Wagner **5.** Ten **6.** 31 **7.** *The Golden Cockerel* **8.** Polish
9. Six **10.** Elgar **11.** *Almira* **12.** Handel **13.** Haydn **14.** Mozart
15. Debussy **16.** Stravinsky

Cliff Richard 1

Answers on page 121

1. Who wrote 'Living Doll'?

2. What was the name of the teenage rock star Cliff played in *Expresso Bongo*?

3. Which of Cliff's number ones was co-written by the son of a comedian?

4. Who did Cliff join on stage at Earls Court in June 1966?

5. With which song did Cliff come third in the 1973 Eurovision Song Contest?

6. In which year did Cliff sing at Wimbledon during a break for rain at the tennis?

7. Who originally recorded 'I'm Lookin' Out The Window'?

8. From which film was 'On The Beach' taken?

9. Which 1960 number one was chosen by members of Cliff's fan club to be his next single?

10. Which 1979 hit provided Cliff with his first UK number one in over a decade?

11. Who didn't live here any more in 1980?

12. Which 1976 hit was originally recorded by a *Crackerjack* presenter?

13. Which of Cliff's hits was written by Compo from *Last of the Summer Wine*?

14. In which year did Cliff release the album 'I'm Nearly Famous'?

15. In which Shakespeare play did Cliff perform with old schoolfriends in 1974?

16. Which 1964 release had been a US hit for Johnny Mathis in 1957?

Answers to page 121
RAP 1: **1.** 2Pac **2.** Outkast **3.** Eminem **4.** Dr Dre **5.** Dirty Dozen
6. Jay-Z **7.** Marshall Mathers **8.** Bloodhound Gang **9.** Lil' Kim **10.** Missy
Elliott **11.** Shaggy **12.** Five **13.** Puff Daddy **14.** Lil' Bow Wow **15.** Eminem
16. Nelly

Classical Gas 2

Answers on page 118

1. What nationality was Liszt?

2. Who composed *Fingal's Cave*?

3. Which French composer wrote *Carnival Of The Animals*?

4. Whose operatic works included *Tannhäuser*, *Lohengrin* and *Tristan and Isolde*?

5. How many symphonies did Schubert compose?

6. How old was Schubert when he died?

7. Which Rimsky-Korsakov opera, written in 1907, was banned until 1909 because it was considered too satirical?

8. What nationality was Chopin?

9. How many Brandenburg Concertos are there?

10. Who composed *Pomp and Circumstance*?

11. What was the title of Handel's first opera?

12. Which German-born composer moved to England and became a British subject in 1726?

13. Who composed the 'Emperor's Hymn', adopted as the Austrian, and later the German, national anthem?

14. Who composed *The Magic Flute*?

15. Which composer was born in the small French town of Saint-Germain-en-Laye in 1862?

16. Which Russian composer became an American citizen in 1945?

Answers to page 118
NAME CHANGES 5: **1.** Grandmaster Flash **2.** Spandau Ballet **3.** M.C.
Hammer **4.** Kiss **5.** The Righteous Brothers **6.** Ultravox **7.** Shabba Ranks
8. Steve Strange **9.** Eric **10.** Mott The Hoople **11.** Tommy James
12. Ringo Starr **13.** Dire Straits **14.** John Denver **15.** Bobby Darin
16. Bobby Vee

Rap 1

Answers on page 119

1. Which rap artist released the single 'Changes'?

2. Who had to say sorry to Ms Jackson?

3. Who is also known as the Real Slim Shady?

4. Who released 'The Next Episode'?

5. What does D12 stand for?

6. Who sampled parts from the film *Oliver* in one of his singles?

7. What is Eminem's real name?

8. Who had a single titled 'The Bad Touch'?

9. Which female rap artist sang on 'Lady Marmalade' in 2001?

10. Who had a thing about 'Hot Boys'?

11. 'Angels' and 'It Wasn't Me' were singles by which rap artist?

12. How many members are there in Bloodhound Gang?

13. Which American rapper used to date Jennifer Lopez?

14. Who claims to be 'all that and a bag of chips'?

15. Who was the main singer with D12 on the 2001 single 'Purple Hills'?

16. Whose singles have included 'Country Grammar' and 'E.1'?

Answers to page 119
CLIFF RICHARD 1: 1. Lionel Bart 2. Bongo Herbert 3. 'Please Don't Tease' (written by Bruce Welch and Pete Chester, son of Charlie Chester) 4. Billy Graham 5. 'Power To All Our Friends' 6. 1996 7. Peggy Lee 8. *Wonderful Life* 9. 'Please Don't Tease' 10. 'We Don't Talk Anymore' 11. 'Carrie' 12. 'Devil Woman' (originally recorded by Kristine aka Christine Holmes) 13. 'Marianne' (written by Bill Owen) 14. 1976 15. *A Midsummer Night's Dream* (he played Bottom) 16. 'The Twelfth Of Never'

Fifties 2

Answers on page 124

1. Who had a UK number one in 1958 with 'It's All In The Game'?

2. Which pianist started life as Trevor Stanford?

3. Which husband and wife team wrote 'Bye Bye Love'?

4. Which laid-back singer had hits with 'Catch A Falling Star' and 'Magic Moments'?

5. Which 1957 Everly Brothers' song was banned from airplay in Boston, Massachusetts, because its lyrics were deemed mildly suggestive?

6. Who was 'Putting On The Style' in 1957?

7. Dick James, Gary Miller and Frankie Vaughan all covered which US hit for Joe Valino?

8. What was the name of Frankie Lymon's backing group?

9. Who sang about her 'Dreamboat' in 1955?

10. Which singing sisters backed Frankie Vaughan on 'Come Softly To Me'?

11. The theme from which American B-film provided Jimmy Young with a UK number one in 1955?

12. Which title, reminiscent of a casino game, gave Russ Conway a UK chart topper in 1959?

13. Who transformed himself from an Isle of Wight milkman named Terence Perkins into a Sixties singing heart-throb?

14. Such diverse talents as Bobby Darin and Charlie Drake both had 1958 hits with which song?

15. Who reached number one in 1958 with 'Hoots Mon'?

16. What was the original title of Buddy Holly's 'Peggy Sue'?

Queen 1

Answers on page 125

1. Who did Queen support on their 1973 UK tour?

2. What was Freddie Mercury still calling himself in 1973?

3. What was Queen's first US hit single?

4. Which Queen single was taken from the film *Highlander*?

5. What was the title of Queen's number one album of 1975?

6. Constant airplay from which Capital Radio DJ helped force EMI to release the six-minute 'Bohemian Rhapsody' as a single?

7. With which song did 'Bohemian Rhapsody' tie as Best British Pop Single (1952–77) at the British Record Industry Britannia Awards in 1977?

8. In which year did Freddie Mercury die?

9. How many weeks did 'Bohemian Rhapsody' spend at the top of the UK charts in 1975?

10. Which single did Freddie Mercury write while he was taking a bath in Munich's Hilton Hotel?

11. In what subject did John Deacon graduate with first-class honours?

12. Which single prevented 'Radio Ga Ga' from being a UK number one?

13. Who said of Freddie Mercury's performance at Live Aid: 'It was the perfect stage for Freddie. He could ponce about in front of the whole world'?

14. In which year was the album 'A Kind Of Magic' released?

15. Which 1976 single reached number two in the UK charts?

16. Which Queen single was the soundtrack of a futuristic 1980 movie?

Film Tracks 4

Answers on page 122

1. Which Adam Faith single of 1961 was taken from the film *What a Whopper!*?

2. Which track from *Tommy* was a hit for both The Who and Elton John?

3. Which Bobby Brown hit of 1999 featured in *Ghostbusters II*?

4. Which R. Kelly hit came from the film *Batman and Robin*?

5. How many Bond movie themes has Shirley Bassey sung?

6. From which film was the Guns N' Roses single 'You Could Be Mine' taken?

7. Bryan Adams, Rod Stewart and Sting combined for the theme song from which 1994 film?

8. Who had a 1985 top three hit with 'We Don't Need Another Hero' from *Thunderdome*?

9. Justin Hayward's hit 'Forever Autumn' came from which film?

10. Which film featured 'Summer Nights'?

11. Who had a hit in 1997 with his own version of the theme from the Bond film *Tomorrow Never Dies*?

12. Who had a 1994 hit with the theme song from *The Flintstones*?

13. Which UK top ten hit of 1996 for Madonna was taken from the film *Evita*?

14. Madonna's 'Beautiful Stranger' featured in which Mike Myers movie?

15. Which former Motown artist had a 1989 hit with the theme from the Bond movie *Licence To Kill*?

16. Which duo had a 1981 hit with 'Endless Love' from the film of the same name?

Answers to page 122
FIFTIES 2: **1.** Tommy Edwards **2.** Russ Conway **3.** Boudleaux and Felice Bryant **4.** Perry Como **5.** 'Wake Up Little Susie' **6.** Lonnie Donegan **7.** 'Garden Of Eden' **8.** The Teenagers **9.** Alma Cogan **10.** The Kaye Sisters **11.** *Unchained* ('Unchained Melody') **12.** 'Roulette' **13.** Craig Douglas **14.** 'Splish Splash' **15.** Lord Rockingham's XI **16.** 'Cindy-Lou'

Seventies 4

Answers on page 123

Which artists had UK hits with the following tracks in the Seventies?

1. 'Something Better Change'

2. 'That Same Old Feeling'

3. 'There's A Ghost In My House'

4. 'Sylvia'

5. 'Kid'

6. 'Co-Co'

7. 'Homely Girl'

8. 'It's Too Late'

9. 'The Man Who Sold The World'

10. 'The Puppy Song'

11. 'Rockin' All Over The World'

12. 'You Make Me Feel Like Dancing'

13. 'I'm In The Mood For Dancing'

14. 'Hey Girl Don't Bother Me'

15. 'Good Morning Judge'

16. 'Burning Love'

Answers to page 123
QUEEN 1: **1.** Mott The Hoople **2.** Larry Lurex **3.** 'Killer Queen' **4.** 'A Kind Of Magic' **5.** 'A Night At The Opera' **6.** Kenny Everett **7.** 'A Whiter Shade Of Pale' **8.** 1991 **9.** Nine **10.** 'Crazy Little Thing Called Love' **11.** Electronics **12.** 'Relax' **13.** Bob Geldof **14.** 1986 **15.** 'Somebody To Love' **16.** 'Flash' (*Flash Gordon*)

Pot Luck 13

Answers on page 128

1. What was George Martin's first UK number one as a producer?

2. Which track won Best British Single at the 1992 Brits – 17 years after its original release?

3. What working words did Paul McCartney use in place of 'yesterday' while composing the lyrics for his song?

4. Which Puff Daddy chart topper sampled The Police's 'Every Breath You Take'?

5. 'Unchained Melody' and 'I Believe' gave which act their first two number ones in 1995?

6. Which Radio 1 DJ refused to play 'Relax' by Frankie Goes To Hollywood?

7. From where was Gene Pitney only 24 hours in 1963?

8. Which international superstar sang supporting vocals on Rockwell's 'Somebody's Watching You'?

9. In which year was Glenn Miller killed in a plane crash?

10. Who recorded the theme song from *Postman Pat*?

11. At 44 letters, which Rolling Stones single has the longest title?

12. Which Sixties group starred in the film *Catch Us If You Can*?

13. Which fruit did Roger Miller sing about in 1968?

14. What was America's answer to Band Aid?

15. Which drummer specialised in dumping Rolls-Royces in swimming pools?

16. How did Lena Gilbert Ford, lyricist of the song 'Keep The Home Fires Burning', meet her death?

Answers to page 128
BRITNEY SPEARS 1: **1.** 'I Will Still Love You' **2.** '(You Drive Me) Crazy' **3.** Sweden **4.** 'Don't Let Me Be The Last To Know' **5.** '…Baby One More Time' **6.** The Mickey Mouse Club **7.** Louisiana **8.** 'Dear Diary' **9.** 'Time Out With Britney Spears' **10.** *Dawson's Creek* **11.** Skechers **12.** Bryan **13.** 'Oops!…I Did It Again' **14.** 'Lucky' **15.** *Sabrina the Teenage Witch* **16.** '…Baby One More Time'

New Wave 1

Answers on page 129

1. Which forerunners of Crowded House had a hit with 'I Got You'?

2. Who eulogised about 'My Sharona'?

3. Who was the singer with Teardrop Explodes?

4. Who were 'Making Plans For Nigel'?

5. What was Cheap Trick's biggest-selling single in the UK?

6. Who wrote The Pretenders' 'I Go To Sleep'?

7. In 1989, which committed vegetarian claimed that she once firebombed McDonald's?

8. Which New Wave band took their name from the last Velvet Underground album?

9. Which band was formed by Stuart Adamson in 1981?

10. Which member of The Police released 'Don't Care' under the name of Klark Kent?

11. Which song gave XTC their highest UK chart position?

12. According to Elvis Costello, for which flowers was it a good year in 1981?

13. Which 1984 single gave The Cars their first UK top ten success for six years?

14. Which single kept Squeeze's 'Up The Junction' from the UK number one spot in 1979?

15. Which track, rejected by Roxy Music, gave Simple Minds their first UK top ten hit?

16. What was the name of Elvis Costello's backing band?

Answers to page 129
MERSEYBEAT 2: 1. The Searchers 2. 'Sweets For My Sweet' 3. *Carousel* 4. The Fourmost 5. Elkie Brooks 6. The Mojos 7. 'You're My World' (Il Mio Mondo) 8. 'Wishin' And Hopin'' 9. The Pete Best Four 10. The Big Three 11. 'Hippy Hippy Shake' 12. 'Needles And Pins' 13. 'What Have They Done To The Rain' 14. The Merseys 15. 'Sorrow' 16. 'Ferry Across The Mersey'

Britney Spears 1

Answers on page 126

1. Which track on Britney's debut album was a duet with Don Philip?

2. What was the title of Britney's third single?

3. In which country was 'Oops!...I Did It Again' recorded?

4. Which song off the second album was co-written by Shania Twain?

5. What was the title of Britney's first album?

6. What was the name of the club which Britney attended with Christina Aguilera and Justin Timberlake?

7. In which American state was Britney born?

8. Which track from her second album did Britney help to write?

9. What was the title of Britney's debut home video?

10. In which Channel 4 teen drama has Britney appeared?

11. What make of trainers has Britney modelled?

12. What is the name of Britney's older brother?

13. What was the title of Britney's second album?

14. Which track from that album was the story of a girl who is a superstar?

15. In which TV series did Britney appear with Melissa Joan Hart?

16. Which Britney release was the best-selling UK single for 1999?

Answers to page 126
POT LUCK 13: 1. 'You're Driving Me Crazy' by The Temperance Seven 2. 'Bohemian Rhapsody' 3. Scrambled eggs 4. 'I'll Be Missing You' 5. Robson and Jerome 6. Mike Read 7. Tulsa 8. Michael Jackson 9. 1944 10. Ken Barrie 11. 'Have You Seen Your Mother Baby, Standing In The Shadow' 12. The Dave Clark Five 13. 'Little Green Apples' 14. USA For Africa 15. Keith Moon 16. In a fire at her home

Merseybeat 2

Answers on page 127

1. Which Merseybeat group toppled Elvis's 'Devil In Disguise' from the top of the UK charts in 1963?

2. And what was the title of the song?

3. From which musical was 'You'll Never Walk Alone' taken?

4. Brian O'Hara, Mike Millward, Billy Hatton and Dave Lovelady formed which Merseybeat group?

5. Which singer is the sister of former Billy J. Kramer and The Dakotas' drummer Tony Mansfield?

6. Which band had a 1964 hit with 'Everything's Alright'?

7. Which Cilla Black number one of 1964 was adapted from an Italian tune?

8. Which Bacharach and David song gave The Merseybeats chart success in 1964?

9. Which group did Pete Best form on being ousted from The Beatles?

10. Brian Griffiths, John Gustafson and John Hutchinson comprised which Merseybeat group?

11. Which song was the first top five hit for The Swinging Blue Jeans?

12. Which Searchers hit was co-written by Sonny Bono?

13. And which Searchers single was an anti-nuclear protest song originally recorded by Malvina Reynolds?

14. Which duo did Tony Crane and Billy Kinsley form following the demise of The Merseybeats?

15. And what was their only hit under their new name?

16. Which film title track was a hit for Gerry and The Pacemakers in 1964?

Answers to page 127
NEW WAVE 1: **1.** Split Enz **2.** The Knack **3.** Julian Cope **4.** XTC
5. 'I Want You To Want Me' **6.** Ray Davies **7.** Chrissie Hynde **8.** Squeeze
9. Big Country **10.** Stewart Copeland **11.** 'Senses Working Overtime'
(10) **12.** Roses **13.** 'Drive' **14.** 'Are "Friends" Electric' (Tubeway Army)
15. 'Don't You (Forget About Me)' **16.** The Attractions

Albums 6

Answers on page 132

1. What was the title of the Red Hot Chili Peppers' number two UK album of 1995?

2. Which Four Seasons album featured 'December 63 (Oh What A Night)'?

3. Who released the album 'Honky Chateau'?

4. 'Venus And Mars' was a number one album for which band?

5. Whose 1979 big-selling album was titled 'Discovery'?

6. What was the title of Roxy Music's number one UK album of 1982?

7. Whose 1985 album was called 'Alf'?

8. Which Lionel Richie offering was the best-selling UK album of 1984?

9. 'Seven And The Ragged Tiger' was a 1983 chart-topping album for which band?

10. Which Eagles album ends with 'The Last Resort'?

11. For the recording of which album did Crowded House spend much of the time naked, apparently in order to create the right atmosphere?

12. Which Rolling Stones album cover was a plain white sleeve depicting an invitation?

13. Whose second album was titled 'In Gorbachev We Trust'?

14. 'Let's Go Crazy' was a track from which Prince album?

15. On which album's sleeve notes did Michael Jackson thank Cary Grant and Marlon Brando?

16. Which Michael Jackson album of 1982 reached number one in every western country?

Answers to page 132
NUMBER TWOS 1: **1.** 'All Right Now' **2.** 'American Pie' **3.** Marillion **4.** The Osmonds **5.** 'Heartbreak Hotel' **6.** Manfred Mann **7.** Billy Fury **8.** Stan ('My Friend Stan') **9.** 'Knock Three Times' by Dawn **10.** Neil Reid **11.** The Moody Blues **12.** King **13.** Herman's Hermits **14.** Deep Purple **15.** Blondie **16.** 'I Believe'

Boy Bands 2

Answers on page 133

1. How did New Kids On The Block's Danny Wood injure himself on stage at Manchester in 1990?

2. How many members are there in Point Break?

3. Which Channel 4 programme traced the formation of O-Town?

4. Lance, Justin and JC are members of which group?

5. What does LFO stand for?

6. Which boy band released the album 'Invincible'?

7. What nationality is Christian from a1?

8. Which group released 'You Needed Me' in 1999?

9. Which boy band are named after a branch of the London Underground?

10. Which country do The Moffatts come from?

11. 'If Only' was a single from which pop threesome?

12. Which member of Another Level once dated the model Jordan?

13. What was East 17's only UK number one?

14. Which items of New Kids On The Block merchandise were unveiled in February 1990?

15. Which boy band had their first UK top ten hit with 'Crazy For You' in 1994?

16. Which two boy bands had hits with 'Love Me For A Reason' 20 years apart?

Answers to page 133
COUNTRY AND WESTERN 3: 1. Loretta Lynn 2. Tammy Wynette ('D.I.V.O.R.C.E.') 3. Lyle Lovett 4. *Even Cowgirls Get The Blues* 5. Garth Brooks 6. Johnny Cash 7. Mary-Chapin Carpenter 8. Billy Ray Cyrus 9. Suzy Bogguss 10. Crystal Gayle 11. 'Lefty' 12. Waylon Jennings 13. Seven 14. Johnny Cash 15. Homer and Jethro 16. Emmylou Harris

Number Twos 1

Answers on page 130

1. Which classic Free track reached number two in the UK charts in 1970?

2. Which Don McLean song, subsequently covered by Madonna, got to number two in 1972?

3. Who reached number two in 1985 with 'Kayleigh'?

4. Whose 'Crazy Horses' missed out on the top spot in 1972?

5. Which 1956 single from Elvis rose to number two in the UK charts?

6. Who got to number two in 1966 with 'Semi-Detached Suburban Mr James'?

7. Which male singer took 'Jealousy' to number two in 1961?

8. Which friend of Slade's only made it to number two in 1973?

9. Which middle-of-the-road single kept the Stones' 'Brown Sugar' off the top spot?

10. Which youthful *Opportunity Knocks* winner got to number two with 'Mother Of Mine' in 1972?

11. Which band made number two with 'Question' in 1970?

12. Which band fell one short of the top with 'Love & Pride' in 1985?

13. Who reached number two with 'My Sentimental Friend' in 1969?

14. Which heavy metal band rose to second spot with 'Black Night' in 1970?

15. Which American band were 'Dreaming' of the number one spot in 1979, only to narrowly miss out?

16. Which Bachelors song only reached number two in 1964 before Robson and Jerome went one better 31 years later?

Answers to page 130
ALBUMS 6: 1. 'One Hot Minute' 2. 'Who Loves You' 3. Elton John
4. Wings 5. Electric Light Orchestra 6. 'Avalon' 7. Alison Moyet
8. 'Can't Slow Down' 9. Duran Duran 10. 'Hotel California'
11. 'Together Alone' 12. 'Beggars Banquet' 13. Shamen 14. 'Purple Rain'
15. 'Bad' 16. 'Thriller'

Country and Western 3

Answers on page 131

1. Who teamed up with Tammy Wynette and Dolly Parton for the 1993 'Honky Tonk Angels' album?

2. Who spelt out her marital problems in a 1975 hit?

3. Whose 1996 album was called 'The Road To Ensenada'?

4. From which film was k.d. lang's 'Just Keep Me Moving' taken?

5. What is the name of country singer Colleen Carroll's famous son?

6. Who recorded an album at San Quentin Prison in 1969?

7. Whose debut album in 1987 was titled 'Hometown Girl'?

8. Which Kentucky-born country singer worked as a car salesman before making his 1992 breakthrough album 'Some Gave All'?

9. Who duetted with Lee Greenwood on the US country hit 'Hopelessly Yours' and was named Most Promising Artist at the 1992 Country Music Awards?

10. Which country artist had mainstream hits in the Seventies with 'Don't It Make My Brown Eyes Blue' and 'Talking In Your Sleep'?

11. What was William Orville Frizzell's nickname?

12. Whose albums have included 'Dreaming My Dreams', 'Will The Wolf Survive?' and 'Highwayman'?

13. How old was Willie Nelson when he wrote his first 'cheating-heart-style' song?

14. Who had a hit with 'Ring Of Fire' in 1963?

15. As which duo were Henry Haynes and Kenneth Burns better known?

16. 'Roses In The Snow' was which artist's fourth US top forty album?

Answers to page 131
BOY BANDS 2: **1.** He damaged his ankle after tripping over a stuffed toy thrown on stage by a fan **2.** Three **3.** *Making the Band* **4.** N Sync **5.** Lyte Funkie Ones **6.** Five **7.** Norwegian **8.** Boyzone **9.** Northern Line **10.** Canada **11.** Hanson **12.** Dane Bowers **13.** Stay Another Day **14.** Dolls **15.** Let Loose **16.** The Osmonds and Boyzone

Eighties 4

Answers on page 136

1. Which American singer had hits with 'Time After Time' and 'True Colours'?

2. Under what name did John Mellencamp used to record?

3. Colin Hay was the vocalist with which Australian band?

4. At which club did Wham! hang out in 1983?

5. Peter Cox and Richard Drummie made up which band?

6. What did Bros want to know in 1988?

7. Who was employed as a tape operator with Stock, Aitken and Waterman before being launched on a singing career?

8. Who had a number two hit with 'Sign Your Name' in 1988?

9. Who took over as singer with Haircut 100 following Nick Heyward's departure?

10. Which band did Norman Cook join in 1985?

11. Who had a 1987 album called 'Dancing With Strangers'?

12. Which artist's full name is Helen Folasade Adu?

13. Joanne Catherall and Susanne Sulley were singers/dancers with which band?

14. Which girl duo had a 1987 hit with 'Heartache'?

15. Which member of The Housemartins left the band to open a vegetarian restaurant?

16. Who was the head of Factory Records?

Answers to page 136
LYRICS 5: 1. 'The Reflex' (Duran Duran) 2. 'We Don't Talk Anymore' (Cliff Richard) 3. 'My Way' (Frank Sinatra) 4. 'Music To Watch Girls By' (Andy Williams) 5. 'I Should Be So Lucky' (Kylie Minogue) 6. 'A Million Love Songs' (Take That) 7. 'All That She Wants' (Ace Of Base) 8. 'I Heard It Through The Grapevine' (Marvin Gaye) 9. 'Reach Out I'll Be There' (The Four Tops) 10. 'Grease' (Frankie Valli) 11. 'Will You Love Me Tomorrow?' (The Shirelles) 12. 'Man On The Moon' (R.E.M.) 13. 'How Do I Live?' (LeAnn Rimes) 14. 'Making Your Mind Up' (Bucks Fizz) 15. 'The Boxer' (Simon and Garfunkel) 16. 'Romeo And Juliet' (Dire Straits)

R.E.M. I

Answers on page 137

1. What subjects did Michael Stipe study at the University of Georgia in Athens?

2. Which band member used to work in an Athens record store, learning guitar licks between serving customers?

3. What does R.E.M. stand for?

4. Which British band did R.E.M. support on a short US tour in 1983?

5. Which R.E.M. single was a tribute to comedian Andy Kaufman?

6. Who contributed backing vocals on 'Shiny Happy People'?

7. Which was R.E.M.'s first number one album in the UK?

8. The title of which album was taken from a sign at Weaver D's soul food diner in Athens?

9. Why did R.E.M. cancel part of their 1995 European tour?

10. Who sang backing vocals on 'E-Bow The Letter?'

11. In which year did 'Losing My Religion' reach number 19 in the UK charts?

12. As a youngster, what nickname was Michael Stipe given by his father?

13. Who joined the band on stage during their 1984 US tour to sing 'So You Want To Be A Rock 'n' Roll Star'?

14. Which tennis player took over on drums for an encore of 'Wichita Lineman' during R.E.M.'s 1995 tour of Australia?

15. What was the title of R.E.M.'s first full-length album?

16. On which album did 'The One I Love' appear?

Answers to page 137
GIRL BANDS 3: 1. The Crystals (Crystal Bates) 2. Gerry Goffin and Carole King 3. 'Someday' 4. 1979 5. The Chiffons 6. 'Never Ever' 7. Veronica and Estelle Bennett 8. Smokey Robinson 9. The Bangles (Michael Steele) 10. Siobhan Fahey 11. 'Da Doo Ron Ron' 12. 'Remember (Walkin' In The Sand)' 13. The youngest, Mary Weiss, stayed on at school 14. 'Nathan Jones' 15. BeBe Winans 16. 'I Wanna Be The Only One'

Lyrics 5

Answers on page 134

From which songs are the following lyrics taken?

1. 'I tell you somebody's fooling around with my chances on the dangerline'

2. 'But I ain't losing sleep and I ain't counting sheep'

3. 'I did what I had to do and saw it through without exemption'

4. 'Eyes watch girls walk with tender loving care'

5. 'My heart is close to breaking and I can't go on faking the fantasy that you'll be mine'

6. 'A million words just trying to make the love song of the year'

7. 'So if you are in sight and the day is right, she's the hunter, you're the fox'

8. 'I bet you're wondering how I knew 'bout your plans to make me blue'

9. 'And your life is filled with confusion, and happiness is just an illusion'

10. 'It's got groove, it's got meaning'

11. 'Is this a lasting treasure or just a moment's pleasure'

12. 'If you believe there's nothing up my sleeve, then nothing is cool'

13. 'If you ever leave, baby, you would take away everything good in my life'

14. 'Don't let your indecision take you from behind'

15. 'I am just a poor boy though my story's seldom told, I have squandered my resistance for a pocketful of mumbles, such are promises'

16. 'I can't do the talk like they talk on TV and I can't do a love song like the way it's meant to be'

Answers to page 134
EIGHTIES 4: **1.** Cyndi Lauper **2.** John Cougar **3.** Men At Work **4.** Club Tropicana **5.** Go West **6.** 'When Will I Be Famous?' **7.** Rick Astley **8.** Terence Trent D'Arby **9.** Mark Fox **10.** The Housemartins **11.** Chris Rea **12.** Sade **13.** Human League **14.** Pepsi and Shirlie **15.** Ted Key **16.** Tony Wilson

Girl Bands 3

Answers on page 135

1. The daughter of songwriter Leroy Bates gave which Sixties girl group their name?

2. Who wrote The Shirelles' 'Will You Love Me Tomorrow'?

3. Which Eternal single came from the film *The Hunchback of Notre Dame*?

4. In which year were The Nolans In The Mood For Dancing?

5. Which girl group comprised Judy Craig, Barbara Lee, Patricia Bennett and Sylvia Peterson?

6. What was All Saints' first UK number one?

7. Which two sisters were the cornerstone of The Ronettes?

8. Who wrote and produced 'Floy Joy' for The Supremes?

9. Which all-girl band had a bass guitarist called Michael?

10. Who left Bananarama in 1988?

11. Which Crystals hit of 1963 is generally regarded as the first true example of the Phil Spector sound?

12. What was The Shangri-Las first US hit?

13. Why were the four-piece Shangri-Las a three-piece on their first promotional tour to Britain?

14. Which Supremes song did Bananarama cover in 1988?

15. Who featured on Eternal's first UK number one?

16. And what was the title of the song?

Answers to page 135
R.E.M. 1: 1. Painting and photography 2. Peter Buck 3. Rapid Eye Movement 4. The Police 5. 'Man On The Moon' 6. Kate Pierson of The B-52s 7. 'Out Of Time' 8. 'Automatic For The People' 9. Drummer Bill Berry was taken ill 10. Patti Smith 11. 1991 12. 'Mr Mouse' 13. Roger McGuinn 14. Jim Courier 15. 'Murmur' 16. 'Document'

Sixties 4

Answers on page 140

Which acts had UK hits in the Sixties with the following tracks?

1. 'Step Inside Love'

2. 'Midnight In Moscow'

3. 'Lovin' Things'

4. 'Google Eye'

5. 'A Groovy Kind Of Love'

6. 'Halfway To Paradise'

7. 'Tell Me When'

8. 'The Ballad Of Bonnie And Clyde'

9. 'Blue Bayou'

10. 'But I Do'

11. 'Creeque Alley'

12. 'A Lover's Concerto'

13. 'Mama'

14. 'Silhouettes'

15. 'She Wears My Ring'

16. 'The Boat That I Row'

Answers to page 140
NAME CHANGES 6: **1.** Simple Minds **2.** Elkie Brooks **3.** Tab Hunter **4.** Norman **5.** Sid Vicious **6.** Gerard **7.** Queen **8.** Gram Parsons **9.** Gary Webb **10.** Nirvana **11.** New Kids On The Block **12.** Denny Laine **13.** The Moody Blues **14.** Manfred Mann **15.** Little Richard **16.** Human League

Pot Luck 14

Answers on page 141

1. What job did the teenage Sting get before going to Warwick University?

2. What did Neil Diamond train to be before taking up a career in music?

3. Producer Phil Spector once held a gun to which singer's head in the studio to get the performance he wanted?

4. Who was the subject of The Beatles' 'Baby You're A Rich Man'?

5. Which London Underground station did The New Vaudeville Band sing about in 1967?

6. Which band took their name from the robot who appeared in the *Beano* comic, adding an 'h' because they thought it wouldn't be sounded in their native Ireland?

7. Which punk rocker was charged with murdering his girlfriend Nancy Spungen in 1978?

8. What was the first posthumous UK number one single?

9. Which are the only US group to have had UK number one singles in the Seventies, Eighties and Nineties?

10. Which knight sang backing vocals on Scaffold's 'Lily The Pink'?

11. What was the name of Joe Brown's backing group?

12. With whom did Tom Jones duet in 1999 on 'Baby It's Cold Outside'?

13. What was Imagination's first UK chart success?

14. Who sang on Electronic's 1989 hit 'Getting Away With It'?

15. Which Tony Christie hit was the theme from the TV series *The Protectors*?

16. What role did 'Flowers In The Rain' by The Move play in radio music history?

Answers to page 141
FOLK 3: 1. Paul McCartney 2. 'Gaudete' 3. 'Meet Me On The Corner' 4. The Dirt Band 5. Buddy Holly 6. The Springfields 7. Jim Dale 8. 'If You Gotta Go, Go Now' 9. The Poppy Family 10. Judith Durham 11. Loudon Wainwright III 12. Richard and Linda Thompson 13. Jack The Lad 14. Joan Baez 15. Julie Felix 16. *Holiday*

Name Changes 6

Answers on page 138

1. Which band changed their name from Johnny and The Self-Abusers?

2. What did Elaine Bookbinder change her name to?

3. Which US singer of the Fifties was born Arthur Kelm?

4. What was Hurricane Smith's real Christian name?

5. What did punk John Ritchie choose as a stage name?

6. What is Leo Sayer's true Christian name?

7. Which internationally famous group used to be known as Smile before opting for something more regal?

8. Which late country rocker was born Cecil Connor III?

9. What is Gary Numan's real name?

10. Which heavy metal band were previously known as Ed Ted and Fred?

11. Which US boy band changed their name from Nynuk?

12. Which former member of The Moody Blues and Wings was born Brian Hines?

13. Which band used to be called The MB Five in deference to Birmingham brewers Mitchell & Butler?

14. Which Sixties keyboard player, who lent his name to the band, was really called Michael Lubowitz?

15. As what was Richard Wayne Penniman better known?

16. Which Eighties band from Sheffield used to be called The Future?

Answers to page 138
SIXTIES 4: **1.** Cilla Black **2.** Kenny Ball and his Jazzmen **3.** Marmalade **4.** The Nashville Teens **5.** The Mindbenders **6.** Billy Fury **7.** The Applejacks **8.** Georgie Fame **9.** Roy Orbison **10.** Clarence 'Frogman' Henry **11.** The Mamas and The Papas **12.** The Toys **13.** Dave Berry **14.** Herman's Hermits **15.** Solomon King **16.** Lulu

Folk 3

Answers on page 139

1. Which Beatle sang backing vocals on Donovan's 'Mellow Yellow'?

2. Which Latin title was a 1973 hit for Steeleye Span?

3. What was Lindisfarne's first UK hit?

4. Which band dropped the 'Nitty Gritty' in 1976?

5. Which dead singer was the principal subject of Don McLean's 'American Pie'?

6. Which folk band had a 1962 hit with 'Island Of Dreams'?

7. Which *Carry On* star co-wrote 'Georgy Girl' for The Seekers?

8. Which cover of a Manfred Mann song gave Fairport Convention their only mainstream UK chart success?

9. Which band, led by Terry Jacks, had a 1970 hit with 'Which Way You Goin' Billy'?

10. Who was the lead singer with The Seekers?

11. Who had a hit with 'Dead Skunk'?

12. Which husband and wife duo released the Seventies albums 'Hokey Pokey' and 'Sunnyvista'?

13. Simon Cowe, Ray Laidlaw and Rod Clements left Lindisfarne in 1973 to form which group?

14. Who had a 1971 hit with 'The Night They Drove Old Dixie Down'?

15. Which toothy singer, famous for her appearances on TV's *The Frost Report*, enjoyed a 1970 hit with a cover of Simon and Garfunkel's 'El Condor Pasa'?

16. Gordon Giltrap's 'Heartsong' was used as the theme to which TV series in the Eighties?

Answers to page 139
POT LUCK 14: **1.** Bus conductor **2.** Doctor **3.** Leonard Cohen **4.** Brian Epstein **5.** Finchley Central **6.** Thin Lizzy (Tin Lizzie) **7.** Sid Vicious **8.** 'It Doesn't Matter Anymore' (Buddy Holly) **9.** Blondie **10.** Tim Rice **11.** The Bruvvers **12.** Cerys Matthews **13.** 'Body Talk' **14.** Neil Tennant (Pet Shop Boys) **15.** 'Avenues And Alleyways' **16.** It was the first record to be played on Radio 1

Michael Jackson 1

Answers on page 144

1. With whom did Michael Jackson duet on the 1982 single 'The Girl Is Mine'?

2. Who recorded the original version of Jackson's 1972 hit 'Ain't No Sunshine'?

3. How old was Jackson when he had his first solo hit?

4. And what was the title of the song?

5. Which style of dancing did Jackson perfect in the Eighties?

6. Which heavy metal guitarist played for free on 'Beat It'?

7. Which single could have been – but wasn't – written about a tennis player?

8. Which Michael Jackson UK number one was written and produced by R. Kelly?

9. What was Jackson's first UK solo number one?

10. Which Michael Jackson single featured Slash from Guns N' Roses on guitar?

11. Which horror-movie star provided a ghostly rap on the title track of 'Thriller'?

12. What was Jackson doing when his hair caught fire in 1984?

13. Who said that Jackson was 'an inspiration to all of us' in a 1984 congratulatory telegram?

14. In which year was the album 'Bad' released?

15. Which member of Jackson's entourage was refused admission to the UK in 1988?

16. Who marched on stage and interrupted Jackson's performance of 'Earth Song' at the 1996 Brit Awards?

Answers to page 144
SOLO ARTISTS 3: **1.** 'You Can't Hurry Love' **2.** Barry Gibb **3.** 'Joanna'
4. Sandie Shaw **5.** Richard Marx **6.** The Sutherland Brothers **7.** 'Oh Julie'
8. Argentina **9.** Cliff Richard ('Honky Tonk Angels') **10.** Hurricane Smith
11. Michael Bolton **12.** Whistling **13.** 'I Was Kaiser Bill's Batman'
14. Joan Osborne **15.** Kenneth McKellar **16.** Jose Feliciano

Nineties 4

Answers on page 145

1. Which 1992 track allegedly recounting the joys of Ecstasy reached number one in the UK during Drug Awareness Week?

2. Felix Buxton and Simon Ratcliffe make up which duo?

3. To which TV presenter is Toploader guitarist Dan Hipgrave married?

4. Who reached the top of the charts in 1992 with 'Sleeping Satellite'?

5. Who released the album 'Diva' in 1993?

6. Who duetted with Mariah Carey on 'Endless Love'?

7. Which boy band took a cover of a Dr Hook hit to the top of the UK charts in 1999?

8. And what was the title of the song?

9. Sarah Cracknell is the singer with which band?

10. Who were 'Missing' in 1995?

11. Which animated family had a number one single in 1991?

12. Who had a 1996 UK number one single with 'I Feel You'?

13. Who was the female singer with The Fugees before going solo?

14. Which star of the TV docusoap *The Cruise* had a number one album in 1998?

15. Which band went 'Dizzy' with Vic Reeves in 1991?

16. Which Super Furry Animals hit incorporated the names of Einstein's parents?

Answers to page 145
COVER VERSIONS 5: **1.** 'Words' **2.** 'Something' **3.** 'She' **4.** 'Happy Together' **5.** 'Go West' **6.** 'Sorrow' **7.** The Delfonics **8.** 'The Air That I Breathe' **9.** The Stranglers **10.** Denise Welch **11.** Argent **12.** 'Going Underground' **13.** 'Love Letters' **14.** 'Love Me Tender' **15.** 'Looking Thru The Eyes Of Love' **16.** Itchycoo Park

Solo Artists 3

Answers on page 142

1. Which Supremes cover gave Phil Collins his first UK number one as a solo artist?

2. Who sang backing vocals on Dionne Warwick's 1982 hit 'Heartbreaker'?

3. Tony Hatch and Jackie Trent originally recorded which Scott Walker hit from 1968?

4. Which Sixties singer made a comeback with The Smiths in 1984?

5. Which American singer's biggest hit was 'Right Here Waiting' in 1989?

6. Who recorded the original version of Rod Stewart's number one 'Sailing'?

7. What was the title of Shakin' Stevens' third UK number one?

8. In which country was Chris De Burgh born?

9. Which artist demanded that his record company withdraw his new single after discovering that it was about prostitutes?

10. Who had Seventies hits with 'Don't Let It Die' and 'Oh Babe, What Would You Say'?

11. Who asked: 'How Am I Supposed To Live Without You' in 1990?

12. In which field of musical performance did Jack Smith excel in 1967?

13. And what was the title of his surprise hit?

14. Which American female singer's 1996 album was titled 'Relish'?

15. Which Scotsman sang Handel on a 1960 EP?

16. Which solo artist had a 1968 hit with 'Light My Fire'?

Answers to page 142
MICHAEL JACKSON 1: **1.** Paul McCartney **2.** Bill Withers **3.** 13 **4.** 'Got To Be There' **5.** Moonwalking **6.** Eddie Van Halen **7.** 'Billie Jean' **8.** 'You Are Not Alone' **9.** 'One Day In Your Life' **10.** 'Black Or White' **11.** Vincent Price **12.** Filming a Pepsi commercial **13.** President Reagan **14.** 1987 **15.** His chimp, Bubbles **16.** Jarvis Cocker

Cover Versions 5

Answers on page 143

1. Which Bee Gees song has been covered successfully by Rita Coolidge and Boyzone?

2. Which song was a hit for both The Beatles and Shirley Bassey within the space of eight months?

3. Which ballad was a hit for Charles Aznavour in 1974 and Elvis Costello in 1999?

4. What were The Turtles in 1967 and Jason Donovan in 1991?

5. Which Village People song did The Pet Shop Boys cover in 1993?

6. Which song links The Merseys and David Bowie?

7. Who originally had a hit with The Fugees' 1996 smash 'Ready Or Not'?

8. Which Hollies single was covered by Simply Red in 1998?

9. Who covered The Kinks' 'All Day And All Of The Night' in 1988?

10. Which former *Coronation Street* actress reached number 23 in the UK charts in 1995 with her version of Julie London's 1957 hit 'Cry Me A River'?

11. Which band originally had a hit with 'God Gave Rock And Roll To You', a 1992 success for Kiss?

12. Which Jam number one also charted for Buffalo Tom in 1999?

13. Which song has been a UK top ten hit for Ketty Lester, Elvis Presley and Alison Moyet?

14. Which song was a hit for both Elvis Presley and Roland Rat?

15. Which song links Gene Pitney and The Partridge Family?

16. Which Small Faces park was revisited by M People in 1995?

Answers to page 143
NINETIES 4: 1. 'Ebenezer Goode' (Shamen) 2. Basement Jaxx 3. Gail Porter 4. Tasmin Archer 5. Annie Lennox 6. Luther Vandross 7. 911 8. 'A Little Bit More' 9. Saint Etienne 10. Everything But The Girl 11. The Simpsons ('Do The Bartman') 12. Peter Andre 13. Lauryn Hill 14. Jane McDonald 15. The Wonder Stuff 16. 'Hermann Loves Pauline'

Bruce Springsteen 1

Answers on page 148

1. Which 1975 track did not make it into the UK singles charts until 1987?

2. On which Springsteen release did Howard Kaylan and Mark Volman from The Turtles sing backing vocals?

3. Which film track gave Springsteen a UK number two in 1994?

4. What is the name of Springsteen's backing band?

5. With which band did Springsteen play as a teenager?

6. What was the title of Springsteen's debut album?

7. Which Springsteen song was covered by Manfred Mann's Earth Band in 1977?

8. From which album was 'Hungry Heart' taken?

9. In which year was the album 'Born In The USA' released?

10. Which Edwin Starr hit did Springsteen cover in 1986?

11. Which was Springsteen's first UK top ten single?

12. What is Springsteen's nickname?

13. From which film was the 1997 single 'Secret Garden' taken?

14. Which of his backing singers did Springsteen marry in 1991?

15. In which year was 'Human Touch' released?

16. Which track formed a double A-side with 'Born In The USA'?

Answers to page 148
INDIE 3: **1.** Oasis **2.** Smashing Pumpkins **3.** 'The Man Who' **4.** 'Say What You Want' **5.** Dodgy **6.** Super Furry Animals **7.** 'Strangeways, Here We Come' **8.** Cast **9.** The Bluetones **10.** 'Different Class' **11.** Counting Crows **12.** Gin Blossoms **13.** Mark and Scott Morriss **14.** Babybird **15.** 'There's No Other Way' **16.** Manic Street Preachers

Chart Toppers 7

Answers on page 149

1. Which American singer enjoyed a UK number one in 1974 with a song of praise to his wife?

2. Which 1977 chart topper from a musical was originally titled 'It's Only Your Lover Returning'?

3. Which act had UK number ones in 1989 with 'Swing The Mood', 'That's What I Like' and 'Let's Party'?

4. What was the title of Stiltskin's UK number one of 1994?

5. For which other artist, besides Mungo Jerry, did Ray Dorset write a UK number one?

6. And what was the title of the song?

7. Which 1980 chart topper, written by an ex-teacher, told of the secret love between a teacher and a pupil?

8. Which Eighties number one was taken from the 1935 musical *Jubilee*?

9. And which former reserve goalkeeper for Real Madrid had the hit with it in 1981?

10. 'The Only Way Is Up' was a 1988 number one for which artist?

11. Who had an instrumental number one with 'Wonderful Land' in 1962?

12. How many UK number one singles have The Rolling Stones had?

13. Which much-maligned singer reached number one with 'I Pretend' in 1968?

14. What was the best-selling UK single of 1968?

15. Whose one and only number one was 'The One And Only'?

16. And who wrote 'The One And Only'?

Answers to page 149
POT LUCK 15: **1.** The Pogues (*Pogue Mo Chone*) **2.** Ray Davies **3.** John Lennon **4.** 99 **5.** Amarillo **6.** Stevie Wonder **7.** 'Get Down Shep' **8.** The Sex Pistols **9.** 'Raspberry Beret' **10.** Sky Saxon **11.** Mariah Carey **12.** Procol Harum **13.** Transit Authority **14.** 'California Dreamin'' **15.** Kajagoogoo **16.** Van McCoy

Indie 3

Answers on page 146

1. Which band had a guitarist nicknamed 'Bonehead'?

2. Singer Billy Corgan is associated with which band?

3. What was the title of Travis's best-selling album of 1999?

4. In 1997, which track gave Texas their first UK top ten single for eight years?

5. Nigel Clarke was the singer with which band?

6. Whose 1997 album was titled 'Radiator'?

7. Which Smiths album title name-checked a prison?

8. Who had hits with 'Alright', 'Walkaway' and 'Flying'?

9. Ed Chesters is drummer with which band?

10. From which album was Pulp's 'Common People' taken?

11. Which California-based band was fronted by Adam Duritz?

12. For which US band was Doug Hopkins, who shot himself dead in 1993, the principal songwriter?

13. Which brothers make up one half of The Bluetones?

14. Which band insisted 'You're Gorgeous' in 1996?

15. Which was Blur's first top ten UK single?

16. Who released a 1994 album called 'The Holy Bible'?

Answers to page 146
BRUCE SPRINGSTEEN 1: **1.** 'Born To Run' **2.** 'Hungry Heart'
3. 'Streets Of Philadelphia' **4.** The E Street Band **5.** The Castiles
6. 'Greetings From Asbury Park NJ' **7.** 'Blinded By The Light' **8.** 'The River' **9.** 1984 **10.** 'War' **11.** 'Dancing In The Dark' **12.** 'The Boss' **13.** *Jerry Maguire* **14.** Patti Scialfa **15.** 1992 **16.** 'I'm On Fire'

Pot Luck 15

Answers on page 147

1. Which band's name is an abbreviation of 'kiss my arse' in Gaelic?

2. Which father of Brit Pop went to the same North London secondary school as Rod Stewart?

3. Thelma Pickles was which rock star's first girlfriend?

4. How old were twin sisters Kin Narita and Gin Kanie when they had a hit single in Japan?

5. Where did Tony Christie want to know the way to in 1971?

6. Who played harmonica on Chaka Khan's 'I Feel For You'?

7. What order did The Barron Knights bark out on behalf of John Noakes?

8. Which punk band starred in the film *The Great Rock 'n' Roll Swindle*?

9. What fruit were Prince and The Revolution wearing on their head in 1985?

10. Which singer with Californian cult band The Seeds used to ask dogs the time and live in a dustbin like his hero Top Cat?

11. Which US diva allegedly said 'I don't do stairs' when asked to climb a small flight to her first-floor suite at BBC's Elstree Studios?

12. Which Sixties group were supposedly named after a friend's pedigree cat?

13. Which two words did Chicago drop from their original name?

14. Which Mamas and The Papas song became a hit again 31 years after its original release when it featured in a TV commercial?

15. Limahl was the lead singer with which Eighties group?

16. Who had a 1975 hit with 'The Hustle'?

Answers to page 147
CHART TOPPERS 7: **1.** John Denver ('Annie's Song') **2.** 'Don't Cry For Me Argentina' **3.** Jive Bunny and The Mastermixers **4.** 'Inside' **5.** Kelly Marie **6.** 'Feels Like I'm In Love' **7.** 'Don't Stand So Close To Me' (The Police, written by Sting) **8.** 'Begin The Beguine' **9.** Julio Iglesias **10.** Yazz **11.** The Shadows **12.** Eight **13.** Des O'Connor **14.** 'Hey Jude' **15.** Chesney Hawkes **16.** Nik Kershaw

Jazz 2

Answers on page 152

1. With what instrument was Erroll Garner associated?

2. What was Eddie Calvert's nickname?

3. Which track from the film *The King and I* gave Kenny Ball and His Jazzmen a number four UK hit in 1962?

4. Which Pittsburgh-born double bass player toured the world with Oscar Peterson from 1951 to 1966?

5. What were Serge Chaloff, Stan Getz, Zoot Sims and Al Cohn collectively known as?

6. What was the original title for 'Stranger On The Shore'?

7. Who had a 1982 hit with 'Cherry Pink And Apple Blossom White'?

8. Which jazz chart topper of 1954 was the first number one hit to be recorded at Abbey Road Studios?

9. What was singer Joe Carroll usually known as?

10. 'Petite Fleur' was a 1959 UK hit for whose jazz band?

11. Who performed the clarinet solo on 'Petite Fleur'?

12. Whose band charted in the UK in 1956 with 'Bad Penny Blues'?

13. What was the name of Acker Bilk's band?

14. Which instrument did Wardell Gray play?

15. What nationality insect gave Herb Alpert a number three hit in 1965?

16. Which group of musicians backed Herb Alpert?

Answers to page 152
NUMBER TWOS 2: **1.** 1965 **2.** 1986 **3.** 1970 **4.** 1970 **5.** 1964 **6.** 1981 **7.** 1970 **8.** 1958 **9.** 1990 **10.** 1993 **11.** 1977 **12.** 1969 **13.** 1962 **14.** 1974 **15.** 1979 **16.** 1983

Elton John 1

Answers on page 153

1. Which was Elton John's first UK chart hit?

2. Which two Beach Boys did backing vocals on 'Don't Let The Sun Go Down On Me'?

3. Which Lennon and McCartney song gave Elton John a 1974 hit?

4. Whose forenames did Reg Dwight borrow for his stage persona?

5. Who sang backing vocals on 'The Bitch Is Back'?

6. Which item of Elton John's stage clothing was checked for drugs when he arrived in Los Angeles in 1972?

7. What did Elton John wear on stage at a Stooges gig in Atlanta in October 1974?

8. What links Elton John and pickled onions?

9. Which song did Elton John perform on *The Muppet Show* with Miss Piggy?

10. On which song did Elton John duet with Kiki Dee in 1993?

11. From which film was 'Circle Of Life' taken?

12. In which year was 'Candle In The Wind' first released?

13. What lifelong ambition did Elton John realise in June 1977?

14. As whom was Elton John dressed when he gatecrashed Rod Stewart's Wembley concert in April 1991?

15. Which Elton John single of 1984 had a strong anti-apartheid message?

16. What honour was bestowed upon Elton John on 7 March 1976?

Answers to page 153
HOME TOWNS 3: 1. Colchester 2. Maidstone 3. Coventry 4. Haircut 100 5. Manchester 6. Southend 7. Liverpool 8. Solihull 9. Leeds 10. Newcastle-upon-Tyne 11. Acton County Grammar School 12. Hertfordshire 13. Soft Machine 14. The Barron Knights 15. Manic Street Preachers 16. Londonderry

Number Twos 2

Answers on page 150

In which years did the following tracks reach number two in the UK charts?

1. 'My Generation' (The Who)

2. 'Holding Back The Years' (Simply Red)

3. 'Lola' (The Kinks)

4. 'Let It Be' (The Beatles)

5. 'I'm Gonna Be Strong' (Gene Pitney)

6. 'Invisible Sun' (The Police)

7. 'I Want You Back' (The Jackson Five)

8. 'Tom Hark' (Elias and his Zigzag Flutes)

9. 'Hanky Panky' (Madonna)

10. 'Why Can't I Wake Up With You?' (Take That)

11. 'Boogie Nights' (Heatwave)

12. 'Oh Happy Day' (The Edwin Hawkins Singers)

13. 'Hey! Baby' (Bruce Channel)

14. 'The Cat Crept In' (Mud)

15. 'Crazy Little Thing Called Love' (Queen)

16. 'My Oh My' (Slade)

Answers to page 150
JAZZ 2: **1.** Piano **2.** 'The Man With The Golden Trumpet' **3.** 'March Of The Siamese Children' **4.** Ray Brown **5.** The Four Brothers **6.** 'Jenny' **7.** Modern Romance featuring John Du Prez **8.** 'Oh Mein Papa' (Eddie Calvert) **9.** 'Bebop' **10.** Chris Barber **11.** Monty Sunshine **12.** Humphrey Lyttelton **13.** The Paramount Jazz Band **14.** Tenor saxophone **15.** 'Spanish Flea' **16.** The Tijuana Brass

Home Towns 3

Answers on page 151

1. Which town do Blur come from?

2. Which Kentish town was home to Chicory Tip?

3. Eighties band King hailed from which Midlands city?

4. Which Eighties band, who sang about their Favourite Shirts, came from Beckenham, Kent?

5. Which city did Herman's Hermits come from?

6. The Kursaal Flyers came from which Essex town?

7. Where do The Farm come from?

8. Where was the home town of Sixties band The Applejacks?

9. In which city did Soft Cell meet up?

10. Which city was home to The Animals?

11. Roger Daltrey, Pete Townshend and John Entwistle were all pupils at which school in west London?

12. From which county did Sixties band Unit Four Plus Two come?

13. Which Sixties band, featuring Robert Wyatt and Kevin Ayers, were formed in Canterbury, Kent?

14. Leighton Buzzard is the home town of which comedy group, popular in the Sixties?

15. Which band are arguably the most famous sons of Blackwood in South Wales?

16. Where was The Undertones' home town?

Answers to page 151
ELTON JOHN 1: **1.** 'Your Song' **2.** Carl Wilson and Bruce Johnston **3.** 'Lucy In The Sky With Diamonds' **4.** Saxophonist Elton Dean and R & B singer Long John Baldry **5.** Dusty Springfield **6.** His platform boots with eight-inch lifts **7.** A gorilla suit **8.** In 1975 he was due to marry Linda Woodrow, heiress to the Epicure pickled onion empire **9.** 'Don't Go Breaking My Heart' **10.** 'True Love' **11.** *The Lion King* **12.** 1974 **13.** He became chairman of Watford Football Club **14.** Rod Stewart's new bride, Rachel Hunter **15.** 'Passengers' **16.** He was immortalised in wax at Madame Tussaud's

Reggae 2

Answers on page 156

1. In which year did Bob Marley and The Wailers first release 'No Woman No Cry'?

2. Who had a hit with 'My Boy Lollipop' in 1964?

3. Who led The Maytals from the early Seventies?

4. Whose albums included 'Furnace', 'Flesh of My Skin, Blood Of My Blood' and 'Torch Of Freedom'?

5. What was the name of Desmond Dekker's backing band?

6. Which song did Desmond Dekker take to number two in the UK charts in 1970?

7. Which former member of The Wailers was murdered by burglars at his Jamaican home in 1987?

8. John Taylor and Everton Banner are better known as which reggae duo?

9. How old was Bob Marley when he died?

10. Which brothers were founder members of UB40?

11. Which UB40 hit was written about the unemployment statistics at the time?

12. In which year did Shaggy reach number one in the UK with 'Boombastic'?

13. What was Ken Boothe's follow-up to 'Everything I Own'?

14. Which song, originally recorded by Johnny Osborne in 1969, was a UK top ten hit for UB40 in 1998?

15. From which film was UB40's number one '(I Can't Help) Falling In Love With You' taken?

16. Who had a posthumous hit with 'Buffalo Soldier' in 1983?

Answers to page 156
BUDDY HOLLY 1: 1. Sonny West 2. It was mis-spelt on the recording contract 3. Charles 4. The Three Tunes 5. Three 6. 1958 7. Des O'Connor 8. Cricket Jerry Allison's girlfriend, Peggy Sue Gerron 9. In his Greenwich Village apartment 10. 'Peggy Sue Got Married' 11. 'Rave On' 12. 'Bo Diddley' 13. Bob Montgomery 14. 'Blue Days, Black Nights' 15. He played only on the downstroke 16. 3 February 1959

Seventies 5

Answers on page 157

1. Who had the last UK number one single of the Seventies?

2. Who got to number one in 1975 with 'Ms Grace'?

3. Which actress contributed whispers to 'Tonight's The Night' by Rod Stewart?

4. Which 10cc song was written about the experiences of Moody Blue Justin Hayward on a holiday to the Caribbean?

5. What was the lead singer of Fox's Christian name?

6. Who had a 1971 hit with 'My Brother Jake'?

7. Who recorded the album 'I'm A Writer, Not A Fighter'?

8. What were the names of the five Osmonds (before Little Jimmy joined)?

9. Which namesake of a Scottish international footballer of the time was a member of Dave Edmunds's Rockpile?

10. Which song gave Deniece Williams a UK number one in 1977?

11. Which daughter of a TV game show host was a member of Guys 'N' Dolls?

12. Who asked: 'Who Were You With In The Moonlight'?

13. In which year did Slade have their first number one?

14. And what was the title?

15. What did Barry White ask in November 1975?

16. Who released the 1970 album 'Self-Portrait'?

Answers to page 157
OASIS 1: **1.** Burnage **2.** British Gas **3.** The Inspiral Carpets **4.** Alan McGee **5.** Creation **6.** Liam and guitarist Paul Arthurs were involved in a brawl on the ferry from Harwich and returned to Britain immediately **7.** 'Supersonic' **8.** A fan jumped on stage and hit him in the face **9.** Liam **10.** Burt Bacharach **11.** 'Some Might Say' **12.** 'Champagne Supernova' **13.** 1995 **14.** An audience member threw wire-rimmed prescription glasses at him **15.** Tony McCarroll **16.** 'All Around The World'

Buddy Holly

Answers on page 154

1. Who originally recorded 'Rave On'?

2. Why was his original name of Holley changed to Holly?

3. What was Buddy Holly's real Christian name?

4. What were The Crickets previously called?

5. How many weeks did 'That'll Be The Day' spend at number one in the UK?

6. In which year did Buddy Holly and The Crickets embark on their only UK tour?

7. Which current chat show host was on the same bill as Holly for that UK tour?

8. After whom was 'Peggy Sue' named?

9. Where did Holly make his last-ever recordings?

10. Which sequel to one of his earlier songs was a posthumous Holly hit in 1959?

11. Which track got to number five in the UK charts in 1958?

12. Which song about an R & B singer was a 1963 hit for Holly?

13. Who was the Bob with whom the teenage Holly played as Buddy & Bob?

14. What was the title of Holly's first single?

15. What was unusual about Holly's guitar-playing?

16. On what date was Holly killed?

Answers to page 154
REGGAE 2: **1.** 1975 **2.** Millie **3.** Toots **4.** Keith Hudson **5.** The Aces
6. 'You Can Get It If You Really Want' **7.** Peter Tosh **8.** Chaka Demus and Pliers **9.** 36 **10.** Robin and Ali Campbell **11.** 'One In Ten' **12.** 1995
13. 'Crying Over You' **14.** 'Come Back Darling' **15.** *Sliver* **16.** Bob Marley

Oasis I

Answers on page 155

1. In which Manchester suburb did the Gallagher brothers live?

2. For which company did Noel Gallagher work as a storeman?

3. For which band did Noel fail an audition to be lead singer?

4. Which record company boss signed up Oasis in 1993?

5. And what was the name of the record company?

6. Why did the band's planned overseas debut in Amsterdam in February 1994 fail to materialise?

7. What was the title of the band's first single?

8. What happened to Noel at a gig at London's Riverside in August 1994?

9. Who broke his foot in 1994 jumping off the top of a moving tour bus?

10. Half a picture of which songwriter was featured on the cover of the band's debut album 'Definitely Maybe'?

11. What was the first UK number one for Oasis?

12. What is the final track on '(What's The Story) Morning Glory'?

13. In which year were Oasis named Best Newcomer at the Brit Awards?

14. Why did Liam walk off stage at Indianapolis in March 1995?

15. Who did Alan White replace as drummer in 1995?

16. Which Oasis track became, at 9 minutes 38 seconds, the longest single to reach number one in the UK?

Answers to page 155
SEVENTIES 5: **1.** Pink Floyd ('Another Brick In The Wall Part II') **2.** The Tymes **3.** Britt Ekland **4.** 'Dreadlock Holiday' **5.** Noosha **6.** Free **7.** Gilbert O'Sullivan **8.** Alan, Wayne, Merrill, Jay and Donny **9.** Billy Bremner **10.** 'Free' **11.** Julie Forsyth (daughter of Bruce) **12.** Dollar **13.** 1971 **14.** 'Coz I Luv You' **15.** 'What Am I Going To Do With You?' **16.** Bob Dylan

Pot Luck 16

Answers on page 160

1. Which female leader of a punk band was jailed in 1977 for obstruction?

2. Which American band took their name from a make of fire engine?

3. Which Salvation Army group had two UK top forty hits in 1964?

4. Who had a 'Constant Craving' in 1993?

5. What was the name of Lulu's backing band on 'Shout'?

6. Which Prince song was a number one for Sinead O'Connor in 1990?

7. Who was the singer with Fine Young Cannibals?

8. Who led The Lovin' Spoonful?

9. What was the title of R & B singer Chuck Willis's last record before his death in 1958?

10. Which 79-year-old bluesman became the oldest artist to get into the UK album charts when 'Don't Look Back' reached number 63 in 1997?

11. Which Belgian had a 1978 hit with 'Ca Plane Pour Moi'?

12. Which country girl sang about a 'Blanket On The Ground' in 1975?

13. Which TV weatherman was the subject of a 1988 song by A Tribe Of Toffs?

14. What nationality are Ace Of Base?

15. Which British funk band had Lee John as their frontman?

16. Who released the 1974 album 'Diamond Dogs'?

Answers to page 160
MOTOWN 2: **1.** Eddie Kendricks **2.** The Isley Brothers **3.** Dion
4. Martha and The Vandellas **5.** William **6.** 'Get Ready' **7.** *Mahogany*
8. 'Make It Happen' **9.** Billy Griffin **10.** Tony Bennett **11.** 'We Can Work It Out' **12.** 'Sir Duke' **13.** 'Chain Reaction' **14.** The Temptations
15. 'When You're Young And In Love' **16.** The Four Tops

Heavy Metal 3

Answers on page 161

1. Which Def Leppard singer appeared in the soccer movie *When Saturday Comes*?

2. Whose 1987 album was titled 'Slippery When Wet'?

3. Who was lead singer with Deep Purple from 1973 to 1976?

4. Which band did Bruce Dickinson leave to join Iron Maiden?

5. 'Come An' Get It' was the title of which band's 1981 album?

6. Which heavy metal singer was once placed seventh in the British fencing rankings for the men's foil?

7. Which film featured Steppenwolf's 'Born To Be Wild' in its opening sequence?

8. Who wrote 'Born To Be Wild'?

9. What was Iron Maiden's first UK number one album?

10. Who sang about 'Love In An Elevator'?

11. 'November Rain' was a 1992 hit for which band?

12. What was the title of the first UK top ten single for INXS?

13. What is the nickname of Saxon singer Peter Byford?

14. Whose albums included 'Lightning To The Nations' and 'Behold The Beginning'?

15. Which Def Leppard guitarist died in 1988 after consuming a lethal mixture of drugs and alcohol?

16. Which band had a top five album in 1982 with 'The Eagle Has Landed'?

Answers to page 161
NAME CHANGES 7: **1.** Limahl (Chris Hamill) **2.** Soft Machine **3.** Kiki Dee **4.** Steppenwolf **5.** The Miracles **6.** Bo Diddley **7.** Marie MacDonald McLaughlin Lawrie **8.** Bez (The Happy Mondays) **9.** Stevie Wonder **10.** Kelly Marie **11.** David Solberg **12.** Oasis **13.** L.L. Cool J. **14.** Raymond **15.** Cilla Black **16.** The Elgins

Motown 2

Answers on page 158

1. Who took lead vocals on The Temptations' 'Just My Imagination'?

2. Who had a 1969 hit with 'Behind A Painted Smile'?

3. Who originally recorded 'Abraham, Martin And John', a 1970 hit for Marvin Gaye?

4. Who reached number 21 in the UK charts in 1967 with 'Jimmy Mack'?

5. What is Smokey Robinson's real Christian name?

6. What was The Temptations' first UK top ten hit?

7. 'Do You Know Where You're Going To' by Diana Ross was the theme from which film?

8. From which album was Smokey Robinson and The Miracles' 'Tears Of A Clown' taken?

9. Who replaced Smokey Robinson as lead singer with The Miracles in 1972?

10. Who recorded the original version of 'For Once In My Life', which Stevie Wonder released in 1968?

11. Which Beatles track did Stevie Wonder record as a single in 1971?

12. Which Stevie Wonder single was a tribute to Duke Ellington?

13. Which 1986 song gave Diana Ross her first UK number one single for 15 years?

14. Who had a 1970 hit with 'Ball Of Confusion'?

15. What was the title of The Marvelettes only UK hit?

16. Levi Stubbs was the lead singer with which Motown group?

Answers to page 158
POT LUCK 16: 1. Siouxsie 2. REO Speedwagon 3. The Joy Strings
4. k.d. lang 5. The Luvvers 6. 'Nothing Compares 2 U' 7. Roland Gift
8. John Sebastian 9. 'What Am I Living For?' 10. John Lee Hooker
11. Plastic Bertrand 12. Billie Jo Spears 13. 'John Kettley (Is A Weatherman)' 14. Swedish 15. Imagination 16. David Bowie

Name Changes 7

Answers on page 159

1. Which frontman of an Eighties band was an anagram of his true surname?

2. Which jazz-rock band used to be known as The Bishops Of Canterbury?

3. Which collaborator with Elton John changed her name from Pauline Matthews?

4. Which heavy metal band used to be called The Sparrows?

5. Which Motown group were previously known as The Matadors?

6. Which R & B star was born Ellas Bates?

7. What is Lulu's real name?

8. Which manic Manchester dancer is really called Mark Berry?

9. Which Motown artist changed his name from Steveland Judkins to something more showbiz?

10. Under what name did Jacqueline McKinnon have a number one disco single?

11. What is David Soul's full name?

12. Which band were previously known as Rain?

13. Which rap artist was born James Todd Smith?

14. What is Gilbert O'Sullivan's real Christian name?

15. Who changed her name from Priscilla White?

16. What were The Temptations formerly known as?

Answers to page 159
HEAVY METAL 3: **1.** Joe Elliott **2.** Bon Jovi **3.** David Coverdale **4.** Samson **5.** Whitesnake **6.** Bruce Dickinson **7.** *Easy Rider* **8.** Dennis Edmonton **9.** 'The Number Of The Beast' **10.** Aerosmith **11.** Guns N' Roses **12.** 'Need You Tonight' **13.** 'Biff' **14.** Diamond Head **15.** Steve Clark **16.** Saxon

Fifties 3

Answers on page 164

1. Which singer had the first-ever UK number one?
2. And what was the title of the song?
3. What was Winifred Atwell's profession before taking up the piano?
4. Which emotional Fifties singer was nicknamed 'The Prince of Wails'?
5. Which Jerry Lee Lewis number one of 1958 was written by Otis Blackwell and Jack Hammer?
6. Which group backed Dickie Valentine on his 1954 chart topper 'The Finger Of Suspicion'?
7. Which Tommy Steele hit was also the theme song to his TV show?
8. Which single taken from the film *Tommy the Toreador* was a 1959 hit for Tommy Steele?
9. Which rock 'n' roller was convicted of transporting a minor across a state line for immoral purposes?
10. Which British female singer had a 1956 UK number one with 'Lay Down Your Arms'?
11. How many UK top ten hits did Ruby Murray have in 1955?
12. How old was Ruby Murray when she had her only number one hit?
13. And what was its title?
14. Which 1955 number one was the last UK chart topper before 'Je T'Aime…Moi Non Plus' to have a foreign title?
15. Which 1954 hit for Rosemary Clooney told the true story of how the body of a mountain man was discovered by hunters in a ramshackle building?
16. Which 1955 number one came from the Jane Russell film *Underwater*?

Answers to page 164
FILM TRACKS 5: **1.** *Aida* **2.** *Rupert and the Frog Song* **3.** 'When The Going Gets Tough, The Tough Get Going' **4.** *Who's That Girl* **5.** *A Countess From Hong Kong* **6.** Charlie Chaplin **7.** 'I'll Remember' **8.** *Shanghai Surprise* **9.** *Summer Holiday* **10.** 'On The Beach' **11.** Shirley Bassey **12.** *Girls! Girls! Girls!* **13.** 'Wooden Heart' **14.** *Buster* **15.** 'Separate Lives' **16.** *The Jazz Singer*

Lyrics 6

Answers on page 165

From which songs are the following lyrics taken?

1. 'Don't underestimate me, boy, I'll make you sorry you were born'

2. 'I want to wake up in a city that doesn't sleep'

3. 'You fooled me with your kisses, you cheated and you schemed'

4. 'You give me one good reason to leave me, I'll give you ten good reasons to stay'

5. 'Once bitten and twice shy, I keep my distance but you still catch my eye'

6. 'We're a thousand miles apart and you know I love you'

7. 'We can try to understand the New York Times' effect on man'

8. 'Mirrors on the ceiling, the pink champagne on ice'

9. 'I know the moment isn't right to hold my emotions inside'

10. 'And don't you make me beg for love, give a sign 'cause I need to know'

11. 'If you want my future forget my past'

12. 'I should've known from the start before you got in my heart'

13. 'Even when the sun is shining I can't avoid the lightning'

14. 'Where did you go when things went wrong for you'

15. 'Acting upon reliable information, a federal deputation laid a deadly ambush'

16. 'I think of the days when the sun used to set on my empty heart, all alone in my bed'

Answers to page 165
TAKE THAT 1: **1.** Nigel Martin-Smith **2.** Mark Owen **3.** Gary Barlow
4. 'Do What U Like' **5.** Howard Donald **6.** Howard Donald **7.** Robbie
Williams **8.** Mark Owen **9.** 'Pray' **10.** 'Everything Changes' **11.** Lulu
12. Mr Blobby **13.** 'Pray' **14.** 'Back For Good' **15.** 'How Deep Is Your
Love' **16.** 1996

Film Tracks 5

Answers on page 162

1. Which Disney film featured Elton John's 'Written In The Stars'?

2. Which animation film spawned 'We All Stand Together' by Paul McCartney and the Frog Chorus?

3. Which Billy Ocean hit came from the film *The Jewel of the Nile*?

4. Madonna's 1987 hit 'The Look Of Love' was taken from which film?

5. 'This Is My Song', a 1967 number one for Petula Clark, was the theme tune for which film?

6. Which silent comedy film star wrote 'This Is My Song'?

7. Which theme from *With Honours* was a 1994 hit for Madonna?

8. Which film featured Madonna's 'Live To Tell', a number two hit in 1986?

9. From which film did Cliff Richard's 'Bachelor Boy' come?

10. Which Cliff Richard single was taken from *Wonderful Life*?

11. Who had a 1967 hit with 'Big Spender' from the film *Sweet Charity*?

12. Elvis Presley's 'Return To Sender' featured in which movie?

13. Which Elvis number one came from *G.I. Blues*?

14. Phil Collins's version of 'A Groovy Kind Of Love' was used in which film?

15. Which Phil Collins single of 1985 was taken from *White Nights*?

16. Neil Diamond's 'Love On The Rocks' was included in which film?

Answers to page 162
FIFTIES 3: 1. Al Martino 2. 'Here In My Heart' 3. Chemist 4. Johnnie Ray 5. 'Great Balls Of Fire' 6. The Stargazers 7. 'A Handful Of Songs' 8. 'Little White Bull' 9. Chuck Berry 10. Anne Shelton 11. Seven 12. 19 13. 'Softly Softly' 14. 'Mambo Italiano' 15. 'This Ole House' 16. 'Cherry Pink And Apple Blossom White'

Take That 1

Answers on page 163

1. Who was Take That's manager?

2. Which member of Take That used to work as a bank clerk?

3. Which member of Take That had been seen as a teenager playing the organ on Ken Dodd's TV show?

4. What was the band's debut single?

5. Who was the oldest member of Take That?

6. Which of the five worked as a car mechanic?

7. Who was the youngest in Take That?

8. Who was voted Most Fanciable Male at the 1992 Smash Hits Readers Poll Party Awards?

9. What was Take That's first UK number one single?

10. Which 1994 chart topper was also the title of their second album?

11. Who was guest vocalist on 'Relight My Fire'?

12. Who knocked 'Babe' off the top of the UK singles chart?

13. Which composition was voted Best Contemporary Song at the 1994 Ivor Novello Awards?

14. Which 1995 single sold over 300,000 copies in its first week – the highest first-week tally in ten years?

15. Which cover of a Bee Gees song became the group's eighth single to go straight in to the UK charts at number one?

16. In which year did Take That split up?

Answers to page 163
LYRICS 6: 1. 'Don't Call Me Baby' (Madison Avenue) 2. 'New York, New York' (Frank Sinatra) 3. '(You're The) Devil In Disguise' (Elvis Presley) 4. 'Too Many Broken Hearts' (Jason Donovan) 5. 'Last Christmas' (Wham!) 6. 'Everything Changes' (Take That) 7. 'Stayin' Alive (The Bee Gees) 8. 'Hotel California' (The Eagles) 9. 'Leave A Tender Moment Alone' (Billy Joel) 10. 'Heart And Soul' (T'Pau) 11. 'Wannabe' (Spice Girls) 12. 'Quit Playing Games (With My Heart)' (Backstreet Boys) 13. 'Why Does It Always Rain On Me?' (Travis) 14. 'Slight Return' (The Bluetones) 15. 'The Ballad Of Bonnie And Clyde (Georgie Fame) 16. 'Waiting For Tonight' (Jennifer Lopez)

Eighties 5

Answers on page 168

Which artists had UK hits in the Eighties with the following tracks?

1. '(Something Inside) So Strong'

2. 'Only When You Leave'

3. 'Owner Of A Lonely Heart'

4. 'Everything Must Change'

5. 'Fantastic Day'

6. 'Causing A Commotion'

7. 'Ain't Nothin' Goin' On But The Rent'

8. 'Wonderful Life'

9. 'Why Can't This Be Love'

10. 'This Charming Man'

11. 'The Land Of Make Believe'

12. 'New Moon On Monday'

13. 'My Baby Just Cares For Me'

14. 'Doctor Doctor'

15. 'Here Comes The Rain Again'

16. 'I Want To Know What Love Is'

Answers to page 168
POT LUCK 17: **1.** God **2.** Jeff Beck **3.** Stray Cats **4.** The Strawbs
5. John Peel **6.** Hank Marvin **7.** Cyndi Lauper **8.** Robert Palmer **9.** The
Rumour **10.** Steve Tyler and Joe Perry **11.** A French exchange student
12. The Teardrop Explodes **13.** Ruth, Anita, Bonnie and June **14.** Barry
Manilow **15.** The Sunshine Band **16.** Ringo Starr

Cover Versions 6

Answers on page 169

1. Which song links Anthony Newley and Donny Osmond?

2. Who had the original hit with 'Guantanamera', revived in 1997 by Wyclef Jean featuring Refugee Allstars?

3. Which Detroit Emeralds song did Shakin' Stevens cover in 1988?

4. Which Survivor number one was covered by Frank Bruno in 1995?

5. Which teen band covered Neil Sedaka's 'Breaking Up Is Hard To Do' in 1972?

6. David Whitfield, Frankie Laine and Barbara Dickson have all had hits with which song?

7. Who covered The Searchers hit 'Needles And Pins' in 1977?

8. Who had a hit with 'Somewhere' 33 years before the Pet Shop Boys?

9. Who had the original hit with The Hollies' 'Searchin''?

10. Which Beatles song did David Cassidy cover in 1974?

11. Which Lesley Gore hit from the Sixties became a number one for Dave Stewart and Barbara Gaskin in 1981?

12. Which TV cop had a number one by speaking his way through a Bread song?

13. Bobby Darin and The Four Tops both had hits with which song in the Sixties?

14. Who recorded the original version of 'I'm Doing Fine Now', a hit for The Pasadenas in 1992?

15. What song links Chaka Khan and Whitney Houston?

16. Sam Cooke and Johnny Nash both had hits with which song in the Sixties?

Answers to page 169
DUOS 2: **1.** The Korgis **2.** Michael and Janet Jackson **3.** Marcella Detroit **4.** Alisha's Attic **5.** 'True Love Ways' **6.** Asher and Waller **7.** 'Don't Stay Away Too Long' **8.** German **9.** 'Little Man' **10.** 1975 **11.** Esther and Abi Ofarim **12.** 'Cinderella Rockefella' **13.** 'Letter From America' **14.** Cilla Black **15.** Patti Labelle and Michael McDonald **16.** Three

Pot Luck 17

Answers on page 166

1. To whom did Prince dedicate his debut album?

2. Who replaced Eric Clapton in The Yardbirds?

3. Brian Setzer, Lee Rocker and Slim Jim Phantom were better known as which rockabilly trio?

4. Who had a top twenty hit with 'Part Of The Union'?

5. Which long-serving DJ was born John Ravenscroft?

6. Who was the first British guitarist to own a Fender Stratocaster?

7. Which American singer was described as 'The deranged First Lady of kookie pop'?

8. Who was the original singer with Power Station?

9. What was the name of Graham Parker's backing band?

10. Which two members of Aerosmith featured on Run D.M.C.'s version of 'Walk This Way'?

11. For what did Curt Smith mistake his future Tears For Fears partner Roland Orzabal when they first met at the age of 13?

12. Which band were named after a caption in *Marvel* comic?

13. What were the names of the four Pointer Sisters?

14. Which singer/songwriter used to work in the CBS-TV mailroom in Manhattan?

15. What was the name of KC's band?

16. Which Beatle went to school with Billy Fury?

Answers to page 166
EIGHTIES 5: 1. Labi Siffre 2. Spandau Ballet 3. Yes 4. Paul Young
5. Haircut 100 6. Madonna 7. Gwen Guthrie 8. Black 9. Van Halen
10. The Smiths 11. Bucks Fizz 12. Duran Duran 13. Nina Simone
14. The Thompson Twins 15. Eurythmics 16. Foreigner

Duos 2

Answers on page 167

1. Which duo had a 1980 hit with 'Everybody's Got To Learn Sometime'?

2. Which brother and sister duetted on 'Scream' in 1995?

3. With whom did Elton John duet on his version of 'Ain't Nothing Like The Real Thing'?

4. Which duo are the daughters of Brian Poole, former leader of The Tremeloes?

5. Which Buddy Holly song was a 1965 hit for Peter and Gordon?

6. What were Peter and Gordon's respective surnames?

7. What did Peters and Lee advise in 1974?

8. What nationality were Modern Talking who had a 1986 UK hit with 'Brother Louie'?

9. After 'I Got You Babe', what was Sonny and Cher's second UK top ten hit?

10. In which year were Sonny and Cher divorced?

11. Which Israeli husband and wife had a number one UK hit in 1968?

12. And what was the title of the song?

13. What was The Proclaimers' first hit single?

14. Who did the UK cover of The Righteous Brothers' 'You've Lost That Lovin' Feelin''?

15. Which duo had a number two hit with 'On My Own' in 1986?

16. How many UK number ones did Robson and Jerome have?

Answers to page 167
COVER VERSIONS 6: **1.** 'Why' **2.** The Sandpipers **3.** 'Feel The Need In Me' **4.** 'Eye Of The Tiger' **5.** The Partridge Family **6.** 'Answer Me' **7.** Smokie **8.** P.J. Proby **9.** The Coasters **10.** 'Please Please Me' **11.** 'It's My Party' **12.** Telly Savalas ('If') **13.** 'If I Were A Carpenter' **14.** New York City **15.** 'I'm Every Woman' **16.** 'Cupid'

Dire Straits 1

Answers on page 172

1. What was the title of Dire Straits' 1984 live double album?

2. Which band did Dire Straits support on their first UK tour, in 1978?

3. What was Dire Straits' first single?

4. Who was Dire Straits' bass guitarist?

5. Which Tina Turner hit was written by Mark Knopfler?

6. Who left the band before the recording of 'Making Movies'?

7. For which Bill Forsyth film starring Burt Lancaster and Denis Lawson did Mark Knopfler write the score?

8. Which group did Mark Knopfler form in 1990?

9. What was the title of Dire Straits' second album?

10. From which album was 'Private Investigations' taken?

11. Which track from *Rocky III* kept 'Private Investigations' off the number one spot in the UK singles chart?

12. Which 14-minute track featured on the 'Love Over Gold' album?

13. Who did Terry Williams replace as drummer in 1982?

14. For how many weeks did the 'Brothers In Arms' album stay at the top of the UK charts?

15. Who co-wrote 'Money For Nothing'?

16. Which five tracks from 'Brothers In Arms' were released as singles?

Answers to page 172
ROCK 'N' ROLL 2: **1.** 'School Day' and 'No Particular Place To Go'
2. Dion **3.** His voice broke **4.** 'Oh, Boy' **5.** 'The Purple People Eater
Meets The Witch Doctor' **6.** 1959 **7.** Bill Haley **8.** Eddie Cochran
9. 'Blue Suede Shoes' **10.** 'Hound Dog' **11.** 'Poor Me' **12.** Marty Wilde
and Craig Douglas **13.** 'Move It' **14.** 'Why Do Fools Fall In Love'
15. Alligator ('See You Later, Alligator') **16.** Chuck Berry and Jerry Lee
Lewis

Chart Toppers 8

Answers on page 173

1. In which year did David Bowie reach number one in the UK with 'Ashes To Ashes'?

2. Who got to number one in 1982 with 'Goody Two Shoes'?

3. Which father and daughter had separate UK number ones in 1966?

4. Andy Fairweather-Low was the singer with which 1969 chart toppers?

5. And what was the title of their number one?

6. Which 1969 chart topper had already seen his brother have a UK number one, but with a different surname?

7. Who had a 1998 number one with 'Gym And Tonic'?

8. Which was the best-selling UK single of 1998?

9. Which boy band had a number one hit in 2001 with 'Let's Dance'?

10. Which 1958 chart topper was promoted as a full-blooded Cherokee Indian?

11. Who reached number one in 1959 with 'The Day The Rains Came'?

12. Which 1982 hit was based on a Zulu folk tune?

13. Whose camera never lied in 1982?

14. Which old Marvin Gaye B-side topped the UK charts in 1983 with a new singer?

15. Who topped the charts in 1977 with 'So You Win Again'?

16. Which charity record gave Wet Wet Wet their first UK number one?

Answers to page 173
VIDEOS 1: 1. 'Dancing In The Dark' 2. Neil Kinnock 3. Claudia Schiffer 4. 'Rio' 5. 'Sledgehammer' 6. 'Bohemian Rhapsody' 7. Madonna (her brother Christopher) 8. Michael Jackson ('Thriller') 9. 'Fat Bottomed Girls' 10. Diana Dors 11. 'Take On Me' 12. Christie Brinkley 13. '(You Drive Me) Crazy' 14. Brian May 15. 'It's Only Love' 16. 'Black And White'

Rock 'n' Roll 2

Answers on page 170

1. Which two Chuck Berry songs have the same tune but different lyrics?

2. Whose hits included 'Runaround Sue' and 'The Wanderer'?

3. Which natural development brought a temporary halt to Frankie Lymon's singing career in 1959?

4. Which Crickets hit of 1957 became a number one for Mud 18 years later?

5. The Big Bopper's 'Chantilly Lace' began as the B-side to which novelty number parodying two chart hits of the time?

6. In which year did Eddie Cochran have a UK hit with 'C'mon Everybody'?

7. Which rock 'n' roll star started out with the Downhomers?

8. Who sang 'Twenty Flight Rock' in the 1956 Jayne Mansfield film *The Girl Can't Help It*?

9. Which Carl Perkins song, covered by Elvis, was based on a true incident observed at a gig?

10. Which Elvis hit was originally recorded by Big Mama Thornton?

11. Which of his song titles did Adam Faith borrow for the title of his early autobiography?

12. Which two British acts had 1959 hits with 'A Teenager In Love'?

13. Which song started on the B-side of 'Schoolboy Crush' but went on to become Cliff Richard's first hit?

14. What was Frankie Lymon and The Teenagers' 1956 UK number one?

15. Which reptile was Bill Haley looking forward to meeting again in 1956?

16. Which two US artists had UK hits with 'Sweet Little Sixteen'?

Answers to page 170
DIRE STRAITS 1: **1.** 'Alchemy' **2.** Talking Heads **3.** 'Sultans Of Swing' **4.** John Illsley **5.** 'Private Dancer' **6.** David Knopfler **7.** *Local Hero* **8.** The Notting Hillbillies **9.** 'Communique' **10.** 'Love Over Gold' **11.** 'Eye Of The Tiger' **12.** 'Telegraph Road' **13.** Pick Withers **14.** Three **15.** Sting **16.** 'So Far Away', 'Money For Nothing', 'Brothers In Arms', 'Walk Of Life' and 'Your Latest Trick'

Videos 1

Answers on page 171

1. In which Bruce Springsteen video did future *Friends* star Courteney Cox climb on stage?
2. Which British politician appeared in a Tracey Ullman video?
3. Which supermodel was in the video for Westlife's version of 'Uptown Girl'?
4. Which Duran Duran video showed the band sailing on the high seas?
5. Which award-winning Peter Gabriel video featured claymation and stop-motion?
6. Which was the first song to have a genuine promo video?
7. The brother of which international artist appeared in the video for Soft Cell's 'Tainted Love'?
8. Who announced in his 1983 video: 'Due to my strong personal convictions, I wish to stress that this film in no way endorses a belief in the occult'?
9. Which Queen video featured semi-nude female cyclists?
10. Which Fifties film star appeared in the video for Adam and The Ants' 'Prince Charming'?
11. Which a-ha video won five prizes at the 1986 MTV Video Music Awards?
12. Which supermodel appeared in the video for Billy Joel's 'Uptown Girl'?
13. Melissa Joan Hart appeared in which Britney Spears video?
14. Which member of Queen was in the video for Five's 'We Will Rock You'?
15. Which Bryan Adams song won Best Stage Performance at the 1986 MTV Video Awards?
16. Which 1991 Michael Jackson video was withdrawn and re-edited after complaints about its violent content?

Beatles 2

Answers on page 176

1. Which Paul McCartney composition was originally written for – but rejected – by Billy J. Kramer?

2. Who is the subject of 'Hey Jude'?

3. In which year was 'Sgt. Pepper' released?

4. Which Beatles track ended with an ultrasonic whistle audible only to dogs and recorded by Paul McCartney especially for his Shetland sheepdog?

5. Which closing track on 'Revolver' featured the use of backward tapes?

6. Which 'Sgt. Pepper' track did the BBC ban in 1967 in the belief that it might encourage drug-taking?

7. Which pop artist created the album cover for 'Sgt. Pepper'?

8. Who were the first act signed by Apple Music?

9. How many weeks did 'Hey Jude' stay at number one in the US?

10. Who appeared on TV's *Dee Time* in 1968 to say that her relationship with Paul McCartney was over?

11. What role did Police Inspector Carl Bear play in Beatles history?

12. What premiered on ABC TV on 25 September 1965?

13. Who are the only two singers featured on the sleeve of 'Sgt. Pepper'?

14. Which veteran actress initially refused to allow her photo to be used on the 'Sgt. Pepper' cover, on the grounds that she would never be in a lonely hearts club?

15. Which Beatles anthem was transmitted worldwide in 1967 as part of the first global TV link-up?

16. What was voted Song of the Year at the 1967 Grammy Awards?

Answers to page 176
NINETIES 5: 1. TLC 2. Boyz II Men 3. Ian Brown 4. Gabrielle 5. 'The Division Bell' 6. Celine Dion 7.'36D', a song about topless models 8. 15 9. Kurt Cobain 10. Eels 11. Rotterdam 12. Suede 13. Meat Loaf 14. Alisha's Attic 15. 'The Only Living Boy In New York' 16. Spin Doctors

Albums 7

Answers on page 177

Which artists released the following albums?

1. 'The Song Remains The Same' (1976)

2. 'Auberge' (1991)

3. 'Misplaced Childhood' (1985)

4. 'Blue Moves' (1976)

5. 'Growing Up In Public' (1992)

6. 'By Request' (1999)

7. 'No Jacket Required' (1985)

8. 'Some Other Sucker's Parade' (1997)

9. 'On The Waters' (1970)

10. 'Adrenalize' (1992)

11. 'Discovery' (1979)

12. 'His 'N' Hers (1994)

13. 'The Seeds Of Love' (1989)

14. 'No Angel' (2001)

15. 'Present Arms' (1981)

16. 'The Summoner's Tales' (1993)

Answers to page 177
POT LUCK 18: 1. Manfred Mann 2. Viv Stanshall 3. Leather jacket
4. Jack Anglin 5. Crowded House 6. David Crosby 7. The Bee Gees
8. 'From Russia With Love' 9. Pulp 10. Travis 11. Jamiroquai 12. Cat
Stevens 13. Gerry Rafferty 14. The Strawbs 15. 14 16. The Rutles

Nineties 5

Answers on page 174

1. Lisa 'Left Eye' Lopes, Rozanda 'Chilli' Thomas and T-Boz make up which trio?

2. Who had a number one single in 1992 with 'End Of The Road'?

3. Who was lead singer with The Stone Roses?

4. Who took 'Dreams' to number one in 1993?

5. Which 1994 release gave Pink Floyd their first number one UK album for 11 years?

6. Which singer married her 52-year-old manager, René Angelil, in 1994?

7. In protest at the lyrics of which song did singer Briana Corrigan leave The Beautiful South?

8. How many weeks did Wet Wet Wet's 'Love Is All Around' spend at number one in the UK?

9. Whose suicide note said: 'It's better to burn out than to fade away'?

10. Which Los Angeles band had a drummer called Butch?

11. Which Dutch port did The Beautiful South sing about?

12. Whose 1996 number one album was titled 'Coming Up'?

13. Who had the biggest-selling UK single and album of 1993?

14. Which girl duo's first UK hit was 'I Am I Feel'?

15. Which Simon and Garfunkel song was covered in 1993 by Everything But The Girl?

16. In 1994, Anthony Krizan replaced Eric Shenkman as guitarist with which US band?

Answers to page 174
BEATLES 2: **1.** 'Yesterday' **2.** Julian Lennon **3.** 1967 **4.** 'A Day In The Life'
5. 'Tomorrow Never Knows' **6.** 'A Day In The Life' **7.** Peter Blake
8. Grapefruit **9.** Nine **10.** Jane Asher **11.** He stopped a 1964 Beatles
show in Cleveland, Ohio, after screaming fans invaded the stage **12.** The
Beatles cartoon series **13.** Bob Dylan and Dion **14.** Mae West **15.** 'All
You Need Is Love' **16.** 'Michelle'

Pot Luck 18

Answers on page 175

1. In 1974, who gave away deeds to a square foot of land on a Welsh mountain to anyone who bought his environment-friendly record 'The Good Earth'?

2. Which eccentric singer once put raw meat into Ringo Starr's drum kit in a bid to wreck the sound?

3. Which 30-year-old item of John Lennon's clothing was sold for £24,200 in 1992?

4. Which country star was killed in a car crash on his way to Patsy Cline's funeral?

5. Which band got their name from a cramped apartment they once shared?

6. Which American was jailed in 1983 for possession of drugs and carrying a gun into a bar?

7. Who wrote Marbles' 1968 hit 'Only One Woman'?

8. Which James Bond film theme gave Matt Monro a hit in 1963?

9. Who were 'Sorted For E's & Wizz' in 1995?

10. Whose 2001 album was titled 'The Invisible Band'?

11. Jay Kay is associated with which band?

12. Which Sixties and Seventies artist returned to music in 1995 under the name of Yusef Islam?

13. Who was the future solo star singer with Steelers Wheel?

14. 'Lay Down' was the first UK top twenty single for which Seventies band?

15. How old was Helen Shapiro when she had a top three hit with 'Don't Treat Me Like A Child'?

16. Which Eric Idle-inspired band were a spoof of The Beatles?

Name Changes 8

Answers on page 180

1. As which heavyweight rock star is Marvin Lee Aday better known?

2. Which backing group to a Fifties Italian/American singer used to be called The Timberlanes?

3. What were Dave Dee, Dozy, Beaky, Mick and Tich previously known as?

4. Which heavy metal band used to be called Earth?

5. Which rap artist started life as Kevin Donovan?

6. What is Babyface's real name?

7. To what did Cherilyn Sarkasian La Piere decide to shorten her name?

8. Which British star of the Fifties was originally Tommy Hicks?

9. What is Jay Kay's real Christian name?

10. As whom was dog-lover Kent Lavoie better known in the Seventies?

11. Who used his imagination when changing his name from John Leslie McGregor?

12. Which enduring star was born Annie Mae Bullock?

13. Which UK singer of the Fifties looked for something more romantic than Richard Bryce?

14. What was Harry Casey better known as initially?

15. Which saxophonist's full name is Kenny Gorelick?

16. Which diminutive Sixties performer was born Eva Narcissus Boyd?

Answers to page 180
a1 1: **1.** Ben **2.** 'Be The First To Believe' **3.** 'Here We Come' **4.** 'Like A Rose' **5.** Spanish **6.** 'I Still Believe' **7.** Columbia **8.** 6 **9.** 'Ready Or Not' **10.** 'Summertime Of Our Lives' **11.** Nine **12.** 'The A List' **13.** 'Take On Me' **14.** Paul **15.** Christian **16.** Ben

Rod Stewart 1

Answers on page 181

1. Which member of Jefferson Starship played piano on 'Maggie May'?

2. Who originally recorded 'Reason To Believe'?

3. For which band did Rod Stewart sing on the 1972 hit 'In A Broken Dream'?

4. With which football club was Stewart an apprentice?

5. From which country was the teenage Stewart deported for vagrancy?

6. Which band did Stewart join in 1965?

7. Who played mandolin on the record of 'Maggie May'?

8. What was Stewart's first UK number one album?

9. Who originally recorded *Angel*?

10. From which album was 'Sailing' taken?

11. In which year did The Faces split?

12. With whom did Stewart duet on the 1990 hit 'It Takes Two'?

13. What was Stewart's last UK number one single?

14. Which Stewart-penned single was about the death of a gay friend in New York?

15. Which album contained the single 'D'Ya Think I'm Sexy'?

16. Why did Stewart refuse to leave the airport international departure lounge on a visit to Britain in 1975?

Answers to page 181
R & B 3: **1.** The Hoochie Coochie Men **2.** Destiny's Child **3.** Jennifer Lopez **4.** 'She's Got That Vibe' **5.** Little Feat **6.** Janis Joplin **7.** 'Let The Heartaches Begin' **8.** 'I Feel Free' **9.** 'With A Little Help From My Friends' **10.** Jennifer Lopez **11.** 'Love II Love' **12.** *Notting Hill* **13.** 'Be Alone No More' **14.** Phil Collins **15.** Cream **16.** Matthew Marsden

a1

Answers on page 178

1. Who is the youngest member of a1?

2. What was a1's first UK hit?

3. What was the title of the band's first album?

4. What was the title of the track, later released as a single, written by Ben on the first album?

5. What nationality is Paul's grandfather?

6. Which track on the debut album was written by Mark?

7. What was a1's first record label?

8. What number in the UK charts did 'Be The First To Believe' get to?

9. What was the other track on the double A-side of 'Everytime'?

10. Which September 1999 single reached number five in the UK charts?

11. How many weeks did 'Be The First To Believe' stay in the UK charts?

12. Which album featured 'Same Old Brand New You'?

13. Which single from that album was a cover version of an a-ha hit?

14. Who was the only band member not to have contributed to the writing of 'Forever In Love'?

15. Which member of a1 plays the guitar?

16. Which member of a1 has the surname Adams?

R & B 3

Answers on page 179

1. Which band did Long John Baldry form in 1964?

2. Which R & B band released the album 'Survivor' in 2001?

3. Who had a hit in 2001 with 'Ain't It Funny'?

4. Which was R. Kelly's first top ten single in the UK?

5. Lowell George, Roy Estrada, Bill Payne and Richie Haywood comprised which Californian band of the Seventies?

6. Which R & B singer died of a heroin overdose at her Hollywood hotel in October 1970?

7. With which song did Long John Baldry have a UK number one in 1967?

8. What was Cream's first UK top twenty hit?

9. Which Beatles song did Joe Cocker take to number one in 1968?

10. Whose 1999 album was titled 'On The 6'?

11. What was Damage's first UK top twenty single?

12. Which film featured Another Level's 'From The Heart'?

13. Which Another Level hit featured Jay-Z?

14. Who sang backing vocals on Eric Clapton's 'Bad Love'?

15. Who had a 1967 album called 'Disraeli Gears'?

16. Which former *Coronation Street* actor teamed up with Destiny's Child for the 1998 single 'She's Gone'?

Answers to page 179
ROD STEWART 1: **1.** Pete Sears **2.** Tim Hardin **3.** Python Lee Jackson **4.** Brentford **5.** Spain **6.** Steampacket **7.** Lindisfarne's Ray Jackson **8.** 'Every Picture Tells A Story' **9.** Jimi Hendrix **10.** 'Atlantic Crossing' **11.** 1976 **12.** Tina Turner **13.** 'Baby Jane' **14.** 'The Killing Of Georgie (Parts 1 and 2)' **15.** 'Blondes Have More Fun' **16.** He reportedly owed the UK taxman £750,000 and didn't want to set foot in this country

Sixties 5

Answers on page 184

1. What was the nickname of Small Faces' bass guitarist Ronnie Lane?

2. What did Paul McCartney's younger brother call himself when he was a member of Scaffold?

3. Which bespectacled Cambridge undergraduate got to number four in the charts in 1965 with 'Everyone's Gone To The Moon'?

4. What was the name of Tony Rivers's backing group?

5. Mike Smith was the keyboard player with which successful Sixties band?

6. Who was the female singer with Chicken Shack before joining Fleetwood Mac?

7. Which singer invited listeners to 'Come Back And Shake Me' in 1969?

8. Which bird gave Manfred Mann a 1966 number one?

9. In which song did Ray Davies of The Kinks complain about 'my poor rheumatic back'?

10. Whose Singing Orchestral Circus had a 1968 hit with 'Quick Joey Small (Run Joey Run)'?

11. Whose backing band were The Rebel Rousers?

12. Whose Trinity was fronted by Julie Driscoll?

13. Davey Jones and The King Bees was the first musical venture for which international artist?

14. Hilton Valentine and John Steel were members of which band?

15. Which group had hits with 'He's In Town' and 'Poor Man's Son'?

16. Whose first UK chart action was with 'Arnold Layne' in 1967?

Answers to page 184
FLEETWOOD MAC 1: **1.** 'Tusk' **2.** Peter Green **3.** Jeremy Spencer **4.** Bob Weston **5.** Their manager assembled a bogus Fleetwood Mac to fulfil the dates **6.** Lindsey Buckingham and Stevie Nicks **7.** Stevie Nicks **8.** Peter Green **9.** Ten **10.** 'Rumours' **11.** Christine McVie **12.** Stevie Nicks **13.** Peter Green **14.** 1987 **15.** 'Little Lies' **16.** Stevie Nicks

Punk 3

Answers on page 185

1. Which punk band took their name from a gang in the David Carradine movie *Bound For Glory*?

2. Which punk icon was once a Playboy bunny waitress?

3. Who went to 'Echo Beach' in 1980?

4. Budgie was the drummer with which punk band?

5. Which album did 'Never Mind The Bollocks – Here's The Sex Pistols' knock off the top of the UK chart?

6. Which Clash album was originally going to be called 'The New Testament'?

7. What was Generation X's only UK top twenty hit?

8. Whose 1978 album was titled 'Love Bites'?

9. 'If The Kids Are United' was a hit for which band?

10. Which town did The Stranglers drop from their original name?

11. Which punk band recorded 'Gary Gilmore's Eyes', a reference to the death-row murderer who offered to donate his eyes to science?

12. Which band's biggest hit was 'Into The Valley'?

13. Jello Biafra was the singer with which controversially named US punk band?

14. Why were The Damned fired as support act for The Sex Pistols' 'Anarchy In The UK' tour?

15. Who quit his day job as a computer operator at an Elizabeth Arden cosmetics factory in 1977 to become a full-time musician?

16. Who was the singer with Eddie and The Hot Rods?

Answers to page 185
NOVELTY NUMBERS 3: **1.** The Monks **2.** Frankie Howerd **3.** Mike Reid **4.** Rolf Harris **5.** Orville **6.** Kermit's nephew Robin **7.** None **8.** Terry Wogan **9.** Keith Michell **10.** Hissing Sid **11.** Jimmy Savile **12.** Chelsea **13.** Rod Stewart **14.** 'We Have A Dream' **15.** Splodgenessabounds **16.** Spinal Tap

Fleetwood Mac 1

Answers on page 182

1. What was Fleetwood Mac's follow-up album to 'Rumours'?

2. Which guitarist appeared on stage in 1969 in a long white robe to reflect his new religious beliefs?

3. Who told the rest of the band on a 1971 US tour that he was 'just popping out for a bit to buy newspapers' and wasn't seen again for two years?

4. Which band member was sacked in 1973 for having an affair with Mick Fleetwood's wife?

5. What happened when Fleetwood Mac pulled out of a 1973 tour?

6. Which pair joined the band in 1974?

7. Who wrote 'Rhiannon'?

8. Which former band member was committed to a mental hospital in 1977?

9. How many different line-ups did Fleetwood Mac have between 1967 and 1974?

10. What was named Album of the Year at the 1978 Grammy Awards?

11. Who penned 'Don't Stop'?

12. Which band member wrote and sang 'Dreams'?

13. Who worked as a gravedigger and hospital porter after leaving Fleeetwood Mac?

14. In which year was the album 'Tango In The Night' released?

15. Which single gave Fleetwood Mac their first UK top five hit since 'Albatross' 14 years earlier?

16. Who released a solo album titled 'The Wild Heart'?

Answers to page 182
SIXTIES 5: 1. 'Plonk' 2. Mike McGear 3. Jonathan King 4. The Castaways 5. The Dave Clark Five 6. Christine Perfect 7. Clodagh Rodgers 8. 'Pretty Flamingo' 9. 'Autumn Almanac' 10. Kasenetz-Katz 11. Cliff Bennett 12. Brian Auger 13. David Bowie 14. The Animals 15. The Rockin' Berries 16. Pink Floyd

Novelty Numbers 3

Answers on page 183

1. Which band had a 1979 hit with the politically incorrect 'Nice Legs Shame About Her Face'?

2. Which comedian sang about the 'Three Little Fishes'?

3. Which ex-*EastEnder* reached number ten in the charts in 1975 with the tale of 'The Ugly Duckling'?

4. Which entertainer has recorded cover versions of both 'Stairway To Heaven' and 'Bohemian Rhapsody'?

5. Which large green duck in a nappy got to number four in the charts in 1982?

6. Which Muppet croaked 'Halfway Down The Stairs'?

7. How many UK number one singles did The Wombles have?

8. Which disc jockey had a 1978 hit with 'The Floral Dance'?

9. Who narrated the adventures of Captain Beaky?

10. Which snake went on trial in the further adventures of Captain Beaky?

11. Which DJ sang out 'Ahab The Arab' in the Sixties?

12. Which football team enjoyed a top five hit with 'Blue Is The Colour' in 1972?

13. Which fan led the Scottish World Cup Squad for 'Ole Ola' in 1978?

14. Which Scottish World Cup Squad song of 1982 teamed up such diverse talents as B.A. Robertson, Miss Scotland and Willie Carson?

15. Who requested 'Two Pints Of Lager And A Packet Of Crisps Please'?

16. Which spoof heavy metal band released a 1992 album 'Break Like The Wind'?

Answers to page 183
PUNK 3: 1. The Boomtown Rats 2. Debbie Harry 3. Martha and The Muffins 4. Siouxsie and The Banshees 5. '40 Golden Greats' by Cliff Richard and The Shadows 6. 'London Calling' 7. 'King Rocker' 8. The Buzzcocks 9. Sham 69 10. Guildford (They were The Guildford Stranglers) 11. The Adverts 12. The Skids 13. The Dead Kennedys 14. For agreeing to play in private for Derby councillors who wanted to assess the band's suitability 15. Elvis Costello 16. Barrie Masters

Pot Luck 19

Answers on page 188

1. Which Shadow became a Jehovah's Witness in 1973?

2. Which Rolling Stone is the son of a lorry driver?

3. What was Bob Marley's middle name?

4. Paddy McAloon is the leader of which band?

5. Dave Mount was the drummer with which Seventies band?

6. Which country star had four children and several miscarriages by the time she was 18?

7. Which singer was once employed wrapping chamber pots in a Cardiff factory?

8. Which band got their name from a TV listing guide which gave details of a forthcoming discussion programme?

9. At the time which rock classic was described as a 'novelty foxtrot'?

10. From which country do Midnight Oil come?

11. Who had a hit with 'The Joker'?

12. Derek Quinn, Roy Crewsdon, Pete Birrell and Bernie Dwyer formed which Sixties backing group to an energetic singer?

13. Who was sacked from his job with the Precision Tool Company in 1951 for being under age?

14. Who was sacked from his job stacking shelves at Tesco because he kept wearing the store's carrier bags?

15. Who wrote and performed 'Time In A Bottle'?

16. Who was the singer with Creedence Clearwater Revival?

Answers to page 188
LYRICS 7: **1.** 'Hand On Your Heart' (Kylie Minogue) **2.** 'Don't Look Back In Anger' (Oasis) **3.** 'All I Want For Christmas Is You' (Mariah Carey) **4.** 'Uptown Girl' (Billy Joel) **5.** 'The Greatest Love Of All' (George Benson) **6.** 'Mamma Mia' (Abba) **7.** 'Take On Me' (a-ha) **8.** 'Eternal Flame' (The Bangles) **9.** 'Love Me For A Reason' (The Osmonds) **10.** 'Linger' (The Cranberries) **11.** 'Honesty' (Billy Joel) **12.** 'A View To A Kill' (Duran Duran) **13.** 'That Don't Impress Me Much' (Shania Twain) **14.** 'Happy Together' (The Turtles) **15.** 'Until The Time Is Through' (Five) **16.** 'Oops!...I Did It Again' (Britney Spears)

Dance 3

Answers on page 189

1. Who was the guiding light behind Beats International's 'Dub Be Good To Me'?

2. Prince Markie Dee was a member of which New York dance band?

3. Who was the founder of Enigma?

4. Which young brother of New Kids On The Block's Donnie Wahlberg was once an underwear model for Calvin Klein?

5. Who changed her name to MC Kinky?

6. Daddy G and Mushroom were among the founding fathers of which Bristol-based dance/rap outfit?

7. Who had a 2001 hit with 'Castles In The Sky'?

8. Who released the album 'Strange Cargo'?

9. What is the real name of D.M.C. from Run D.M.C.?

10. Who had a 1997 hit with his version of the James Bond theme from *Tomorrow Never Dies*?

11. Which dance band were the UK's entrants in the 1995 Eurovision Song Contest?

12. Which Paul Hardcastle hit featured spoken news reports about the Vietnam War?

13. Who had a 1998 hit with 'The Rockafeller Skank'?

14. Who remixed Cornershop's 'Brimful Of Asha' to take it to number one in 1998?

15. What nationality are Black Box?

16. Which track earned Black Box a UK number one single in 1989?

Answers to page 189
ONE-HIT WONDERS 5: **1.** Wild Cherry **2.** Lipps Inc. **3.** Harmony Grass **4.** 'Race With The Devil' **5.** First Class **6.** 'Twilight Café' **7.** 'Also Sprach Zarathustra' **8.** Paul Davidson **9.** The Weather Girls **10.** Sunny **11.** Red Sovine **12.** 'My Resistance Is Low' **13.** Pseudo Echo **14.** Ohio Express **15.** 1910 Fruitgum Company **16.** 'The Shifting Whispering Sands'

Lyrics 7

Answers on page 186

From which songs are the following lyrics taken?

1. 'Look me in the eye and tell me we are really through'

2. 'You ain't ever gonna burn my heart out'

3. 'I just want you for my own more than you could ever know'

4. 'And when she's walking she's looking so fine'

5. 'I decided long ago never to walk in anyone's shadow'

6. 'Look at me now, will I ever learn, I don't know how, but I suddenly lose control'

7. 'Today's another day to find you shying away'

8. 'Do you feel my heart beating, do you understand'

9. 'My initial reaction is, honey, give me love, not a facsimile of'

10. 'But I'm in so deep, you know I'm such a fool for you'

11. 'If you look for truthfulness you might just as well be blind'

12. 'That fatal kiss is all we need'

13. 'I can't believe you kiss your car goodnight'

14. 'Me and you and you and me, no matter how they toss the dice it has to be, the only one for me is you and you for me'

15. 'Without your love I'd be half a man, maybe one day you'll understand'

16. 'It might seem like a crush but it doesn't mean that I'm serious'

Answers to page 186
POT LUCK 19: **1.** Hank Marvin **2.** Charlie Watts **3.** Nesta **4.** Prefab Sprout **5.** Mud **6.** Loretta Lynn **7.** Shirley Bassey **8.** Talking Heads **9.** 'Rock Around The Clock' **10.** Australia **11.** The Steve Miller Band **12.** The Dreamers (Freddie and The Dreamers) **13.** Elvis Presley **14.** Boy George **15.** Jim Croce **16.** John Fogerty

One-Hit Wonders 5

Answers on page 187

1. Whose only hit was 'Play That Funky Music' in 1976?

2. Who reached number two with 'Funky Town' in 1980 before disappearing without trace?

3. Which group had their solitary hit with 'Move In A Little Closer' in 1969?

4. What was Gun's only hit?

5. Which band's moment of triumph was 'Beach Baby' in 1974?

6. With a song about which eaterie did Susan Fassbender enjoy chart success in 1981?

7. Which instrumental reached number seven for Deodato in 1973?

8. Who had a top ten hit with 'Midnight Rider' in 1975?

9. For whom was it 'Raining Men' in 1984?

10. Who issued 'Doctor's Orders' in 1974?

11. Which American artist's only UK chart success was a number four hit with 'Teddy Bear' in 1981?

12. In 1976, which cover version of an old Hoagy Carmichael song gave Robin Sarstedt his only hit?

13. Which Australian band reached number eight in 1987 with 'Funky Town'?

14. Which bubblegum group had a 1968 hit with 'Yummy Yummy Yummy'?

15. Who got to number two in 1968 with 'Simon Says'?

16. Which 1956 release gave Eamonn Andrews his only chart entry?

Answers to page 187
DANCE 3: **1.** Norman Cook **2.** The Fat Boys **3.** Michael Cretu
4. Marky Mark **5.** Caron Geary **6.** Massive Attack **7.** Ian Van Dahl
8. William Orbit **9.** Darryl McDaniels **10.** Moby **11.** Love City Groove
12. '19' **13.** Fatboy Slim **14.** Norman Cook **15.** Italian **16.** 'Ride On Time'

George Michael I

Answers on page 192

1. How old was George Michael when he wrote 'Careless Whisper'?

2. Who played piano on Wham!'s 1986 number one 'Edge Of Heaven'?

3. With whom did George Michael duet on 'I Knew You Were Waiting (For Me)'?

4. Which George Michael number one sampled Patrice Rushen's 'Forget Me Nots'?

5. Which 1997 single (with Toby Bourke) did George Michael dedicate to his late mother?

6. Who joined George Michael on a duet for the 1999 hit 'As'?

7. On which Stevie Wonder album did 'As' originally appear?

8. Where did George Michael and Andrew Ridgeley record demos of 'Wham Rap!', 'Club Tropicana' and 'Careless Whisper'?

9. What was Wham!'s first hit single?

10. From which Wham! album was 'Club Tropicana' taken?

11. Which single was inspired by a note Andrew Ridgeley left lying in his bedroom?

12. In which year did George Michael become the youngest-ever recipient of the Songwriter Of The Year trophy at the Ivor Novello Awards?

13. In August 1985, Wham! became the first pop group to perform live in which country?

14. What was George Michael's second solo single?

15. In which year did Wham! split up?

16. What was the title of George Michael's first solo album?

Answers to page 192
SOLO ARTISTS 4: 1. Veronica 2. Andy Gibb 3. Debbie Gibson
4. 'Temma Harbour' 5. Rita Coolidge 6. Vanessa Paradis 7. Tiffany
8. Shakin' Stevens 9. 'When I Need You' 10. Jimmy Page 11. 'Rubber Ball'
12. Sinead O'Connor 13. Billy Ocean 14. Joe Jackson 15. Phil Collins
16. George Harrison ('My Sweet Lord')

Cover Versions 7

Answers on page 193

1. How did Brian Hyland and Jason Donovan choose to seal their letters?

2. The Equals and Pato Banton both took which song to number one?

3. Betty Everett, Linda Lewis and Cher have all had hits with which song?

4. What was an important date for Cliff Richard and Donny Osmond?

5. Which Elvis hit did ZZ Top cover in 1992?

6. Which song links Dionne Warwick, The Stranglers and Gabrielle?

7. Which Dion hit was covered by Status Quo in 1984?

8. 'Too Good To Be Forgotten' was a UK hit for which two bands?

9. Engelbert Humperdinck in 1967 and Elvis Presley in 1971 both enjoyed UK top ten hits with which song?

10. What were Tommy Steele in 1956 and Daniel O'Donnell in 1994 both doing?

11. Who originally recorded 'She's Not There', a 1977 hit for Santana?

12. Which Bread song was a hit for Let Loose in 1996?

13. Who was the first artist to have a UK hit with 'Lovely Day'?

14. Which song links Bill Withers, Mud, Club Nouveau and Michael Bolton?

15. Which Eddie Cochran chart topper was a number two hit for Showaddywaddy in 1975?

16. Who took their two-tone version of Smokey Robinson's 'Tears Of A Clown' to number six in the UK charts in 1979?

Answers to page 193
SEVENTIES 6: **1.** Les Gray **2.** Boston **3.** Yes **4.** Neil Young **5.** The Bee Gees **6.** 'Rockin' All Over The World' **7.** 'Bye Bye Baby' **8.** David Gates **9.** 1978 **10.** Genesis **11.** David Essex **12.** Keith Emerson **13.** Neil Diamond **14.** Jane **15.** 'Paper Roses' **16.** 'Mother And Child Reunion'

Solo Artists 4

Answers on page 190

1. What is Randy Crawford's real first name?
2. Which youngest of the Gibb brothers enjoyed a moderately successful solo career before his death in 1988?
3. Which young American singer, who had hits with 'Shake Your Love' and 'Foolish Beat' in the late Eighties, had previously made TV commercials for Oxydol detergent and Wendy's burger restaurants?
4. Which harbour did Mary Hopkin sing about in 1970?
5. Which singer did Kris Kristofferson marry in 1973?
6. Who was hailed for her rendition of 'Joe Le Taxi' in 1988?
7. Who had a number one with 'I Think We're Alone Now' after performing free in shopping malls across the US?
8. Which Welsh rock 'n' roller played the king on stage in the West End musical *Elvis* before enjoying a lucrative solo career in the Eighties?
9. Which Leo Sayer single gave Chrysalis Records their first-ever number one?
10. Who played guitar on P.J. Proby's 1964 hit 'Hold Me'?
11. Which bouncy number from Bobby Vee was written by Gene Pitney?
12. Which Irish singer spent part of her early life in a residential centre run by nuns?
13. Whose first UK hit was 'Love Really Hurts Without You'?
14. Whose 1982 album was titled 'Night And Day'?
15. Which future singer played the Artful Dodger in a London stage production of *Oliver* at 14 before touring the UK promoting Smith's crisps?
16. Whose was the biggest-selling UK single of 1971?

Answers to page 190
GEORGE MICHAEL 1: **1.** 16 **2.** Elton John **3.** Aretha Franklin
4. 'Fastlove' **5.** 'Waltz Away Dreaming' **6.** Mary J. Blige **7.** 'Songs In The Key Of Life' **8.** In Ridgeley's parents' front room **9.** 'Young Guns (Go For It)' **10.** 'Fantastic' **11.** 'Wake Me Up Before You Go Go' **12.** 1985 **13.** China **14.** 'A Different Corner' **15.** 1986 **16.** 'Faith'

Seventies 6

Answers on page 191

1. Who was the lead singer with Mud?

2. Which US band hit the UK charts in 1977 with 'More Than A Feeling'?

3. Which progressive rock band released the albums 'Fragile' and 'Close To The Edge'?

4. Which Canadian singer/songwriter had a 'Heart Of Gold' in 1972?

5. Which prolific songwriters penned Candi Staton's hit 'Nights On Broadway'?

6. Which Status Quo anthem was originally recorded by John Fogerty?

7. With which Four Seasons song did The Bay City Rollers enjoy their first UK number one?

8. Who was the chief songwriter with Bread?

9. In which year did The Commodores get to number one with 'Three Times A Lady'?

10. Whose 1976 album was called 'A Trick Of The Tail'?

11. Who played Jim MacLaine in *That'll Be The Day*?

12. Which keyboard player, famous for stabbing his instrument with knives, injured his hands in San Francisco in 1973 when his organ, rigged to explode as a stunt during the set, detonated prematurely?

13. Who released the live double album 'Hot August Night' in 1972?

14. To whom did Slade say Gudbuy in 1972?

15. What was the title of Marie Osmond's solo single?

16. Which song did Paul Simon write after eating egg fried rice and chicken in a Chinese restaurant?

Answers to page 191
COVER VERSIONS 7: **1.** With a kiss **2.** 'Baby Come Back' **3.** 'It's In His Kiss (The Shoop Shoop Song)' **4.** 'The Twelfth Of Never' **5.** 'Viva Las Vegas' **6.** 'Walk On By' **7.** 'The Wanderer' **8.** The Chi-Lites and Amazulu **9.** 'There Goes My Everything' **10.** 'Singing The Blues' **11.** The Zombies **12.** 'Make It With You' **13.** Bill Withers **14.** 'Lean On Me' **15.** 'Three Steps To Heaven' **16.** The Beat

Girl Bands 4

Answers on page 196

1. Which band had Nineties hits with 'Creep', 'No Scrubs' and 'Unpretty'?

2. How many UK top ten singles hits did The Nolans have?

3. Which girl group had a 1963 hit with 'Then He Kissed Me'?

4. Who enquired: 'Is that Jimmy's ring you're wearing'?

5. Which member of The Bangles co-wrote 'Eternal Flame'?

6. Sarah, Keren and Siobhan were better known as which group?

7. Who sang lead vocals with The Chiffons until 1969?

8. 'Right Now' was a number one album in 2001 for which girl band?

9. 'Power Of A Woman' and 'I Am Blessed' were 1995 hits for which band?

10. Which two sisters are members of Eternal?

11. In which year did Louise leave Eternal?

12. Which girl band turned down The Crystals' US number one 'He's A Rebel' because they were afraid the title would stir up trouble in the south?

13. With which band did The Supremes record the album 'The Magnificent 7'?

14. Who did The Ronettes support on a 1964 tour of Britain?

15. Which Bananarama single was originally titled 'Big Red Motorbike'?

16. Which Martha Reeves and The Vandellas track was originally released in the UK in 1964 but did not become a top ten hit until 1969?

Answers to page 196
POT LUCK 20: **1.** Eyes **2.** Gary Numan **3.** Chuck Berry **4.** Björk **5.** Dave Berry **6.** Blue Oyster Cult **7.** Brad Roberts **8.** The Grateful Dead **9.** 1969 **10.** Roy Wood **11.** Ugly Kid Joe **12.** Dog kennels **13.** Val Doonican **14.** 'Lazy River' **15.** Gorillaz **16.** Petula Clark

Chart Toppers 9

Answers on page 197

In which years did the following tracks top the UK charts?

1. 'Skweeze Me, Please Me' (Slade)

2. 'Don't Give Up On Us' (David Soul)

3. 'Everlasting Love' (Love Affair)

4. 'Distant Drums' (Jim Reeves)

5. 'Mr Vain' (Culture Beat)

6. 'I Believe I Can Fly' (R. Kelly)

7. 'Pipes Of Peace' (Paul McCartney)

8. 'Running Bear' (Johnny Preston)

9. 'The Name Of The Game' (Abba)

10. 'Start' (The Jam)

11. 'Do You Really Want To Hurt Me' (Culture Club)

12. 'Two Tribes' (Frankie Goes To Hollywood)

13. 'Never Ever' (All Saints)

14. 'Vogue' (Madonna)

15. 'I Should Have Known Better' (Jim Diamond)

16. 'Blackberry Way' (The Move)

Answers to page 197
PRINCE 1: 1. The Revolution 2. *Purple Rain* 3. 'The Most Beautiful Girl In The World' 4. 'For You' 5. Most of the tour was cancelled due to poor ticket sales 6. James Brown 7. 1984 8. Elaine Paige and Barbara Dickson 9. Alexander Nevermind 10. 1987 11. A squiggle 12. A lollipop 13. 'Batdance' 14. 'Betcha By Golly Wow' 15. Christopher Tracy 16. A huge pink Cadillac

Pot Luck 20

Answers on page 194

1. Which word was in both of Art Garfunkel's UK number ones?

2. Which rock star tried to fly around the world, only to end up in an Indian military zone?

3. Which Fifties rock 'n' roll star spent three years in jail as a teenager for armed robbery?

4. Which artist's surname is Gudmundsdóttir?

5. Who had a Sixties hit with 'The Crying Game'?

6. Who said '(Don't Fear) The Reaper'?

7. Who was the lead singer with Crash Test Dummies?

8. Which US acid rock band chose their name at random in 1965 from the pages of the Oxford English Dictionary?

9. In which year was the Woodstock Festival?

10. Which colourful British star's real first names are Ulysses Adrian?

11. Who had a 1993 hit with 'Cats In The Cradle'?

12. What did Cyndi Lauper used to clean for a living?

13. Who got out of his rocking chair and tried to 'Walk Tall' in 1964?

14. Which Hoagy Carmichael song was a number two UK hit for Bobby Darin in 1961?

15. Which cartoon group were formed by Damon Albarn?

16. In 1967, who was convinced that the other man's grass was always greener?

Answers to page 194
GIRL BANDS 4: **1.** TLC **2.** Three **3.** The Crystals **4.** The Shangri-Las ('Leader Of The Pack') **5.** Susanna Hoffs **6.** Bananarama **7.** Judy Craig **8.** Atomic Kitten **9.** Eternal **10.** Easther and Vernie Bennett **11.** 1995 **12.** The Shirelles **13.** The Four Tops **14.** The Rolling Stones **15.** 'Shy Boy' **16.** 'Dancing In The Street'

Prince 1

Answers on page 195

1. What was the name of Prince's occasional backing band?

2. From which film was 'When Doves Cry' taken?

3. What was Prince's first UK number one single?

4. What was the title of his debut album?

5. What happened when Prince first came to the UK in 1981?

6. Seeing which artist in concert inspired Prince to become a musician?

7. In which year did the film *Purple Rain* open?

8. Which duo kept '1999/Little Red Corvette' off the UK top spot?

9. Under which pseudonym did Prince write 'Sugar Walls' for Sheena Easton?

10. In which year was the album 'Sign Of The Times' released?

11. To what did Prince change his name in 1993?

12. What did Prince suck throughout the 1995 American Music Awards?

13. Which was the first Prince single to be taken from the movie *Batman*?

14. Which Stylistics song did Prince cover in 1996?

15. Which pseudonym did Prince use when writing 'Manic Monday' for The Bangles?

16. In what did Prince enter the stage on his 1988 'Lovesexy' tour?

Answers to page 195
CHART TOPPERS 9: **1.** 1973 **2.** 1977 **3.** 1968 **4.** 1966 **5.** 1993 **6.** 1997 **7.** 1984 **8.** 1960 **9.** 1977 **10.** 1980 **11.** 1982 **12.** 1984 **13.** 1998 **14.** 1990 **15.** 1984 **16.** 1969

Rap 2

Answers on page 200

1. From which film was Snoop Doggy Dog's 'We Just Wanna Party With You' taken?

2. Who was The Fresh Prince in DJ Jazzy Jeff and The Fresh Prince?

3. Which rap artist had a number one in 1995 with 'Gangsta's Paradise'?

4. Which Stevie Wonder song was sampled on 'Gangsta's Paradise'?

5. Which Will Smith hit was dedicated to his son Tre?

6. What does LL Cool J stand for?

7. Which Bill Withers track was sampled on LL Cool J's single 'Phenomenon'?

8. Whose albums include 'Raising Hell' and 'Tougher Than Leather'?

9. Who released 'Rapper's Delight' in 1979?

10. Which mainstream band had a 1981 hit with 'Rapture'?

11. Who was often backed by The Furious Five?

12. Which Grandmaster was born Melvin Glover?

13. Which rap act are known as 'The Black Sex Pistols'?

14. What was the title of Vanilla Ice's 1990 UK number one?

15. And which Queen and David Bowie song did it sample?

16. Whose 1993 album was called 'Home Invasion'?

Answers to page 200
BOY BANDS 3: **1.** Andy Williams **2.** Donnie Wahlberg **3.** 'Rollercoaster' **4.** New Kids On The Block **5.** 'Night To Remember' **6.** 'The Journey' **7.** 'The Proud One' **8.** 'Love Me For A Reason' **9.** Bad Boys Inc. **10.** 'Crazy Horses' **11.** Point Break **12.** 'If You Go Away' **13.** 1973 **14.** Alan **15.** Boston **16.** 'Don't Make Me Wait'

Name Changes 9

Answers on page 201

1. Who changed his name from August Darnell?

2. What is Ginger Baker's real first name?

3. What is Eric Clapton's real surname?

4. Which rap artist decided that Robert Van Winkle just wasn't cool enough?

5. Which US band who weren't afraid of dying started out as The Stalk-Forrest Group?

6. What was Louise's maiden name?

7. Which band who have had hits spanning five decades used to be known as The Rattlesnakes?

8. Which sinister British pop star of the Sixties changed his name from David Holgate Grundy?

9. Which rap artist was born Artis Ivey?

10. What was Eden Kane's real name?

11. Which mixer changed his name from William Wainwright?

12. Which Sixties girl group were previously called The Poquellos?

13. Who is William Johnson better known as?

14. Which falsetto singer was born Francis Castelluccio?

15. Who shortened her name from Eithne Ni Bhraonain?

16. Which keyboard player/producer started life as Thomas Morgan Robertson before opting for a better sound?

Answers to page 201
ALBUMS 8: **1.** Foreigner **2.** 'Everything Must Go' **3.** Leo Sayer **4.** Mike Oldfield **5.** Abba **6.** 'Rumours' (Fleetwood Mac) **7.** A cigarette **8.** 'Songs From The Big Chair' **9.** The Who **10.** David Bowie **11.** The Police **12.** Catatonia **13.** 'Our Town' **14.** Robson and Jerome **15.** Pink Floyd ('Wish You Were Here') **16.** Bryan Ferry

Boy Bands 3

Answers on page 198

1. On which singer's US TV show did The Osmonds first come to prominence?

2. Which member of New Kids On The Block fell through an unlocked trapdoor on stage mid-way through a New York concert in 1990?

3. What was the title of Let Loose's second album?

4. Which band were sued by three girl fans and a mother for 'pain and suffering' following a stampede at a 1991 concert?

5. A cover of which Shalamar track gave 911 their first hit?

6. What was the title of 911's debut album?

7. Which Four Seasons track did The Osmonds cover in 1975?

8. What was The Osmonds' only UK number one?

9. Which British band had a 1994 top ten hit with 'More To This World'?

10. What was The Osmonds' first UK top five hit?

11. 'Do We Rock' was a first UK hit for which boy band?

12. Which New Kids On The Block single shared the same title as a Terry Jacks hit from 1974?

13. In which year did The Osmonds release 'Let Me In'?

14. Who is the oldest Osmond?

15. From which American city do New Kids On The Block originate?

16. What was 911's first UK top ten single?

Answers to page 198
RAP 2: **1.** *Men In Black* **2.** Will Smith **3.** Coolio **4.** 'Pastime Paradise'
5. 'Just The Two Of Us' **6.** Ladies Love Cool James (his real name is James Smith) **7.** 'Who Is He And What Is He To You' **8.** Run D.M.C.
9. The Sugarhill Gang **10.** Blondie **11.** Grandmaster Flash
12. Grandmaster Melle Mel **13.** Public Enemy **14.** 'Ice Ice Baby'
15. 'Under Pressure' **16.** Ice-T

Albums 8

Answers on page 199

1. Which US band had a number one album with 'Agent Provocateur' in 1984?

2. Which Manic Street Preachers album contains 'A Design For Life'?

3. Which solo singer released the album 'Silver Bird' which reached number two in 1974?

4. Who recorded 'Hergest Ridge'?

5. Which band had the biggest-selling UK albums for both 1976 and 1977?

6. The title of which band's best-selling album from 1977 was taken from the crumbling relationships occurring within the unit?

7. What is Paul McCartney holding in his right hand on the cover of 'Abbey Road'?

8. Which Tears For Fears album features 'Shout' and 'Everybody Wants To Rule The World'?

9. Whose greatest hits album was titled 'Meaty, Beaty, Big and Bouncy'?

10. Whose 1972 album was definitely 'Hunky Dory'?

11. 'Outlandos D'Amour', 'Regatta De Blanc' and 'Zenyatta Mondatta' were the first three albums by which band?

12. Whose 2001 album was called 'Papers, Scissors, Stone'?

13. What was the title of Deacon Blue's 1994 Greatest Hits album?

14. Which duo had the best-selling UK album of 1995?

15. The title of whose 1975 album sounded like a holiday invitation to Judith Chalmers?

16. Whose 1978 album was called 'The Bride Stripped Bare'?

Answers to page 199
NAME CHANGES 9: 1. Kid Creole 2. Peter 3. Clapp 4. Vanilla Ice
5. Blue Oyster Cult 6. Nurding 7. The Bee Gees 8. Dave Berry
9. Coolio 10. Richard Sarstedt 11. William Orbit 12. The Shirelles
13. Holly Johnson 14. Frankie Valli 15. Enya 16. Thomas Dolby

Number Twos 3

Answers on page 204

In which years did the following singles reach number two in the UK charts?

1. 'Starting Together' (Su Pollard)

2. 'You Take Me Up' (The Thompson Twins)

3. 'Alternate Title' (The Monkees)

4. 'Welcome To The Pleasure Dome' (Frankie Goes To Hollywood)

5. 'Bend It' (Dave Dee, Dozy, Beaky, Mick and Tich)

6. 'The Jean Genie' (David Bowie)

7. 'Gold' (Spandau Ballet)

8. 'True Love Ways' (Peter and Gordon)

9. 'Song 2' (Blur)

10. 'If You Gotta Go Go Now' (Manfred Mann)

11. 'Yester-Me Yester-You Yesterday' (Stevie Wonder)

12. 'Only You' (Yazoo)

13. 'Love Of The Common People' (Paul Young)

14. 'Sandy' (John Travolta)

15. 'Call Me Number One' (The Tremeloes)

16. 'Ghostbusters' (Ray Parker Jnr)

Answers to page 204
POT LUCK 21: **1.** Little Jimmy Osmond ('Long Haired Lover From Liverpool') **2.** 'Arnold Layne' **3.** Al Green **4.** Hues Corporation **5.** Cousin **6.** Rod Argent (Argent) **7.** 'House Of The Rising Sun' **8.** Judas Priest **9.** Nick Beggs **10.** The Who **11.** Marty Wilde **12.** New Zealander **13.** Clare Grogan **14.** Mari Wilson **15.** Swedish **16.** 'Old Red Eyes Is Back'

David Bowie 1

Answers on page 205

1. Which Bowie novelty track originally released in 1967 finally became a hit in 1973?

2. Who co-wrote and provided backing vocals on 'Fame'?

3. What was the original title of the 'Space Oddity' album in the UK?

4. On which Sixties show did Bowie make his TV debut with The Manish Boys?

5. Who originally recorded 'China Girl'?

6. Who recorded backing vocals on 'Sound And Vision'?

7. With whom did Bowie record the double A-side duet 'Peace On Earth' and 'Little Drummer Boy'?

8. In which year did 'Let's Dance' get to number one?

9. Which film theme did Bowie take to number two in the singles charts in 1986?

10. Who played guitar on 'Buddha Of Suburbia'?

11. Who joined Bowie for the 1996 single 'Hallo Spaceboy'?

12. Who did Bowie tell 'I'm Only Dancing' in 1972?

13. When did Davy Jones, as he was originally billed, decide to change his name?

14. Why did he choose the surname Bowie?

15. In which year was 'Aladdin Sane' released?

16. Which Bowie composition was a 1971 hit for Peter Noone?

Answers to page 205
FIVE 1: **1.** Jason Brown **2.** Sean **3.** Birmingham **4.** Abidin **5.** 'Slam Dunk Da Funk' **6.** Ritchie and Scott **7.** Four **8.** 1 **9.** Abs **10.** Turkey **11.** 'We Will Rock You' **12.** 'Everybody Get Up' **13.** Abs **14.** Scott **15.** Ritchie and J **16.** Sweden

Pot Luck 21

Answers on page 202

1. Who admitted in 1972 that he had no idea where Liverpool was?

2. Which Pink Floyd song was about a boy who stole women's underwear?

3. Who became a preacher after hot grits was poured on him in the bath by an ex-girlfriend who then shot herself?

4. Hubert Ann Kelly, St Clair Lee and Fleming Williams made up which trio who had a 1974 hit with 'Rock The Boat'?

5. What relation is Dionne Warwick to Whitney Houston?

6. Which keyboard player with The Zombies went on to form his own band?

7. Which four and a half minute Sixties classic was about a New Orleans brothel?

8. Which heavy metal band were formed in Birmingham in 1969 by K. K. Downing and Ian Hill?

9. Who took over singing duties with Kajagoogoo following Limahl's exit?

10. Who could see for miles in 1967?

11. Which British rock 'n' roller wrote Status Quo's 'Ice In The Sun'?

12. What nationality was John Rowles who had a 1968 top three hit with 'If I Only Had Time'?

13. Who was the lead singer with Altered Images?

14. Who was 'Neasden's queen of soul'?

15. What nationality are Roxette?

16. Which Beautiful South song dealt with alcoholism?

Answers to page 202
NUMBER TWOS 3: 1. 1986 2. 1984 3. 1967 4. 1985 5. 1966 6. 1972
7. 1983 8. 1965 9. 1997 10. 1965 11. 1969 12. 1982 13. 1983 14. 1978
15. 1969 16. 1984

Five 1

Answers on page 203

1. What is J's full name?

2. Who is the youngest member of the group?

3. In which city was Ritchie Neville born?

4. What is Abs short for?

5. What was the title of Five's first UK single?

6. Which two members sang the lead vocals on 'Until The Time Is Through'?

7. How many singles were released from Five's first album?

8. What number in the UK charts did 'Keep On Movin'' reach?

9. Which band member went to the Italia Conti Performing Arts College?

10. Which country is Abs's father from?

11. Which Five single featured Brian May?

12. What was the title of Five's fourth single?

13. Which band member does not drink alcohol?

14. Which band member took time off in 2001 because his girlfriend had a baby?

15. Which two members ended up in court after a fight in a Dublin bar?

16. In which country did Five record the single 'Slam Dunk Da Funk'?

Answers to page 203
DAVID BOWIE 1: 1. 'The Laughing Gnome' 2. John Lennon 3. 'David Bowie' 4. *Gadzooks! It's All Happening* 5. Iggy Pop 6. Mary Hopkin 7. Bing Crosby 8. 1983 9. 'Absolute Beginners' 10. Lenny Kravitz 11. The Pet Shop Boys 12. John 13. When Davy Jones signed up as one of The Monkees 14. From the Bowie knife in honour of his idol Mick Jagger, a jagger being an old English knife 15. 1973 16. 'Oh You Pretty Thing'

Motown 3

Answers on page 208

1. Who was lead singer and saxophonist with The Commodores before going solo?

2. Which Motown artist enjoyed a 1981 UK number one with 'Being With You'?

3. Which Four Tops hit was originally a US number five for Left Banke?

4. How old was Stevie Wonder when he signed for Motown?

5. Which Stevie Wonder hit was inspired by Bob Marley's 'Jamming'?

6. What did The Miracles and Diana Ross and The Supremes both second?

7. Which Four Tops hit was taken from the film *Buster*?

8. Where were The Four Tops standing in 1967?

9. Which Temptation sued Motown for $5 million in 1968?

10. Who had a top three hit with 'War' in 1970?

11. Who replaced David Ruffin in The Temptations and went on to sing lead vocals on 'Papa Was A Rolling Stone'?

12. 'Help Me Make It Through The Night' was a 1972 hit for which Motown group?

13. Who contributed backing vocals on Lionel Richie's 'Hello'?

14. Which Motown girl group had 'Nowhere To Run' in 1965?

15. What was Marvin Gaye too busy thinking about in 1969?

16. Which 20-year-old artist married Motown boss Berry Gordy's 37-year-old sister Anna?

Answers to page 208
FOLK 4: **1.** *Tonight* **2.** Gordon Giltrap **3.** American **4.** Fairport Convention **5.** Salford **6.** The Kingston Trio **7.** Arlo Guthrie (son of Woody Guthrie) **8.** Clannad **9.** Glenn Yarbrough **10.** The Seekers **11.** Australian **12.** 'I Get A Kick Out Of You' **13.** 'Green Green' **14.** Gene Clark **15.** Joni Mitchell **16.** Donovan

Eighties 6

Answers on page 209

1. Who are Neil Tennant and Chris Lowe?

2. Which 1986 number one was written by Pal Waaktaar?

3. Who played harmonica on Chaka Khan's 'I Feel For You'?

4. Which 1984 chart topper wrote the theme for the TV series *Boon*?

5. What were Squeeze pulling from the shell in 1980?

6. Which band's only top ten hit was 'When You Ask About Love' in 1980?

7. Who had a 1988 number one with 'Nothing's Gonna Change My Love For You'?

8. Which song was named International Hit Of The Year at the 1983 Ivor Novello Awards?

9. Which Hall and Oates hit from 1983 was a cover of a Mike Oldfield track?

10. Which Mike Oldfield song was a tribute to John Lennon?

11. Neville Staples, Lynval Golding and Jerry Dammers were members of which band?

12. John Pickles and Ian Morgan were better known as which hitmakers?

13. Who reached the top of the UK singles chart in 1988 with 'The First Time'?

14. What was the title of Big Country's only UK number one album?

15. Who had a 1982 hit with 'Torch'?

16. John Keeble was the drummer with which Eighties band?

Answers to page 209
INDIE 4: 1. New Order 2. 'Black Eyed Boy' 3. R.E.M. 4. Blur
5. Arabacus 6. 'Cloudcuckooland' 7. Joy Division 8. Deacon Blue
9. John Power 10. 'Female Of The Species' 11. Counting Crows
12. Brian Eno 13. 'The One And Only' by Chesney Hawkes
14. Radiohead 15. Suede 16. Stone Roses masks (after the Roses had cancelled their headline appearance)

Folk 4

Answers on page 206

1. Robin Hall and Jimmie MacGregor were regulars on which TV news magazine series of the early Sixties?

2. Who released the 1977 album 'Perilous Journey'?

3. What nationality is Julie Felix?

4. Iain Matthews, Judy Dyble, Ashley Hutchings, Richard Thompson, Simon Nicol and Martin Lamble were the original members of which group?

5. Which district of Manchester inspired Ewan MacColl to write 'Dirty Old Town'?

6. Which trio had a hit with 'Tom Dooley' in 1958?

7. Which son of a famous folk singer sang about 'Alice's Restaurant'?

8. Which band took their name from the Gaelic for 'family'?

9. Who was lead vocalist with the Sixties folk group The Limeliters?

10. Bruce Woodley and Keth Potger were members of which folk quartet from Down Under?

11. What nationality is Gary Shearston?

12. And what was his only UK chart success?

13. What colour gave The New Christy Minstrels a UK hit in 1963?

14. Who left The New Christy Minstrels after a few months and went on to form The Byrds?

15. Who recorded the 1974 album 'Court And Spark'?

16. Which Sixties folk singer was labelled 'Britain's answer to Bob Dylan'?

Answers to page 206
MOTOWN 3: 1. Lionel Richie 2. Smokey Robinson 3. 'Walk Away Renee' 4. Ten 5. 'Masterblaster' 6. That Emotion 7. 'Loco In Acapulco' 8. 'Standing In The Shadows Of Love' 9. David Ruffin 10. Edwin Starr 11. Dennis Edwards 12. Gladys Knight and The Pips 13. Richard Marx 14. Martha and The Vandellas 15. My Baby 16. Marvin Gaye

Indie 4

Answers on page 207

1. Which band had a 2001 hit with 'Crystal'?

2. In which 1997 single did Texas re-create the sound of The Supremes?

3. Who released the 1995 single 'Crush With Eyeliner'?

4. Which band's debut album was titled 'Leisure'?

5. What prefix did Pulp drop from their original name?

6. 'Pure' was a track from which Lightning Seeds album?

7. New Order were the successors to which band?

8. Who had hits with 'Dignity' and 'Real Gone Kid'?

9. Which bassist formed Cast following the break-up of The La's?

10. Which was more deadly than the male according to Space?

11. 'August & Everything After' was the debut album of which Van Morrison-inspired US band?

12. Who produced the 'Laid' album for James?

13. Which song prevented 'Sit Down' by James from reaching number one in the UK in 1991?

14. Who released the album 'The Bends'?

15. Which band were named Hype of the Year in the 1994 *Rolling Stone* Music Awards Critics' Picks?

16. What did Supergrass wear on stage at the 1995 Glastonbury Festival?

Answers to page 207
EIGHTIES 6: 1. The Pet Shop Boys 2. 'The Sun Always Shines On TV' (a-ha) 3. Stevie Wonder 4. Jim Diamond 5. Mussels 6. Matchbox 7. Glenn Medeiros 8. 'Ebony And Ivory' 9. 'Family Man' 10. 'Monnlight Shadow' 11. The Specials 12. Jive Bunny 13. Robin Beck 14. 'Steeltown' 15. Soft Cell 16. Spandau Ballet

Simon and Garfunkel 1

Answers on page 212

1. What did Paul Simon call himself in the late Fifties?

2. What was the title of Simon and Garfunkel's debut album?

3. Which song did Paul Simon dedicate to his then girlfriend Kathy Chitty?

4. Which trio covered 'The Sound of Silence' in the UK?

5. Which track from the album 'Sounds Of Silence' was originally recorded solo by Simon in 1964?

6. In 1967, who covered Simon's '59th Street Bridge Song (Feelin' Groovy)'?

7. How many Simon and Garfunkel tracks featured in *The Graduate*?

8. In which year was the album 'Bookends' released?

9. Which Paul Simon song was named Record of The Year at the 1969 Grammy Awards?

10. For how many weeks did 'Bridge Over Troubled Water' occupy the number one spot in the UK singles chart?

11. Which architect was the subject of a song on the 'Bridge Over Troubled Water' album?

12. Which Everly Brothers hit was covered on 'Bridge Over Troubled Water' in a live recording?

13. How many hours did it reportedly take Simon and Garfunkel to complete the recording of the 'Bridge Over Troubled Water' album?

14. For the recording of which song did the duo reunite briefly in 1975?

15. Which year saw the release of the double live set, 'The Concert In Central Park'?

16. In which school production did Simon and Garfunkel first appear together?

Answers to page 212
ONE-HIT WONDERS 6: **1.** Chris Spedding **2.** Mason Williams **3.** 'Four In The Morning' **4.** Dan Hill **5.** Our Kid **6.** 'I'd Rather Jack' **7.** Redbone **8.** 'Shame, Shame, Shame' **9.** '(How Much Is) That Doggie In The Window' **10.** Angry Anderson **11.** Laurie Anderson **12.** 'Love Games' **13.** 'Chantilly Lace' **14.** Graham Bonney **15.** 'I'm The Urban Spaceman' **16.** Sophie Lawrence

Solo Artists 5

Answers on page 213

1. 'Boys Cry' was a 1964 hit for which singer?
2. According to Jilted John, who was a moron?
3. How old was Little Jimmy Osmond when he recorded 'Long Haired Lover From Liverpool'?
4. Who was 'King Of The Road' in 1965?
5. Cilla Black's 1964 number one 'You're My World' was translated from which language?
6. Who turned down 'It's Not Unusual' because she didn't think it was suited to her talents?
7. Who recorded a version of 'I Know Him So Well' in a duet with her mother Cissy on her 1987 album?
8. Which 1961 Ben E. King song became a UK number one 26 years later after featuring in a jeans commercial?
9. Which Labi Siffre track was sampled on Eminem's 'My Name Is'?
10. Which Gloria Estefan single was the official anthem of the 1996 Olympics?
11. Who was the uncredited singer on Mike Oldfield's 'Moonlight Shadow'?
12. What was David Essex's first UK hit?
13. What is Lonnie Donegan's real Christian name?
14. Which 1970 number one for Dave Edmunds was originally recorded by Smiley Lewis?
15. On which road did Robbie Williams find himself in 2001?
16. Who saw the light in 1973?

Answers to page 213
LYRICS 8: 1. 'Waterloo' (Abba) 2. '(I Just) Died In Your Arms Tonight' (Cutting Crew) 3. '(I've Had) The Time Of My Life' (Bill Medley and Jennifer Warnes) 4. 'Wonderwall' (Oasis) 5. 'I Have Nothing' (Whitney Houston) 6. 'You Needed Me' (Boyzone) 7. 'Love Really Hurts Without You' (Billy Ocean) 8. 'The Longest Time' (Billy Joel) 9. 'Desperado' (The Eagles) 10. 'New Year's Day' (U2) 11. 'Surfin' USA' (The Beach Boys) 12. 'Easy Lover' (Phil Collins and Philip Bailey) 13. 'Drive' (The Cars) 14. 'Livin' On A Prayer' (Bon Jovi) 15. 'What Can I Do' (The Corrs) 16. 'With A Little Help From My Friends' (Joe Cocker)

One-Hit Wonders 6

Answers on page 210

1. After sweating in a Wombles costume on *Top of the Pops*, whose only hit in human guise was 'Motor Bikin'' in 1975?

2. 'Classical Gas' was the only hit for which instrumentalist?

3. What was Faron Young's favourite time of day?

4. Which Canadian singer hit the UK charts in 1978 with 'Sometimes When We Touch'?

5. Which juvenile band took 'You Just Might See Me Cry' to number two in 1976?

6. Which song provided The Reynolds Girls with their 15 minutes of fame?

7. Which American band got to number two in 1971 with 'The Witch Queen of New Orleans'?

8. Which song was a 1975 hit for Shirley and Company?

9. Which pet-shop lament – the young Margaret Thatcher's favourite song – was a 1953 hit for Patti Page?

10. Who was unhappy about Scott and Charlene getting married in *Neighbours* even though the wedding song, 'Suddenly', gave him his only UK hit?

11. 'O Superman' was which American singer's solitary chart entry?

12. Which 1974 Eurovision entry marked the beginning and end for Belle and The Devotions?

13. What was The Big Bopper's only UK hit?

14. Who had his only UK hit with 'Super Girl' in 1966?

15. Which novelty number charted for The Bonzo Dog Doo-Dah Band?

16. Which ex-*EastEnder* got to number 21 in 1991 with 'Love's Unkind'?

Answers to page 210
SIMON AND GARFUNKEL 1: **1.** Jerry Landis **2.** 'Wednesday Morning, 3 A.M.' **3.** 'Homeward Bound' **4.** The Bachelors **5.** 'I Am A Rock' **6.** Harpers Bizarre **7.** Five **8.** 1968 **9.** 'Mrs Robinson' **10.** Three **11.** Frank Lloyd Wright **12.** 'Bye Bye Love' **13.** 800 **14.** 'My Little Town' **15.** 1982 **16.** *Alice in Wonderland*

Lyrics 8

Answers on page 211

From which songs are the following lyrics taken?

1. 'And how could I ever refuse, I feel like I win when I lose'
2. 'It must've been some kind of kiss, I should've walked away'
3. 'Now with passion in our eyes there's no way we could disguise it secretly'
4. 'There are many things that I would like to say about you but I don't know how'
5. 'I won't hold it back again, this passion inside, can't run from myself, there's nowhere to hide'
6. 'You put me high upon a pedestal, so high that I could almost see eternity'
7. 'You run around town like a fool and you think that it's groovy'
8. 'I don't care what consequence it brings, I have been a fool for lesser things'
9. 'Don't you draw the queen of diamonds, boy, she'll beat you if she's able'
10. 'And so we're told this is the golden age, and gold is the reason for the wars we wage'
11. 'If everybody had an ocean across the USA'
12. 'She'll take your heart but you won't feel it'
13. 'Who's gonna pay attention to your dreams, who's gonna plug their ears when you scream'
14. 'We've got each other and that's a lot for love, we'll give it a shot'
15. 'I haven't slept at all in days, it's been so long since we have talked'
16. 'What would you do if I sang out of tune, would you stand up and walk out on me'

Answers to page 211
SOLO ARTISTS 5: **1.** Eden Kane **2.** Gordon **3.** Nine **4.** Roger Miller
5. Italian **6.** Sandie Shaw **7.** Whitney Houston **8.** 'Stand By Me'
9. 'I Got The' **10.** 'Reach' **11.** Maggie Reilly **12.** 'Rock On' **13.** Anthony
14. 'I Hear You Knocking' **15.** 'The Road To Mandalay' **16.** Todd
Rundgren

Pot Luck 22

Answers on page 216

1. Which movie star sang backing vocals on Billy Ocean's 1986 hit 'When The Going Gets Tough (The Tough Get Going)'?

2. Which older sister of Janet Jackson had a minor US hit in 1984 with 'Hearts Don't Lie'?

3. Who played bass on Midge Ure's 'If I Was'?

4. Who played a housewife in the 1979 film *Union City*?

5. Which former teen idol did washing powder commercials in the Sixties?

6. Which singer/songwriter used to be employed at a New York brewery?

7. Which Scottish singer was once married to a Bee Gee?

8. Bobby Farrell was the chief dancer in which Seventies group?

9. Clem Burke was the drummer with which Eighties band?

10. Why does Sheryl Crow have two false front teeth?

11. Which artist, who had a UK number one, founded Dr West's Medicine Show and Junk Band?

12. Who had a 1996 hit with 'Stripper Vicar'?

13. What do PJ Harvey's initials stand for?

14. Which member of Poco left to found The Eagles?

15. Who wrote 'Simon Smith And His Amazing Dancing Bear'?

16. Gary Brooker was the singer and pianist with which Sixties band?

Answers to page 216
FIFTIES 4: **1.** Ronnie Hilton ('Veni, Vidi, Vici') **2.** The Hilltoppers and The Platters **3.** The Checkmates **4.** 'What Do You Want To Make Those Eyes At Me For?' **5.** October **6.** 'On The Street Where You Live' **7.** Vic Damone **8.** Pat Boone **9.** 'Diana' **10.** The Ramblers **11.** 'Living Doll' **12.** Paul Anka **13.** 'I Can't Tell A Waltz From A Tango' **14.** 'Long Tall Sally' **15.** *The Sweetest Girl in Town* **16.** Brenda Lee

Stevie Wonder 1

Answers on page 217

1. Which Stevie Wonder single was part of his campaign to have Martin Luther King's birthday recognised as a US holiday?

2. With whom did Stevie Wonder duet on 'My Love'?

3. What was Stevie Wonder's first UK hit single?

4. Who recorded the original version of 'For Once In My Life'?

5. What caused Stevie Wonder's blindness?

6. Which French title gave Stevie Wonder a hit on both sides of the Atlantic in 1969?

7. Which singer did he marry in 1970?

8. For whom was 'Superstition' originally written?

9. Which 1973 single gave Stevie Wonder his first US number one for ten years?

10. What did Stevie Wonder lose after a car crash in 1973?

11. Which female artist took a Stevie Wonder song to number one in the US in 1975?

12. What kept 'Happy Birthday' off the top of the UK singles chart?

13. What sport did Stevie Wonder play while hosting NBC TV's *Saturday Live* in 1983?

14. On which Elton John song did Stevie Wonder play harmonica?

15. To whom did Stevie Wonder dedicate his 1985 Oscar for Best Song, awarded for 'I Just Called To Say I Love You'?

16. In which year was the album 'Innervisions' released?

Answers to page 217
FILM TRACKS 6: 1. *Jubilee* 2. *Girl's Town* 3. 'When You Believe'
4. Barbra Streisand 5. *Up Close and Personal* 6. 'More Than A Woman'
7. 'You're The One That I Want', 'Summer Nights', 'Sandy' and 'Greased
Lightning' 8. *Xanadu* 9. 'Hopelessly Devoted To You' 10. Anthony Newley
11. 'Living In America' 12. Boy George 13. Doris Day 14. Duane Eddy
15. *King Creole* 16. *Fun in Acapulco*

Fifties 4

Answers on page 214

1. Who came, saw and conquered the charts in 1954?

2. Which two groups had UK top ten hits in the Fifties with 'Only You'?

3. What was the name of Emile Ford's backing group?

4. And what were they asking in 1959?

5. In which month of 1959 did 'Here Comes Summer' top the UK charts?

6. Which 1958 UK number one was taken from the musical *My Fair Lady*?

7. And which American singer took it to the top of the charts?

8. 'I'll Be Home' was a first UK number one single for which artist?

9. Which number one did Paul Anka write about his babysitter?

10. Which group backed Perry Como on his chart-topping 'Don't Let The Stars Get In Your Eyes'?

11. Which was the biggest-selling UK single of 1959?

12. Which 12-year-old won $35 for impersonating Johnnie Ray in a 1953 amateur talent contest?

13. Which Alma Cogan hit suggested she had two left feet?

14. Which girl gave Little Richard his first UK top ten hit?

15. Which film featured Jackie Wilson's 'Reet Petite'?

16. Who was billed as 'Little Miss Dynamite'?

Answers to page 214
POT LUCK 22: **1.** Michael Douglas **2.** LaToya Jackson **3.** Mark King (Level 42) **4.** Debbie Harry **5.** Craig Douglas **6.** Barry Manilow **7.** Lulu (Maurice Gibb) **8.** Boney M **9.** Blondie **10.** The originals fell out when she tripped up on stage early in her career **11.** Norman Greenbaum **12.** Mansun **13.** Polly Jean **14.** Randy Meisner **15.** Randy Newman **16.** Procul Harum

Film Tracks 6

Answers on page 215

1. Adam and The Ants' 'Deutscher Girls' was a 1982 hit from which 1977 film?

2. From which film was Paul Anka's 1959 hit 'Lonely Boy' taken?

3. Mariah Carey and Whitney Houston duetted on which song from *The Prince of Egypt*?

4. Who sang the theme from *The Way We Were*?

5. Celine Dion's 1996 hit 'Because You Loved Me' was the theme from which film?

6. Which Tavares hit, written by The Bee Gees, came from *Saturday Night Fever*?

7. Which four singles from *Grease* featured John Travolta?

8. The Olivia Newton-John/Cliff Richard duet 'Suddenly' was taken from which film?

9. Which *Grease* single did Olivia Newton-John take to number two in the UK charts as a solo artist?

10. Who recorded 'I've Waited So Long' in 1959 from *Idle on Parade*?

11. Which James Brown single was taken from *Rocky IV*?

12. Who released the theme from *The Crying Game* in 1992?

13. In 1955, who recorded 'Ready, Willing And Able' from *Young at Heart*?

14. The theme from *Because They're Young* was a 1960 hit for which guitar man?

15. Elvis's 'Hard-Headed Woman' came from which film?

16. 'Bossa Nova Baby' was an Elvis hit from which film?

Answers to page 215
STEVIE WONDER 1: 1. 'Happy Birthday' 2. Julio Iglesias 3. 'Uptight (Everything's Alright)' 4. Tony Bennett 5. After birth, he was given too much oxygen while in an incubator 6. 'My Cherie Amour' 7. Syreeta 8. Jeff Beck 9. 'Superstition' 10. His sense of smell 11. Minnie Riperton ('Lovin' You') 12. 'Green Door' by Shakin' Stevens 13. Tennis 14. 'I Guess That's Why They Call It The Blues' 15. Nelson Mandela 16. 1973

Nineties 6

Answers on page 220

Which artists had UK hits with the following tracks?

1. 'Don't Marry Her'

2. 'Come As You Are'

3. 'Promise Me'

4. 'Because We Want To'

5. 'Bitter Sweet Symphony'

6. 'Twilight Zone'

7. 'Flying Without Wings'

8. 'Fairground'

9. 'The Universal'

10. 'Whoops Now'

11. 'Beautiful Ones'

12. 'To You I Belong'

13. 'You Are Not Alone'

14. 'Boom! Shake The Room'

15. 'Rhythm Is A Dancer'

16. 'The Fly'

Answers to page 220
GLAM ROCK 2: **1.** Marc Bolan **2.** Nicky Chinn and Mike Chapman
3. Sweet **4.** Gary Glitter **5.** Gary Glitter **6.** Rob Davis **7.** 'Blockbuster'
8. 'Tie A Yellow Ribbon' **9.** 1972 **10.** 'I Love To Boogie' **11.** Marc Bolan
12. Mike Leander **13.** Four **14.** Sweet **15.** Gerry Sheppard **16.** 1976

Classical Gas 3

Answers on page 221

1. Who composed *Peter And The Wolf*?

2. In which century did Vivaldi die?

3. Which Russian composer, born at Oneg in 1873, went to live in the USA following the 1917 Revolution?

4. What was Purcell's Christian name?

5. Who composed the ballet *Boléro*?

6. What nationality was *Bartók*?

7. Who wrote the *Symphonie Fantastique*?

8. Who composed the *New World Symphony*?

9. Which Austrian composer once said: 'To write a symphony is, for me, to construct a world'?

10. In which German town was Bach born?

11. In which year did Bizet compose his most famous opera, *Carmen*?

12. How many piano sonatas did Beethoven compose?

13. How old was Beethoven when he was stricken by deafness?

14. For whom did Handel write his *Water Music*?

15. Which Handel masterpiece was first performed in Dublin in 1842?

16. Which musicologist catalogued Mozart's works chronologically 70 years after the composer's death?

Answers to page 221
SINGER/SONGWRITERS 3: **1.** 'All By Myself' **2.** John Denver
3. 'Watermark' **4.** Tanita Tikaram **5.** 'Tapestry' **6.** Joe Jackson **7.** 'The Way It Is' **8.** 'Our Last Song Together' **9.** Leonard Cohen **10.** David Gray
11. Bob Dylan **12.** Kirsty MacColl **13.** Mandy **14.** Clifford T. Ward
15. Neil Diamond **16.** They share the same birthday – 30 July

Glam Rock 2

Answers on page 218

1. Which glam rock star was born Mark Feld?

2. Who composed most of Sweet's hits?

3. Which glam rock group were banned by the Mecca dancehall circuit for what was considered to be an overtly sexual stage act?

4. Who released a version of George Harrison's 'Here Comes The Sun' under the name of Paul Monday?

5. In 1973, who put old records and photos of his former persona, Paul Raven, in a coffin and let them sink into the Thames?

6. Which Mud guitarist used to wear a dress on stage?

7. Which Sweet number has an identical riff to David Bowie's 'The Jean Genie'?

8. Which song kept Sweet's 'Hellraiser' off the top of the UK charts in 1973?

9. In which year did T. Rex hit number one with 'Telegram Sam'?

10. Which T. Rex single was based on 'Teenage Boogie' by Webb Pierce?

11. Which glam rock star had an earlier existence as London folk singer Toby Tyler?

12. Who produced and co-wrote Gary Glitter's early hits?

13. How many weeks did 'I'm The Leader Of The Gang (I Am)' spend at the top of the UK charts?

14. Who went on a Ballroom Blitz in 1973?

15. Who was lead singer with The Glitter Band?

16. When did Gary Glitter first announce his retirement?

Answers to page 218
NINETIES 6: 1. The Beautiful South 2. Nirvana 3. Beverley Craven
4. Billie 5. The Verve 6. 2 Unlimited 7. Westlife 8. Simply Red 9. Blur
10. Janet Jackson 11. Suede 12. B*Witched 13. Michael Jackson 14. Jazzy
Jeff and The Fresh Prince 15. Snap! 16. U2

Singer/Songwriters 3

Answers on page 219

1. Which Eric Carmen single was based on a Rachmaninov melody from his Piano Concerto No 2 in C Minor?

2. Who released the 1972 album 'Rocky Mountain High'?

3. From which album was Enya's 'Orinoco Flow' taken?

4. Whose debut hit was 'Good Tradition' in 1988?

5. Which Carole King album spent 90 weeks in the UK charts following its 1971 release?

6. Who reckoned 'It's Different For Girls'?

7. Which Bruce Hornsby single dealt with racial discrimination?

8. Which Neil Sedaka song was penned in tribute to his former writing partner Howard Greenfield?

9. Which melancholic, Canadian-born songwriter composed 'Suzanne'?

10. Whose best-selling album is 'White Ladder'?

11. Who released the 1966 album 'Blonde On Blonde'?

12. Who was 'Walking Down Madison' in 1991?

13. Which Barry Manilow song was inspired by Scott English's 'Brandy'?

14. Which Seventies artist had hits with 'Gaye' and 'Scullery'?

15. 'Tap Root Manuscript' was the first album to chart in the UK for which American singer/songwriter?

16. Other than the song 'Wuthering Heights', what else links Kate Bush to Emily Brontë?

Answers to page 219
CLASSICAL GAS 3: **1.** Prokofiev **2.** 18th **3.** Rachmaninov **4.** Henry
5. Ravel **6.** Hungarian **7.** Berlioz **8.** Dvorak **9.** Mahler **10.** Eisenach
11. 1875 **12.** 32 **13.** 31 **14.** King George I **15.** *Messiah* **16.** Ludwig von
Köchel

Bee Gees 1

Answers on page 224

1. Which Bee Gees hit was originally written for, but turned down by, Otis Redding?

2. Which industrial tragedy gave The Bee Gees their first hit single in the UK?

3. For which American female singer was 'How Deep Is Your Love' originally written?

4. On which island were the Gibb brothers born?

5. Which former child actor joined The Bee Gees as drummer in 1967?

6. Which was the band's first number one in Australia?

7. In which year did Maurice Gibb say that it is 'very probable The Bee Gees will be non-existent in two years from now'?

8. Which were the last Bee Gees hits on which Colin Petersen and Vince Melouney appeared?

9. Which brother left the band in 1969 to pursue a solo career?

10. Whose UK TV show did The Bee Gees walk off in protest at his mickey-taking?

11. Which single got to number one in the US in 1977?

12. From which album was 'Nights On Broadway' taken?

13. Who played guest percussion on 'You Should Be Dancing'?

14. Which Bee Gees single set a Billboard Hot 100 record by remaining in the US top ten for 17 weeks in a row?

15. In which year was 'Tragedy' a number one on both sides of the Atlantic?

16. 'Tragedy' was a track on which Bee Gees album?

Answers to page 224
POT LUCK 23: 1. Eric Clapton 2. San Francisco 3. Monsieur Dupont
4. 'Could It Be Magic' 5. 'A Lover's Concerto' 6. 'God Save The Queen'
7. 'Ventura Highway' 8. John Lennon 9. Paul McCartney 10. 1964
11. Mike Oldfield 12. The Monkees 13. Ozzy Osbourne 14. Slade
15. The Modern Lovers 16. Crispian St Peters

Chart Toppers 10

Answers on page 225

1. Which Scot sang about a 'Japanese Boy' in 1981?

2. Dennis D'Ell was the singer with which 1964 chart toppers?

3. From which Duran Duran album was 'The Reflex' taken?

4. What didn't Eddy Grant want to do in the title of his 1982 number one?

5. Which 1982 number one by a group of Birmingham schoolboys was originally a Jamaican song about pot-smoking?

6. Which American youngsters had a 1983 number one with 'Candy Girl'?

7. Tim Hauser, Janis Siegel, Laurel Masse and Alan Paul made up which 1977 chart toppers?

8. And which French love song took them to number one?

9. Who got smoke in their eyes in 1959?

10. How many weeks did Whitney Houston stay at the top of the UK charts with 'I Will Always Love You'?

11. Who had a posthumous number one with 'Living On My Own' in 1993?

12. Which 1994 single was the 700th UK number one since the charts began?

13. Which 1982 number one by a German techno band started out on the B-side of a track called 'Computer Love'?

14. What was the name of Georgie Fame's backing group on his 1965 hit 'Yeh Yeh'?

15. Which singer with a group who had a 1964 UK number one went on to present *Play School*?

16. And which girl did his band sing about?

Answers to page 225
ALBUMS 9: **1.** Whitesnake **2.** Blondie **3.** 10cc **4.** The Smiths **5.** Melanie C **6.** The Small Faces **7.** Queen **8.** Kate Bush **9.** Alison Moyet **10.** Tanita Tikaram **11.** Roxy Music **12.** Deep Purple **13.** Leo Sayer **14.** Haircut 100 **15.** Simply Red **16.** The Rolling Stones

Pot Luck 23

Answers on page 222

1. As a 16-year-old which future guitar legend took a Christmas job as a relief postman in Surrey?

2. After which US city did The Bay City Rollers name themselves?

3. Which Frenchman did Sandie Shaw sing about in 1969?

4. Which Barry Manilow song was inspired by Chopin's Prelude in C Minor?

5. And which hit for The Toys was adapted from Bach's Minuet in G?

6. Which Sex Pistols track was banned by the BBC for being too anarchic?

7. Which highway did America drive down in 1972?

8. Who called himself Dr Winston O'Boogie when playing on Elton John's version of 'Lucy In The Sky With Diamonds'?

9. Who produced Mary Hopkin's 1968 chart topper 'Those Were The Days'?

10. In which year was Jim Reeves killed in a plane crash?

11. Who recorded his own version of the *Blue Peter* theme?

12. Which Sixties pop group starred in the film *Head*?

13. Which Black Sabbath wild man once reputedly bit off a bat's head on stage?

14. Which Seventies band dropped the prefix 'Ambrose' from their original name?

15. What was the name of Jonathan Richman's backing group?

16. In 1966, who was convinced he was the 'Pied Piper'?

Answers to page 222
BEE GEES 1: **1.** 'To Love Somebody' **2.** 'New York Mining Disaster 1941'
3. Yvonne Elliman **4.** Isle of Man **5.** Colin Petersen **6.** 'Spicks And Specks'
7. 1968 **8.** 'I Started A Joke' **9.** Robin **10.** Clive Anderson **11.** 'Jive Talkin''
12. 'Main Course' **13.** Stephen Stills **14.** 'How Deep Is Your Love'
15. 1979 **16.** 'Spirits Having Flown'

Albums 9

Answers on page 223

Who recorded the following albums?

1. 'Come And Get It' (1981)

2. 'Eat To The Beat' (1979)

3. 'The Original Soundtrack' (1975)

4. 'Hatful Of Hollow' (1984)

5. 'Northern Star' (1999)

6. 'Ogden's Nut Gone Flake' (1968)

7. 'Sheer Heart Attack' (1974)

8. 'The Sensual World' (1989)

9. 'Raindancing' (1987)

10. 'Ancient Heart' (1988)

11. 'Avalon' (1982)

12. 'Burn' (1974)

13. 'Endless Flight' (1976)

14. 'Pelican West' (1982)

15. 'Love And The Russian Winter' (1999)

16. 'Emotional Rescue' (1980)

Answers to page 223
CHART TOPPERS 10: 1. Aneka 2. The Honeycombs 3. 'Seven And The Ragged Tiger' 4. Dance 5. 'Pass The Dutchie' (Musical Youth) 6. New Edition 7. Manhattan Transfer 8. 'Chanson D'Amour' 9. The Platters 10. Ten 11. Freddie Mercury 12. 'Twist And Shout' by Chaka Demus and Pliers with Jack Radics and Taxi Gang 13. 'The Model' 14. The Blue Flames 15. Lionel Morton (The Four Pennies) 16. Juliet

Sixties 6

Answers on page 228

1. What was the name of Screaming Lord Sutch's backing group?

2. Grocer Jack was the central figure in which innovative Sixties hit?

3. And who was the singer?

4. Which group did The Ivy League become in 1967?

5. Bobby Elliott was the drummer for which popular Sixties group?

6. Who had a 1962 hit with 'Ginny Come Lately'?

7. Which son of a famous actor sang about 'Windmills Of Your Mind' in 1969?

8. In which baffling song did someone leave the cake out in the rain?

9. Which group, who had a hit with the mild protest song 'It's Good News Week', were all ex-members of the RAF?

10. Who sang about 'The House That Jack Built' in 1967?

11. What was the title of Frank Ifield's fourth and final UK number one single?

12. Which comedian had the biggest-selling UK single of 1965?

13. Who conjured up a 'Strange Brew' in 1967?

14. Which singer with The Zombies later enjoyed a successful solo career?

15. What was the name of Chris Farlowe's backing band?

16. Under what name did accomplished songwriters Roger Cook and Roger Greenaway perform?

Answers to page 228
EUROVISION 3: 1. Switzerland 2. They both sang barefoot 3. Celine Dion 4. Michael Ball 5. At 16th, she was the lowest-ever UK finisher 6. Alphabeta 7. German 8. Vicky Leandros 9. Patricia Bredin (1957) 10. Denmark 11. Five 12. Matt Monro 13. Scott Fitzgerald 14. Ronnie Carroll (1962, 1963) 15. 1985 16. The New Seekers

Girl Bands 5

Answers on page 229

1. How many members are there in the Irish girl group B*Witched?

2. The single 'He Loves U Not' by Dream was remixed by which male rap star?

3. What does the 'C' in TLC stand for?

4. 'It's About Time You Were Mine' was a single by which group?

5. The All Saints single 'Pure Shores' was a song from the soundtrack to which film?

6. Which group released 'Deep Deep Down'?

7. Sporty Spice was also known as who?

8. Which single did Precious enter in the Eurovision Song Contest?

9. Fiona, Mim, Kate and Leanne make up which girl group?

10. Which group released 'Girls On Top'?

11. Which country are the group M2M from?

12. How many members of Madasun are there?

13. Who had a single titled 'Shut Your Mouth'?

14. What was the first UK chart success for Honeyz?

15. Which girl group had hits with 'Days Like That' and 'So Long' in 1999?

16. What was the title of TLC's second album?

Answers to page 229
NEW WAVE 2: **1.** XTC **2.** Edward Tudor-Pole (Tenpole Tudor) **3.** Paul Carrack **4.** Bottles of blood **5.** The Teardrop Explodes **6.** Buggles **7.** 'Brass In Pocket' **8.** The Kinks **9.** Elvis Costello **10.** 'Drive' **11.** 'I Can't Stand Up For Falling Down' **12.** 'Private Life' **13.** The Police **14.** Tenpole Tudor **15.** The Pretenders (Martin Chambers) **16.** 'Sgt. Rock (Is Going To Help Me)'

Eurovision 3

Answers on page 226

1. Which country did Israeli-born Esther Ofarim represent in the 1963 Eurovision Song Contest?

2. What did Sandie Shaw in 1967 have in common with Spain's Remedios Amaya in 1983?

3. Which Canadian-born international star won the Eurovision for Switzerland in 1988?

4. Which West End musical star represented the UK in 1992?

5. What dubious distinction does the 2000 UK entry Nicki French hold?

6. What was the name of Izhar Cohen's backing group in Israel's victorious year of 1978?

7. What nationality was Nicole who got to number one in the UK with her 1982 Eurovision winner, 'A Little Peace'?

8. Who won for Luxembourg in 1972 with 'Come What May'?

9. Who was the UK's first Eurovision entrant?

10. The Olsen Brothers won the 2000 contest for which country?

11. How many times have the United Kingdom won the Eurovision?

12. Who was runner-up in 1964 for the UK with 'I Love The Little Things'?

13. Who finished runner-up for the UK in 1988 with 'Go' yet only reached number 52 in the charts?

14. Who is the only singer to have represented the UK two years in a row?

15. In which year did Norway win the Eurovision for the first time?

16. Who came second in 1972 with 'Beg, Steal Or Borrow'?

Answers to page 226
SIXTIES 6: 1. The Savages 2. 'Excerpt From A Teenage Opera' 3. Keith West 4. The Flowerpot Men 5. The Hollies 6. Brian Hyland 7. Noel Harrison (son of Rex) 8. 'MacArthur Park' 9. Hedgehoppers Anonymous 10. Alan Price 11. 'Confessin'' 12. Ken Dodd ('Tears') 13. Cream 14. Colin Blunstone 15. The Thunderbirds 16. David and Jonathan

New Wave 2

Answers on page 227

1. Andy Partridge, Colin Moulding, Dave Gregory and Terry Chambers lined up in which new wave band?

2. Which leader of an Eighties band went on to present *The Crystal Maze*?

3. Who sang lead vocals on Squeeze's 'Tempted'?

4. What were thrown at Squeeze during a gig at a veterinary college in Bournemouth?

5. Which band's biggest hit was 'Reward'?

6. Who were Trevor Horn and Geoff Downes better known as?

7. What was The Pretenders' first UK number one?

8. Who originally recorded The Pretenders' 'Stop Your Sobbing'?

9. Who produced the Squeeze album 'East Side Story'?

10. Which Cars song provided backing for film footage of the famine in Ethiopia during Live Aid?

11. Which cover of a Sam and Dave song gave Elvis Costello a UK top five hit in 1980?

12. Which Chrissie Hynde song was covered by Grace Jones?

13. Who had a 1981 hit titled 'De Do Do Do, De Da Da Da'?

14. 'Swords Of A Thousand Men' was a 1981 hit for which band?

15. Which band's drummer injured both his hands in separate incidents within the space of two months in 1981, causing dates to be cancelled?

16. Which comic-book hero came to the aid of XTC?

Answers to page 227
GIRL BANDS 5: **1.** Four **2.** Puff Daddy **3.** Chilli **4.** Thunderbugs **5.** *The Beach* **6.** Hepburn **7.** Melanie Chisholm **8.** 'Say It Again' **9.** 21st Century Girls **10.** Girl Thing **11.** Norway **12.** Three **13.** Made In London **14.** 'Finally Found' **15.** Fierce **16.** 'Fanmail'

Pot Luck 24

Answers on page 232

1. Which singer killed in a 1966 car crash was famous for wearing an eye patch?

2. What middle name was John Lennon given at birth?

3. In 1974, who became the first woman to win the Ivor Novello Songwriting Award?

4. Which band's 1973 album was titled 'Can't Buy A Thrill'?

5. Which three solo artists with the surname Preston had UK hits in the Sixties?

6. Which sister of a pop star had a 1991 hit with 'Love And Kisses'?

7. Which member of Duran Duran co-produced Kajagoogoo's only number one?

8. Which band named themselves after a pep pill?

9. What was the surname of Delaney and Bonnie?

10. Who did it 'All For Leyna' in 1980?

11. Which two Sixties artists had hits about girls named Jennifer?

12. In which year did The Moody Blues first release 'Nights In White Satin'?

13. Who was 'Living On The Front Line' in 1979?

14. Who worked as a bookmaker's clerk before joining The Rolling Stones?

15. Which girl did Gerry Monroe take to number four in the charts in 1970?

16. Which family group reckoned they were 'The Chosen Few' in 1979?

Answers to page 232
ROCK 'N' ROLL 3: **1.** Little Richard **2.** Chuck Berry **3.** Jerry Lee Lewis **4.** The Teenagers (Frankie Lymon's group) **5.** Little Richard **6.** Marty Wilde **7.** Adam Faith **8.** Smiley Lewis **9.** English **10.** Tony Meehan **11.** 'Rave On' **12.** Billy Fury **13.** 'Lonely Teenager' **14.** Chuck Berry **15.** Rapp **16.** Marty Wilde

One-Hit Wonders 7

Answers on page 233

1. Which actor had a hit with 'MacArthur Park'?

2. What was the title of Mr Bloe's only hit?

3. Who reached number three with 'Jungle Rock' in 1957?

4. On which thoroughfare could The Maisonettes be found in 1982?

5. Which politically incorrect title took Carl Malcolm into the top ten in 1975?

6. Who sang about 'Something Old, Something New' in 1971?

7. 'A Way Of Life' was a hit for which band in 1969?

8. Which song by Honeybus went on to be used in TV adverts for Nimble bread?

9. Who was 'Gonna Make You An Offer You Can't Refuse' in 1973?

10. The UK top ten hit 'I See A Star' was the 1974 Dutch Eurovision entry for which ill-matched duo?

11. Which American artist recorded 'The Clapping Song'?

12. Who got to number three in the UK charts in 1957 with 'Little Darlin''?

13. What was Danny and The Juniors' only success in the UK?

14. Who had a 1963 hit with 'Rhythm Of The Rain'?

15. Yannis Markopoulos had a 1977 hit with the theme from which BBC television series?

16. Whose only hit was a 1964 version of The Beatles' 'I Should Have Known Better'?

Answers to page 233
SEVENTIES 7: 1. Sweet 2. Don Powell 3. Suzi Quatro 4. 'Bicycle Race' 5. Pickettywitch 6. The New Seekers 7. Tom Jones 8. 'Song For Guy' 9. The Isley Brothers 10. Heatwave 11. 'Under My Thumb' 12. 'Rubber Bullets' 13. The Delfonics 14. Chicago 15. Fox 16. Thin Lizzy

Rock 'n' Roll 3

Answers on page 230

1. As a child, which rock 'n' roller used to sing with The Tiny Tots Quartet?

2. Who released 'Roll Over Beethoven' in 1956?

3. 'Whole Lotta Shakin' Goin' On' became a hit on both sides of the Atlantic for which flamboyant performer?

4. What were Sherman Garnes, Joe Negroni, Herman Santiago and Jimmy Merchant known as collectively?

5. Who wrote and recorded 'Tutti Frutti'?

6. Which rock 'n' roller worked in a south London timber yard before being discovered?

7. Whose first movie was the X-rated *Beat Girl* with Shirley Ann Field?

8. Who originally recorded 'One Night', a UK number one for Elvis in 1959?

9. In what subject did Cliff Richard (then known as Harry Webb) gain his only 'O' Level pass?

10. Which drummer joined Cliff Richard's backing band in November 1958?

11. Which Buddy Holly single was recorded originally by Sonny West?

12. Which budding rock star used to work as a deckhand on the River Mersey tug boats?

13. What was the title of Dion's first solo single?

14. Which rock star was born in St Louis, Missouri, in 1926 and later landed a job with General Motors?

15. What was the surname of Danny from Danny and The Juniors?

16. Which rock 'n' roller married one of The Vernons Girls?

Answers to page 230
POT LUCK 24: **1.** Johnny Kidd **2.** Winston **3.** Lynsey De Paul **4.** Steely Dan **5.** Billy, Johnny and Mike **6.** Dannii Minogue **7.** Nick Rhodes **8.** Dexy's Midnight Runners (dexedrine) **9.** Bramlett **10.** Billy Joel **11.** Donovan ('Jennifer Juniper') and The Hollies ('Jennifer Eccles') **12.** 1967 **13.** Eddy Grant **14.** Bill Wyman **15.** 'Sally' **16.** The Dooleys

Seventies 7

Answers on page 231

1. Who were proud of their 'Little Willy' in 1972?

2. Who was the drummer with Slade?

3. Which Detroit-born rocker sang about the "48 Crash' in 1973?

4. Which Queen track formed a double A-side with 'Fat Bottomed Girls'?

5. Who experienced 'That Same Old Feeling' in 1970?

6. Lyn Paul and Eve Graham were the singers with which Seventies group?

7. Who charted with 'Daughter Of Darkness' in 1970?

8. Which Elton John single was a tribute to Rocket Records' motorcycle messenger boy who had died in an accident aged 17?

9. Which former Motown band had hits with 'Highway Of My Life' and 'Summer Breeze'?

10. Whose biggest hit was 'Boogie Nights' in 1977?

11. Which cover of a Rolling Stones track gave Wayne Gibson a UK top twenty record in 1974?

12. Which 10cc single received little radio play because of the weaponry used by the British Army in Northern Ireland?

13. In 1971 which Philly band asked 'Didn't I (Blow Your Mind This Time)'?

14. '25 Or 6 To 4' was a hit for which American band in 1970?

15. Who wanted to sleep in a 'S-S-S-Single Bed'?

16. Who were 'Live And Dangerous' on their 1978 album?

Answers to page 231
ONE-HIT WONDERS 7: **1.** Richard Harris **2.** 'Groovin' With Mr Bloe' **3.** Hank Mizell **4.** 'Heartache Avenue' **5.** 'Fattie Bum Bum' **6.** The Fantastics **7.** Family Dogg **8.** 'I Can't Let Maggie Go' **9.** Jimmy Helms **10.** Mouth and McNeal **11.** Shirley Ellis **12.** The Diamonds **13.** 'At The Hop' **14.** The Cascades **15.** *Who Pays The Ferryman?* **16.** The Naturals

Cover Versions 8

Answers on page 236

1. Which Canadian chanteuse had the original hit with Boyzone's 'You Needed Me'?

2. Which song links The Real Thing, Sonia and Sean Maguire?

3. Which Free track did Pauline Henry cover in 1993?

4. Who discovered that 'The First Cut Is The Deepest' ten years before Rod Stewart?

5. Faith No More covered which Commodores single in 1993?

6. The McCoys and The Sandpipers both had hits with which song?

7. In 1988, who covered The Isley Brothers hit 'Harvest For The World'?

8. The Detroit Emeralds, Forrest and Shakin' Stevens have all had hits with which song?

9. Which Elton John song was covered by Oleta Adams in 1991?

10. Kavana recorded which Shalamar hit in 1997?

11. Who originally had a UK hit with David Cassidy's 1972 chart topper 'How Can I Be Sure'?

12. Which Donna Summer hit did Arsenal Football Club re-record in 1998?

13. Which title was a hit for both Michael Jackson and Marti Webb?

14. Which track links Harold Faltermeyer and Clock?

15. Which Sweet song did Def Leppard cover in 1994?

16. The Kinks and The Stranglers both had top ten hits with which song?

Answers to page 236
CHART TOPPERS 11: **1.** 1973 **2.** 1998 **3.** 1995 **4.** 1966 **5.** 1959 **6.** 1987 **7.** 1982 **8.** 1975 **9.** 1997 **10.** 1963 **11.** 1969 **12.** 1979 **13.** 1987 **14.** 1990 **15.** 1993 **16.** 1977

Pot Luck 25

Answers on page 237

1. In which month of the year was Wizzard's 'Rock 'n' Roll Winter' released?

2. Which 52-year-old had a number one hit in 1998?

3. Which band took their name from a David Lynch film?

4. Who had more UK top ten hits than any other act in the first half of the Eighties?

5. Which divine American female artist once worked as a pineapple chunker in Hawaii?

6. Which district of London was mentioned in Marillion's 'Kayleigh'?

7. Which Mark Knopfler song was used as the theme tune for Britain's 1986 challenge for the America's Cup yachting prize?

8. What were Harold and Herbie known as when they joined the ranks of one-hit wonders in 1958?

9. Donald Fagen and Walter Becker were the prime movers in which band?

10. Who was the lead singer with The Gingerbreads?

11. Which footballer teamed up with Lindisfarne for a 1990 version of 'Fog On The Tyne'?

12. John Phillips and Denny Doherty were the male members of which Sixties foursome?

13. How did Jimi Hendrix attract headlines at the 1967 Monterey Pop Festival?

14. Which Peter, Paul and Mary song was a 1963 hit for Trini Lopez?

15. Which member of Darts went on to present *Tiswas*?

16. Who were the first overseas act to have their first three singles reach number one in the UK?

Answers to page 237
THE POLICE 1: 1. 'The Dream Of The Blue Turtles' 2. CIA agent
3. Henry Padovani 4. Alberto Y Lost Trios Paranoias 5. 1978 6. Ace
7. The Kennedy Space Centre, Houston 8. 'Invisible Sun' 9. *Rumble Fish*
10. 'Spread A Little Happiness' 11. 'Synchronicity' 12. 'Synchronicity'
13. 'Every Breath You Take' 14. 'Message In A Bottle' 15. Andy Summers
16. Trudie Styler

Chart Toppers 11

Answers on page 234

In which years did the following singles reach number one in the UK?

1. 'Get Down' (Gilbert O'Sullivan)

2. 'No Matter What' (Boyzone)

3. 'Think Twice' (Celine Dion)

4. 'Sunny Afternoon' (The Kinks)

5. 'Only Sixteen' (Craig Douglas) ·

6. 'Respectable' (Mel and Kim)

7. 'The Lion Sleeps Tonight' (Tight Fit)

8. 'January' (Pilot)

9. 'Beetlebum' (Blur)

10. 'She Loves You' (The Beatles)

11. 'Albatross' (Fleetwood Mac)

12. 'Video Killed The Radio Star' (Buggles)

13. 'It's A Sin' (The Pet Shop Boys)

14. 'A Little Time' (The Beautiful South)

15. 'Pray' (Take That)

16. 'When I Need You' (Leo Sayer)

Answers to page 234
COVER VERSIONS 8: 1. Anne Murray 2. 'You To Me Are Everything'
3. 'Feel Like Making Love' 4. P.P. Arnold 5. 'Easy' 6. 'Hang On Sloopy'
7. The Christians 8. 'Feel The Need In Me' 9. 'Don't Let The Sun Go
Down On Me' 10. 'I Can Make You Feel Good' 11. Dusty Springfield
12. 'Hot Stuff' 13. 'Ben' 14. 'Axel F' 15. 'Action' 16. 'All Day And All Of
The Night'

The Police 1

Answers on page 235

1. What was the title of Sting's first solo album?

2. What did Stewart Copeland's father do for a living?

3. Which member of The Police quit the band in 1977, leaving them as a trio?

4. Which band did The Police support on their first UK tour?

5. In which year was 'Roxanne' released as a single?

6. Which character did Sting play in the film *Quadrophenia*?

7. Where did The Police film the video for 'Walking On The Moon'?

8. Which Police single was inspired by the troubles in Northern Ireland?

9. For which Francis Ford Coppola movie of 1982 did Stewart Copeland write the score?

10. What was Sting's first solo single?

11. Which album was written by Sting at Ian Fleming's former Jamaican home?

12. From which album was 'Every Breath You Take' extracted as a single?

13. Which Police track was named Song Of The Year at the 1984 Grammy Awards?

14. Which was the band's first UK number one?

15. Which band member released the solo album 'XYZ'?

16. Who did Sting marry in 1992?

Answers to page 235
POT LUCK 25: **1.** April **2.** Cher **3.** Erasure (*Eraserhead*) **4.** Madness
5. Bette Midler **6.** Belsize Park **7.** 'Going Home' **8.** The Kalin Twins
9. Steely Dan **10.** Goldie **11.** Paul Gascoigne **12.** Mamas and The Papas
13. By burning his guitar **14.** 'If I Had A Hammer' **15.** Den Hegarty
16. Aqua

Heavy Metal 4

Answers on page 240

1. Which heavy metal frontman formed an unlikely double act with Mr Bean on a 1992 single?

2. Which Aerosmith album featured 'Walk This Way'?

3. Which band chose their name after rejecting Heads Of Amazon and AIDS?

4. Which glove puppet was frequently lowered onstage at Iron Maiden concerts at the request of drummer Nicko McBrain?

5. Which band were famous for their painted faces?

6. 'Geezer' Butler is bassist with which band?

7. Who released the live album 'Made In Japan'?

8. Which heavy metal keyboard player has twice been married to Cher?

9. Which band got to number 13 in the UK charts in 1987 with 'Wanted Dead Or Alive'?

10. Who was sacked from Hawkwind in 1975 for spending five days in a Canadian jail for drug possession?

11. Which band rejected the name Bastard before settling on their new identity?

12. What was Hawkwind's only UK top thirty hit?

13. From which film was the Aerosmith single 'I Don't Want To Miss A Thing' taken?

14. Richie Sambora, David Bryan and Tico Torres were founder members of which band?

15. Who strongly advised: 'Run To The Hills' in 1982?

16. Whose albums included 'The Razor's Edge' and 'Ballbreaker'?

Answers to page 240
NAME CHANGES 10: **1.** The Delfonics **2.** Terence **3.** The Communards **4.** Brenda Lee **5.** Ewan MacColl **6.** Carole King **7.** George **8.** Steve Tyler **9.** Theodore **10.** Edwin Starr **11.** Aneka ('Japanese Boy') **12.** Kiss **13.** Chris Farlowe **14.** Nina Simone **15.** Slash **16.** Sweetshop

Duos 3

Answers on page 241

1. Who teamed up with Nancy Sinatra for the 1971 hit 'Did You Ever'?

2. Who links Yazoo and Erasure?

3. Who was Jimmy Somerville's partner in The Communards?

4. Which cover of an Elvis song gave The Pet Shop Boys a number one in 1987?

5. Who joined Billy Preston on the 1979 hit 'With You I'm Born Again'?

6. Which two singers joined forces in 1986 for 'On My Own'?

7. Which Sixties duo could have been called Stewart and Clyde?

8. Which band had a 1986 hit with 'Sometimes'?

9. Which pair pleaded 'Don't Stay Away Too Long' in 1974?

10. What was the title of The Pet Shop Boys' second UK number one?

11. Which girl duo got to number five in the charts in 1984 with 'Since Yesterday'?

12. What was Peter and Gordon's follow-up to 'A World Without Love'?

13. With whom did Elton John release a live version of 'Don't Let The Sun Go Down On Me' in 1991?

14. For whom was it 'Yesterday Once More' in 1973?

15. Which Everly Brothers classic was a hit for Bobbie Gentry and Glen Campbell in 1969?

16. Which two country artists got together for 'Islands In The Stream' in 1983?

Answers to page 241
SPICE GIRLS 1: **1.** Simon Fuller **2.** Geri **3.** 1996 **4.** 1998 **5.** Emma Bunton
6. Victoria Beckham (with Sophie Ellis-Bextor, daughter of Janet Ellis)
7. 'Say You'll Be There' **8.** Mel B **9.** Melanie C **10.** 'When You're Gone'
11. 'Mama/Who Do You Think You Are' **12.** *Spiceworld: The Movie*
13. Richard E. Grant **14.** 'Goin' Down' **15.** 'Look At Me' **16.** 'Mi Chico Latino'

Name Changes 10

Answers on page 238

1. Which Philly band were previously known as The Four Gents?

2. What is the real Christian name of 'Geezer' Butler?

3. Which duo were formerly called The Committee but changed it in honour of a group of 19th-century French Republicans?

4. Which Sixties American singer shortened her name from Brenda Mae Tarpley?

5. Which folk singer did Jimmie Miller become?

6. Which singer/songwriter found something more regal than Carole Klein?

7. What is Zoot Money's real name?

8. Which heavy metal singer was born Steve Tallarico?

9. What prefix did Supergrass drop from their name?

10. Which Motown artist changed his name from Charles Hatcher?

11. What stage name did Mary Sandeman adopt for her Oriental-sounding number one?

12. Which rock band were previously called Wicked Lester?

13. Which British Sixties R & B singer was born John Deighton?

14. Which singer began life as Eunice Waymon?

15. As which heavy metal guitarist is Saul Hudson better known?

16. What were Sweet originally called?

Answers to page 238
HEAVY METAL 4: **1.** Bruce Dickinson **2.** 'Toys In The Attic' **3.** Guns N' Roses **4.** Sooty **5.** Kiss **6.** Black Sabbath **7.** Deep Purple **8.** Greg Allman **9.** Bon Jovi **10.** Lemmy **11.** Motorhead **12.** 'Silver Machine' **13.** *Armageddon* **14.** Bon Jovi **15.** Iron Maiden **16.** AC/DC

Spice Girls 1

Answers on page 239

1. Who was The Spice Girls' manager?

2. Of the original line-up, who was the oldest Spice Girl?

3. In which year did 'Wannabe' reach number one in the UK?

4. When did Geri leave the band?

5. Which Spice Girl once played a mugger in *EastEnders*?

6. Which Spice Girl has had a running feud with the daughter of a former *Blue Peter* presenter?

7. What was the title of The Spice Girls' second number one?

8. Which Spice Girl presented a TV talent show in 2001?

9. Which Spice Girl recorded a duet with Bryan Adams?

10. What was its title?

11. Which 1997 double A-side was a charity record in aid of Comic Relief's Red Nose Day?

12. What was the name of The Spice Girls' first film?

13. Who played the girls' manager in that film?

14. What was the title of Melanie C's second single?

15. What was Geri Halliwell's first solo single?

16. Which song gave Geri Halliwell her first UK number one?

Stairway to Heaven 3

Answers on page 244

1. Thousands of fans showed up for a free 1975 concert from which singer/songwriter, not knowing that he had just died in a car crash on the Long Island Expressway?

2. Which velvet-voiced singer died from anorexia nervosa at the age of 32?

3. Which Memphis-based rock 'n' roller drowned in a California boating accident in 1964?

4. Which prolific songwriter for The Monkees shot himself dead in 1994?

5. Which former member of Wings died from heart failure in 1979?

6. How did Sonny Bono die?

7. Which member of The Temptations shot himself dead in his car near the Motown studios in 1973?

8. How did Steve Took, Marc Bolan's partner in T. Rex, meet his end in 1980?

9. Who died of a 1996 heart attack halfway through 'Tiptoe Thru The Tulips'?

10. How did Viv Stanshall of The Bonzo Dog Doo-Dah Band die in 1995?

11. Which member of The Temptations died from a drug overdose in 1991?

12. Which controversial manager, born Andreas Cornelius Van Kuijk, died of a stroke in 1997?

13. Which Sixties singer, whose hits included 'Dream Baby' and 'It's Over', died of a heart attack while visiting his mother in 1988?

14. Who had the only US number one to be sung entirely in Japanese before being killed in a plane crash 22 years later?

15. In which year did The Doors' Jim Morrison die?

16. How old was John Lennon when he was killed?

Answers to page 244
NOVELTY NUMBERS 4: 1. Charlie Drake 2. Alexei Sayle 3. Hylda Baker and Arthur Mullard 4. Father Abraham 5. Peter Sellers and Sophia Loren 6. 'Bangers and Mash' 7. 'Combine Harvester' 8. 'Brand New Key' 9. 'Elected' 10. 'I Am A Cider Drinker' 11. Harry Enfield 12. The Woolpackers 13. *Emmerdale* 14. The Goodies 15. Dudley Moore 16. *Not Only…But Also*

Pot Luck 26

Answers on page 245

1. Which Rolling Stone used to work as a relief porter at Bexley Mental Hospital?

2. What is the name of the Abba tribute band from Australia?

3. Which band were named after the HMV dog Nipper?

4. Which band were stripped of their 1989 Grammy for Best New Artist after it emerged that they hadn't sung on any of their releases?

5. What was the name of Reparata's backing group?

6. Which movie star was waiting for Bananarama in 1984?

7. Who had a bit of a 'Rama Lama Ding Dong' in 1978?

8. Who released 'Ooh-Wakka-Doo-Wakka-Day' in 1972?

9. Who tried to '(Remember The Days Of The) Old School Yard'?

10. Who sang with The Flowerpot Men, Edison Lighthouse and Pipkins?

11. Zal Cleminson was a colourful member of which band?

12. What is former Queen drummer Roger Taylor's full name?

13. Who were 'The In Betweenies' in 1974?

14. Which two artists fought out the 'Battle Of New Orleans' in 1959?

15. Who sang about 'Handbags & Gladrags' in 1967?

16. What was John Wayne according to Haysi Fantayzee?

Answers to page 245
LYRICS 9: **1.** 'You're Still The One' (Shania Twain) **2.** 'This Night' (Billy Joel) **3.** 'Like A Prayer' (Madonna) **4.** 'Don't Speak' (No Doubt) **5.** 'Genie In A Bottle' (Christina Aguilera) **6.** 'If You Had My Love' (Jennifer Lopez) **7.** 'Marblehead Johnson' (The Bluetones) **8.** 'Help!' (The Beatles) **9.** 'A Little Respect' (Erasure) **10.** 'With Or Without You' (U2) **11.** 'You Make Me Feel Like Dancing' (Leo Sayer) **12.** 'I'm Not In Love' (10cc) **13.** 'Good Vibrations' (The Beach Boys) **14.** 'It Must Be Love' (Madness) **15.** 'Lazy Sunday' (The Small Faces) **16.** 'Baby…One More Time' (Britney Spears)

Novelty Numbers 4

Answers on page 242

1. Which pint-sized comedian wailed: 'My Boomerang Won't Come Back'?

2. Who enquired: 'Ullo John! Gotta New Motor'?

3. Which grotesque duo tried to outdo Travolta and Livvy with their own version of 'You're The One That I Want'?

4. Who was the bearded leader of The Smurfs?

5. Which actor and actress played doctor and patient for the 1960 hit 'Goodness Gracious Me'?

6. And what was the title of their culinary follow-up?

7. What was The Wurzels' only number one?

8. And which Melanie song did they adapt?

9. Which Alice Cooper song was covered by Mr Bean and Bruce Dickinson?

10. What was the title of The Wurzels' version of 'Una Paloma Blanca'?

11. Who had 'Loadsamoney' in 1988?

12. Who danced to the 'Hillbilly Rock Hillbilly Roll' in 1966?

13. And from which TV soap did they come?

14. Who suggested 'Make A Daft Noise For Christmas' in 1975?

15. Who said 'Goodbye-ee' with Peter Cook in 1965?

16. And in which TV series was it the closing song?

Answers to page 242
STAIRWAY TO HEAVEN 3: **1.** Harry Chapin **2.** Karen Carpenter
3. Johnny Burnette **4.** Tommy Boyce **5.** Jimmy McCulloch **6.** In a skiing accident **7.** Paul Williams **8.** He choked on a cherry pip **9.** Tiny Tim
10. In a fire **11.** David Ruffin **12.** Colonel Tom Parker **13.** Roy Orbison
14. Kyu Sakamoto ('Sukiyaki') **15.** 1971 **16.** 40

Lyrics 9

Answers on page 243

From which songs are the following lyrics taken?

1. 'Looks like we made it, look how far we've come my baby'

2. 'How many nights have I been thinking about you, wanting to hold you but knowing you would not be there'

3. 'I hear your voice, it's like an angel sighing'

4. 'It looks as though you're letting go, and if it's real, well, I don't want to know'

5. 'You're licking your lips and blowing kisses my way'

6. 'Tell me who can I trust if I can't trust you'

7. 'And now my heart's possessed with 18-carat gold regrets'

8. 'My independence seems to vanish in the haze'

9. 'I'm so in love with you, I'll be forever blue'

10. 'See the stone set in your eyes, see the thorn twist in your side'

11. 'You've got a cute way of talking, you got the better of me'

12. 'It's just a silly phase I'm going through'

13. 'I love the colourful clothes she wears and the way the sunlight plays upon her hair'

14. 'As soon as I wake up, every night, every day'

15. 'Hallo, Mrs Jones, how's your Bert's lumbago – mustn't grumble'

16. 'My loneliness is killing me, I must confess, I still believe'

Answers to page 243
POT LUCK 26: 1. Mick Jagger 2. Bjorn Again 3. Bow Wow Wow
4. Milli Vanilli 5. The Delrons 6. Robert De Niro 7. Rocky Sharpe and
The Replays 8. Gilbert O'Sullivan 9. Cat Stevens 10. Tony Burrows
11. The Sensational Alex Harvey Band 12. Roger Meddows-Taylor
13. The Goodies 14. Lonnie Donegan and Johnny Horton 15. Chris
Farlowe 16. Big Leggy

Eighties 7

Answers on page 248

1. Carol Decker was the fiery singer with which band?

2. Who were dancing with tears in their eyes in 1984?

3. Who had a number one album in 1982 with 'The Gift'?

4. Which band reached number two in 1980 with 'What You're Proposing'?

5. Which former lead singer with The Undertones had a number one in 1985 with 'A Good Heart'?

6. Which 1986 number one was a girl's heartfelt plea to her father not to criticise her for getting pregnant?

7. Which sisters nearly made the top of the charts with 'Automatic'?

8. From which country did the girl group Mai Tai originate?

9. Who said 'The Lunatics (Have Taken Over The Asylum)'?

10. Thereze Bazar and David Van Day were better known as which duo?

11. Which Bruce Springsteen number one album of 1987 had the same title as a track on Dire Straits' 'Making Movies'?

12. Which country singer was the first solo artist to have a UK number one in the Eighties?

13. And what was the name of the song?

14. Who was 'Guilty', according to the title of her 1980 album?

15. Who sang about 'Don Quixote' in 1985?

16. Who had a 1989 hit with a remixed version of 'I'm Every Woman'?

Answers to page 248
INDIE 5: **1.** Pearl Jam **2.** Blur **3.** Pulp **4.** 'Sit Down' **5.** 'The Man Who'
6. 'Yellow' **7.** Radiohead **8.** The Lightning Seeds **9.** 'If You Tolerate This Your Children Will Be Next' **10.** 'This Is My Truth Tell Me Yours'
11. 1991 **12.** John Squire **13.** Food **14.** 'The Last Time' **15.** ''D'You Know What I Mean?' **16.** James

Soul 2

Answers on page 249

1. Who covered The Beatles' 'Hey Jude' in 1969?

2. Who sang 'It's A Man's Man's Man's World' in 1966?

3. Who liked to make 'Sweet Soul Music' in 1967?

4. Which band backed James Brown on his first three UK hits?

5. Who is known as 'The Queen of Soul'?

6. What are Charles and Eddie's surnames?

7. Which Eddie had a 1974 hit with '(Hey There) Lonely Girl'?

8. In 1976, who promised: 'You'll Never Find Another Love Like Mine'?

9. Who was the oldest of The Jacksons?

10. Which of The Jacksons was really named Sigmund Esco?

11. What was the title of The Jacksons' first UK number one?

12. Who wrote 'Respect', a hit for Aretha Franklin in 1967?

13. Who originally recorded 'I Say A Little Prayer', which Aretha Franklin took to number four in the UK in 1968?

14. Whose hits included 'I Get The Sweetest Feeling' and '(Your Love Keeps Lifting Me) Higher And Higher'?

15. Which soul singer liked to describe himself as a 'sex machine'?

16. Which song gave Otis Redding his first UK hit?

Answers to page 249
POT LUCK 27: **1.** 1972 **2.** 1997 **3.** 1956 **4.** 1958 **5.** 1999 **6.** 1971
7. 1992 **8.** 1972 **9.** 1978 **10.** 1989 **11.** 1976 **12.** 1972 **13.** 1962 **14.** 1978
15. 1981 **16.** 1967

Indie 5

Answers on page 246

1. Which band were formed by Jeff Ament and Stone Gossard in Seattle?

2. Alex James is a member of which band?

3. Which Indie band formed in 1979 had to wait until 1995 for their first UK top ten hit?

4. Which James song only reached number 77 in 1989 but then got to number two in 1991?

5. 'Driftwood' and 'Turn' are tracks from which Travis album?

6. Which colour brought chart success for Coldplay?

7. Who released 'Creep' in 1993?

8. Whose 1994 album was titled 'Jollification'?

9. Which track gave the Manic Street Preachers their first UK number one?

10. And from which number one album was it taken?

11. In which year did Blur release 'There's No Other Way'?

12. Which member of The Stone Roses once worked as a set-maker on a TV adaptation of *The Wind in the Willows*?

13. With which record label have Blur spent most of their career?

14. Which Rolling Stones track was sampled on The Verve's 'Bitter Sweet Symphony'?

15. What was the title of Oasis's 1997 UK number one?

16. Who were 'Waltzing Alone' in 1997?

Answers to page 246
EIGHTIES 7: 1. T'Pau 2. Ultravox 3. Jam 4. Status Quo 5. Feargal Sharkey 6. 'Papa Don't Preach' 7. The Pointer Sisters 8. Holland 9. Fun Boy Three 10. Dollar 11. 'Tunnel Of Love' 12. Kenny Rogers 13. 'Coward Of The County' 14. Barbra Streisand 15. Nik Kershaw 16. Chaka Khan

Pot Luck 27

Answers on page 247

In which years were the following tracks UK top ten hits?

1. 'Goodbye To Love' (The Carpenters)

2. 'Drop Dead Gorgeous' (Republica)

3. 'Blue Suede Shoes' (Carl Perkins)

4. 'Born Too Late' (The Poni-Tails)

5. 'Honey To The Bee' (Billie)

6. 'It Don't Come Easy' (Ringo Starr)

7. 'It Only Takes A Minute' (Take That)

8. 'Look Wot You Dun' (Slade)

9. 'Oh What A Circus' (David Essex)

10. 'Song For Whoever' (The Beautiful South)

11. 'You Should Be Dancing' (The Bee Gees)

12. 'Tumbling Dice' (The Rolling Stones)

13. 'Ramblin' Rose' (Nat King Cole)

14. 'Instant Replay' (Dan Hartman)

15. 'I Could Be Happy' (Altered Images)

16. 'Hey Joe' (Jimi Hendrix Experience)

Answers to page 247
SOUL 2: 1. Wilson Pickett 2. James Brown 3. Arthur Conley 4. The Famous Flames 5. Aretha Franklin 6. Pettigrew and Chacon 7. Eddie Holman 8. Lou Rawls 9. Jackie 10. Jackie 11. 'Show You The Way To Go' 12. Otis Redding 13. Dionne Warwick 14. Jackie Wilson 15. James Brown 16. 'My Girl'

Jimi Hendrix 1

Answers on page 252

1. Who originally recorded 'All Along The Watchtower'?

2. Hendrix was a member of whose backing band in 1965?

3. What was the debut single of The Jimi Hendrix Experience?

4. On stage, what did Hendrix like to play his guitar with?

5. In which year was 'Purple Haze' released as a single?

6. What was the title of Hendrix's debut album?

7. Which Hendrix single had previously been recorded by The Leaves and Tim Rose?

8. In which country did Hendrix spend a night in jail after wrecking a hotel room during a fight with band member Noel Redding?

9. Which was Hendrix's third UK hit single?

10. With which British singer did Hendrix perform a duet on a 1968 TV series?

11. Which Animal was responsible for bringing Hendrix to the UK?

12. Who was drummer with the Experience?

13. What was the title of Hendrix's second album?

14. Why did some shops refuse to display the album 'Electric Ladyland'?

15. What final message did Hendrix leave on his manager's answering machine?

16. Which track topped the UK chart two months after Hendrix's death?

Answers to page 252
DANCE 4: **1.** 'Silk' **2.** Goldie **3.** Lindy Layton **4.** Norman Cook (aka Fatboy Slim) **5.** Missy Elliott **6.** MC Remedee **7.** Jason Nevins **8.** Larry Heard **9.** Stephen Morris and Gillian Gilbert **10.** New Order **11.** 'Just For The Money' **12.** Gang Starr **13.** Coldcut **14.** Beats International **15.** Black Box **16.** Geir Jenssen

Number Twos 4

Answers on page 253

1. Which Fifties throwback band reached number two in the UK charts in 1977 with 'You Got What It Takes'?

2. Which band got to number two in 1979 with 'Some Girls'?

3. Which track spelt success for Ottawan in 1980?

4. Who made it to the number two spot with 'Let's Dance' in 1962?

5. 'Do You Want To Know A Secret' was a 1963 hit for which Merseybeat group?

6. Which Elton John song nearly had lift-off to number one in 1972?

7. Which group scored a number two hit with 'I'm Telling You Now' in 1963?

8. Emerson, Lake and Palmer got to second spot with which piece in 1977?

9. 'Another Day In Paradise' fell one short of the promised land for which singer?

10. Who took his cover of 'Freedom' to number two in 1996?

11. Who got to number two in 1960 with 'Someone Else's Baby'?

12. Minus their leader, who had a 1975 hit with 'Goodbye My Love'?

13. 'Radio Gaga' narrowly missed out on pole position in 1984 for which band?

14. Who was 'Going In With My Eyes Open' in 1977?

15. Who had a 1986 hit with 'Every Beat Of My Heart'?

16. Which comedienne got to number two in 1983 with a Kirsty MacColl song?

Answers to page 253
SIXTIES 7: **1.** Kenney Jones **2.** Crispian St Peters **3.** Brian Poole **4.** The New Vaudeville Band **5.** Keith Emerson **6.** The Migil Five **7.** Mike D'Abo **8.** The Vagabonds **9.** Marianne Faithfull **10.** Simon Dupree and The Big Sound **11.** The Dave Clark Five **12.** Cliff Bennett and The Rebel Rousers **13.** 1964 **14.** 'The Green Green Grass Of Home' **15.** Roy Orbison **16.** Bobby Darin

Dance 4

Answers on page 250

1. What is Steve Hurley's nickname?

2. Which artist is distinguishable by his gold-inlaid front teeth?

3. Who sang on Beats International's 'Dub Be Good To Me'?

4. Whose aliases have included Pizzaman, Fried Funk Food and Mighty Dub Katz?

5. Which New York hip-hop artist used to be part of a group called Sista?

6. Which member of Cookie Crew used to be a chef for the Ministry of Defence?

7. Which remixer has called himself Plastick Project, Crazee Tunes and The Experience?

8. Which house music DJ is better known as Mr Fingers?

9. Who comprised The Other Two?

10. The Other Two were a splinter group from which band?

11. The voices of Lord Olivier and Bob Hoskins were heard on which Paul Hardcastle track about the Great Train Robbery?

12. Guru Keith E and DJ Premier make up which hip-hop band?

13. Whose albums include 'What's That Noise' and 'Some Like It Cold'?

14. Whose debut album was titled 'Let Them Eat Bingo'?

15. Who are Daniele Divoli, Mirko Limoni and Valerio Simplici better known as?

16. Which Bleep mainman went on to create Biosphere?

Answers to page 250
JIMI HENDRIX 1: **1.** Bob Dylan **2.** Little Richard **3.** 'Hey Joe' **4.** His teeth **5.** 1967 **6.** 'Are You Experienced' **7.** 'Hey Joe' **8.** Sweden **9.** 'The Wind Cries Mary' **10.** Dusty Springfield **11.** Chas Chandler **12.** Mitch Mitchell **13.** 'Axis: Bold As Love' **14.** The cover showed Hendrix surrounded by naked women **15.** 'I need help bad, man' **16.** 'Voodoo Chile'

Sixties 7

Answers on page 251

1. Who was drummer with The Small Faces?

2. Who claimed he was better than Elvis and The Beatles after a hit with 'You Were On My Mind' but sank without trace within a year?

3. Who left The Tremeloes at the start of 1966?

4. Henry Harrison formed which quirky band modelled on a pre-war jazz sound?

5. Who was keyboard player with The Nice?

6. Mike Felix was the singer with which band that had a hit with 'Mockingbird Hill'?

7. Who replaced Paul Jones as lead singer with Manfred Mann?

8. What was the name of Jimmy James's backing group?

9. Who had a 1964 hit with 'As Tears Go By'?

10. 'Kites' flew high for which band in 1967?

11. Denny Payton played saxophone with which London chart toppers?

12. Whose hits included 'One Way Love' and 'Got To Get You Into My Life'?

13. In which year did Ken Dodd release 'Happiness'?

14. Which was the biggest-selling UK single of 1966?

15. Who was the only male solo artist to have a UK number one in 1964?

16. Which American singer had a top three hit with 'Things' in 1962?

Answers to page 251
NUMBER TWOS 4: **1.** Showaddywaddy **2.** Racey **3.** 'D.I.S.C.O.' **4.** Chris Montez **5.** Billy J. Kramer and The Dakotas **6.** 'Rocket Man' **7.** Freddie and The Dreamers **8.** 'Fanfare For The Common Man' **9.** Phil Collins **10.** Robbie Williams **11.** Adam Faith **12.** The Glitter Band **13.** Queen **14.** David Soul **15.** Rod Stewart **16.** Tracey Ullman ('They Don't Know')

Pot Luck 28

Answers on page 256

1. Who produced 'I'm The Urban Spaceman' for The Bonzo Dog Doo-Dah Band under the pseudonym Apollo C. Vermouth?

2. Who was charged with indecent exposure during a 1969 concert in Miami?

3. Which film star's eyes were the subject of a Kim Carnes hit of 1981?

4. Who wrote The Jackson Five's 'Doctor My Eyes'?

5. What taste did Acker Bilk have in 1963?

6. What were Pinkerton's Assorted Colours looking into in 1966?

7. What nationality were The Mixtures?

8. And what was the title of their only UK hit?

9. Who was 'Frozen' in 1998?

10. Which band's number one of 1979 was their first UK singles hit for 12 years?

11. With which successful Sixties band did Van Morrison play before going solo?

12. Who released the 1991 album 'Out Of Time'?

13. Who asked 'How Am I Supposed To Live Without You' in 1990?

14. 'Gertcha' was a hit for which Cockney duo?

15. Who recounted 'Mary's Prayer' in 1987?

16. Elkie Brooks and Robert Palmer sang together in which band?

Answers to page 256
ONE-HIT WONDERS 8: **1.** The Connells **2.** Buzz Clifford **3.** Oran 'Juice' Jones **4.** Janet Kay **5.** Father Christmas **6.** Hotshots **7.** 'Three Wheels On My Wagon' **8.** The Seashells **9.** Randy Vanwarmer **10.** 'You Keep Me Hanging On' **11.** 'Here I Go Again' **12.** Oliver **13.** Don Robertson **14.** 'More Than In Love' **15.** Stan Ridgway **16.** Rich Kids ('Rich Kids')

Fifties 5

Answers on page 257

1. Which was the biggest-selling single in the UK for 1958?

2. Who was 'Puttin' On The Style' in 1957?

3. Who had a hit with 'Be Bop A Lula' in 1956?

4. Who backed Joan Regan on her 1953 hit 'Ricochet'?

5. Which three artists had UK hits with 'Only Sixteen' in 1959?

6. Which 1958 number one for Tommy Edwards became a hit again for The Four Tops 12 years later?

7. Which British female singer's first chart entry was a version of Harry Belafonte's 'Banana Boat Song'?

8. Who sang the theme tune from the TV series *Rawhide*?

9. From which Hitchcock film was the Doris Day hit 'Que Sera Sera' taken?

10. How old was Frankie Lymon when he sang his 1956 number one 'Why Do Fools Fall In Love'?

11. Which two songs were placed equal at the top of the UK charts on 18 December 1959?

12. Who had hits in 1959 with 'Sea Of Love' and 'Bad Boy'?

13. For which two artists were 'Kisses Sweeter Than Wine' in 1957?

14. Dave King and Dean Martin both had hits with which song in 1956?

15. Who sang about the 'Gal With The Yaller Shoes'?

16. Which capital city gave Frankie Vaughan his first hit in 1954?

Answers to page 257
ERIC CLAPTON 1: 1. 1966 2. 'I Feel Free' 3. 'Disraeli Gears' 4. 1968
5. Blind Faith 6. Derek and The Dominos ('Layla') 7. 'I Shot The Sheriff'
8. 'Slowhand' 9. 'Wonderful Tonight' 10. *Water* 11. 'I Was Made To Love Her' 12. 'Unplugged' 13. 'Tears In Heaven' 14. 'Love Can Build A Bridge'
15. Elton John 16. *Phenomenon*

One-Hit Wonders 8

Answers on page 254

1. Which act's only incursion into the UK charts was with ''74-'75' in 1995?

2. Who had a hit with 'Baby Sittin' Boogie' in 1961 and hasn't been heard of since?

3. Who took 'The Rain' to number four in 1986?

4. In 1979 'Silly Games' provided which artist with her only chart success?

5. Who did Greg Lake believe in to give him his only hit as a solo artist?

6. A cover version of 'Snoopy Versus The Red Baron' was a one-off success for which British group in 1973?

7. Which song about a Cherokee Indian ambush gave The New Christy Minstrels their only UK hit?

8. Who had a 1972 hit with a cover version of Lesley Gore's 'Maybe I Know'?

9. 'Just When I Needed You Most' was a 1979 top ten hit for which American artist?

10. What was the title of Vanilla Fudge's 1967 version of a Supremes song, itself later covered by Kim Wilde?

11. Which song gave Twiggy her only hit?

12. Who had a hit with 'Good Morning Starshine' from the musical *Hair*?

13. Who was 'The Happy Whistler' in 1956?

14. Which song from *Crossroads* went to number 1 in 1981 sung by Kate Robbins?

15. Who had a 1986 top five hit with 'Camouflage'?

16. In 1978, which UK band's only hit was named after them?

Answers to page 254
POT LUCK 28: **1.** Paul McCartney **2.** Jim Morrison **3.** Bette Davis
4. Jackson Browne **5.** 'A Taste Of Honey' **6.** 'Mirror, Mirror'
7. Australian **8.** 'The Pushbike Song' **9.** Madonna **10.** Pink Floyd
11. Them **12.** R.E.M. **13.** Michael Bolton **14.** Chas and Dave **15.** Danny
Wilson **16.** Vinegar Joe

Eric Clapton 1

Answers on page 255

1. In which year were Cream formed?
2. What was the title of Cream's debut single?
3. From which Cream album was 'Sunshine Of Your Love' taken?
4. In which year did Cream break up?
5. Which band did Clapton form with Ginger Baker and Steve Winwood?
6. Which alias did Clapton adopt for a 1972 hit about George Harrison's wife, Patti Boyd?
7. Which song gave Clapton a US number one in 1974?
8. What was the title of Clapton's 1977 solo album?
9. Which 1978 ballad was the second song Clapton wrote about Patti Boyd?
10. In which Michael Caine film did Clapton make a cameo appearance?
11. Which Stevie Wonder song did Clapton select when he was a guest on *Desert Island Discs*?
12. Which Clapton collection won Album Of The Year at the 1993 Grammy Awards?
13. Which song was written about his dead son Conor who tragically fell to his death from the 53rd floor of a New York apartment block in 1991?
14. On which 1995 Comic Relief song did Clapton team up with Cher, Chrissie Hynde and Neneh Cherry?
15. With whom did Clapton duet on 'Runaway Train'?
16. From the soundtrack of which film was the single 'Change The World' taken?

Pot Luck 29

Answers on page 260

1. Who sang on Rockwell's 1984 hit 'Somebody's Watching Me'?

2. Whose song about the death of her biker boyfriend 'Terry' caused a mild furore in 1964?

3. Who sang about 'The Young New Mexican Puppeteer' in 1972?

4. What did the J stand for in Billy J. Kramer?

5. Which country star's first name is really Troyal?

6. What were the names of the twins in Bros?

7. Martin Lee and Lee Sheridan are the male half of which quartet?

8. Jay Aston was a member of which Eurovision-winning group?

9. Which band were named after a stalwart of the 18th-century Agricultural Revolution?

10. Who was the original drummer with 10cc?

11. What was the name of Kid Creole's backing band?

12. Who was 'Torn Between Two Lovers' in 1977?

13. Who invited you to ride on their 'Paper Plane' in 1973?

14. Mike Barson was the keyboard player with which Eighties band?

15. Who was the leader of ELO?

16. Who had a hit in 2001 with 'Little L'?

Answers to page 260
COUNTRY AND WESTERN 4: **1.** 'Lucille' **2.** Dolly Parton **3.** Tammy Wynette **4.** 'You're Still The One' **5.** Chris Gaines **6.** 'Blue' **7.** Elton John **8.** *Aida* **9.** Shania Twain ('That Don't Impress Me Much') **10.** Alvin and The Chipmunks **11.** Kenny Rogers **12.** Mac David **13.** Sheena Easton **14.** 'We've Got Tonight' **15.** Trisha Yearwood **16.** 'Stand By Your Man'

Christmas Hits 2

Answers on page 261

1. Who was simply having a 'Wonderful Christmastime' in 1979?

2. Which DJ had a 1975 hit with 'Renta Santa'?

3. And what was the title of his 1976 festive follow-up?

4. Who was 'Rockin' Around The Christmas Tree' in 1962?

5. For which duo was 1985 the 'Last Christmas'?

6. What colour Christmas did Elvis Presley experience in 1964?

7. Who sent out the invitation to 'Step Into Christmas' in 1973?

8. Who was 'Driving Home For Christmas' in 1988?

9. In 1975 who announced 'Santa Claus Is Coming To Town'?

10. What did Dora Bryan want for Christmas in 1963?

11. Who told the story of 'A Winter's Tale' in 1982?

12. What misfortune had befallen Santa Claus, according to Spitting Image in 1986?

13. Who saw 'Christmas Through Your Eyes' in 1992?

14. Which Christmas ditty was a 1959 hit for Max Bygraves?

15. Which Irish singer offered 'A Christmas Kiss' in 1999?

16. What advice did Chuck Berry offer to Santa's head reindeer in 1963?

Answers to page 261
NINETIES 7: **1.** Oasis **2.** Monaco **3.** Weezer **4.** Pink Floyd **5.** Piper
6. 'To The End' **7.** Sinead O'Connor **8.** 'Any Dream Will Do' **9.** Ash
('1977') **10.** Bryan Adams **11.** Depeche Mode **12.** Miles Hunt **13.** Suede
14. The Prodigy **15.** Kylie Minogue **16.** S Club 7

Country and Western 4

Answers on page 258

1. Which Kenny Rogers number one was originally recorded by Johnny Darrell?

2. Who had a 1976 hit with 'Jolene'?

3. Which country star sang lead vocals on the 1991 KLF hit 'Justified And Ancient'?

4. What was Shania Twain's first UK top ten hit?

5. As which fictional character from the film *The Lamb* did Garth Brooks record 'Lost In You' in 1999?

6. Which song, written for Patsy Cline who died before she could record it, became a hit for LeAnn Rimes in 1998?

7. With whom did LeAnn Rimes duet on the 1999 hit 'Written In The Stars'?

8. And from which Walt Disney film was the song taken?

9. Who was hard to impress in 1999?

10. Which cartoon critters joined forces with Billy Ray Cyrus for a Christmas version of 'Achy Breaky Heart'?

11. 'Something's Burning' was a 1970 hit in the UK for which country artist?

12. Who recorded the song originally?

13. Who duetted with Kenny Rogers on a 1983 cover of a Bob Seger song?

14. What was the title of the song?

15. Whose 1998 album was called 'Where Your Road Leads'?

16. In 1975, which country song became a number one in the UK seven years after it had first entered the US charts?

Answers to page 258
POT LUCK 29: **1.** Michael Jackson **2.** Twinkle **3.** Tom Jones **4.** Nothing **5.** Garth Brooks **6.** Matt and Luke Goss **7.** Brotherhood Of Man **8.** Bucks Fizz **9.** Jethro Tull **10.** Kevin Godley **11.** The Coconuts **12.** Mary McGregor **13.** Status Quo **14.** Madness **15.** Jeff Lynne **16.** Jamiroquai

Nineties 7

Answers on page 259

1. Who hit number one in 1998 with 'All Around The World'?

2. Which New Order splinter band had a 1997 hit with 'What Do You Want From Me'?

3. Rivers Cuomo was the singer with which goofy US band?

4. Whose 1995 album was titled 'Pulse'?

5. What was Billie's surname before she married Chris Evans?

6. Laetitia from Stereolab provided backing vocals on which Blur single from 'Parklife'?

7. Who had a number one album 'I Do Not Want What I Haven't Got'?

8. What was Jason Donovan's last UK number one?

9. The title of which band's debut album reflected the year in which two-thirds of them were born?

10. Who insisted that he would be '18 Til I Die'?

11. Who had hits in the Nineties with 'In Your Room' and 'Barrel Of A Gun'?

12. Who was the lead singer with The Wonder Stuff?

13. Which band released the 1994 album 'Dog Man Star'?

14. Keith Flint is the leader of which band?

15. Who pleaded 'Confide In Me' in 1994?

16. Jo O'Meara is a member of which band?

Answers to page 259
CHRISTMAS HITS 2: **1.** Paul McCartney **2.** Chris Hill **3.** 'Bionic Santa'
4. Brenda Lee **5.** Wham! **6.** Blue **7.** Elton John **8.** Chris Rea **9.** The
Jackson Five **10.** A Beatle **11.** David Essex **12.** He was on the dole
13. Gloria Estefan **14.** 'Jingle Bell Rock' **15.** Daniel O'Donnell **16.** 'Run
Rudolph Run'

John Lennon I

Answers on page 264

1. Who raised young Lennon after his parents' separation?

2. In which Richard Lester film did Lennon play Private Gripweed?

3. Why was Lennon's album 'Unfinished Music No 1 – Two Virgins' distributed in brown paper bags?

4. To what did Lennon change his middle name in 1969?

5. In which city did John and Yoko spend eight days in a bed to promote world peace?

6. On which Lennon composition did Petula Clark appear?

7. What did Lennon return to Buckingham Palace in 1969?

8. Who produced 'Instant Karma'?

9. In which year was the album 'Imagine' released?

10. The 'Imagine' track 'How Do You Sleep' was a thinly veiled attack on whom?

11. What was the name of Lennon's new backing band for 1972?

12. What did a drunken Lennon have taped to his head when he hurled insults at the Smothers Brothers during their Los Angeles show?

13. Which band recorded a tribute version of Lennon's 'Jealous Guy'?

14. On 9 October 1990 which track was played simultaneously in 130 countries to mark what would have been Lennon's 50th birthday?

15. Who pronounced himself 'the number one John Lennon fan' in 1994?

16. With which number did Lennon have a strange fixation?

Answers to page 264
POT LUCK 30: **1.** Half Man Half Biscuit **2.** French **3.** Adam Faith **4.** Earth, Wind and Fire **5.** Beaky **6.** Rod Stewart **7.** Manfred Mann and Sweet **8.** 'Bernadette' **9.** Samantha **10.** Blackberry ('Blackberry Way') **11.** 'If I Said You Have A Beautiful Body Would You Hold It Against Me' **12.** Syd Barrett (Pink Floyd) **13.** The title isn't featured in the song's lyrics **14.** 'Love Is Life' **15.** The News **16.** It Bites

Albums 10

Answers on page 265

Which artists released the following albums?

1. 'Tango In The Night' (1987)

2. 'The Rhythm Of The Saints' (1990)

3. 'Ooh-La-La' (1973)

4. 'It's Better To Travel' (1987)

5. 'Dig Your Own Hole' (1997)

6. 'Medusa' (1995)

7. 'Black Tie White Noise' (1993)

8. 'Kings Of The Wild Frontier' (1981)

9. 'On The Level' (1975)

10. 'Highway 61 Revisited' (1965)

11. 'Oceans Of Fantasy' (1979)

12. 'Hush' (1999)

13. 'Move To This' (1991)

14. 'The Joshua Tree' (1987)

15. 'No Sleep Till Hammersmith' (1981)

16. 'Journey To The Centre Of The Earth' (1974)

Answers to page 265
PUNK 4: **1.** The Undertones **2.** Stuart Adamson **3.** The Jam **4.** Bob Geldof **5.** 'Denis' (it was a cover of 'Denise' by Randy & The Rainbows) **6.** '(I'm Not Your) Stepping Stone' **7.** The Undertones **8.** Buckingham Palace **9.** 'Peaches' **10.** The Stranglers **11.** The Clash **12.** The Motors **13.** Secret Affair **14.** The Slits **15.** Siouxsie and The Banshees **16.** The Banshees (*Cry of the Banshee*)

Pot Luck 30

Answers on page 262

1. Whose song titles have included '99% Of Gargoyles Look Like Bob Todd' and 'I Love You Because (You Like Jim Reeves)'

2. What nationality is Johnny Hallyday?

3. Which pop star played Budgie on TV?

4. Maurice White was the leader of which nine-piece seventies disco group?

5. Which member of Dave Dee, Dozy, Beaky, Mick and Tich was born John Dymond?

6. Which rock star once worked as a gravedigger at Highgate Cemetery in London?

7. Which two groups had hits with different songs titled 'Fox On The Run'?

8. Which girl did The Four Tops take into the UK charts in 1967 and 1972?

9. What did Sam become after Cliff Richard had said goodbye to her in 1970?

10. Which fruit was in the title of a Move hit?

11. Which Bellamy Brothers hit had 51 letters in its title?

12. Which reclusive rock star used to use margarine as hair gel?

13. What do 'Bohemian Rhapsody', 'Space Oddity' and 'Tubthumping' have in common?

14. What was Hot Chocolate's first UK hit?

15. What was the name of Huey Lewis's band?

16. Who were 'Calling All The Heroes' in 1986?

Answers to page 262
JOHN LENNON 1: **1.** His Aunt Mimi **2.** *How I Won The War* **3.** The cover was a naked full-frontal of John and Yoko **4.** Ono **5.** Montreal **6.** 'Give Peace A Chance' **7.** His MBE **8.** Phil Spector **9.** 1971 **10.** Paul McCartney **11.** Elephant's Memory **12.** A tampon **13.** Roxy Music **14.** 'Imagine' **15.** Paul McCartney **16.** 9

Punk 4

Answers on page 263

1. Which band sang about 'Teenage Kicks'?

2. Who left The Skids in order to form Big Country?

3. Which band reached number three with 'The Eton Rifles'?

4. Which member of The Boomtown Rats was previously a journalist on the *NME*?

5. Which song had a sex change when becoming a 1978 hit for Blondie?

6. Which Paul Revere and The Raiders song was covered by The Sex Pistols in 1980?

7. Who had a Perfect Cousin in 1980?

8. Outside which tourist attraction did The Sex Pistols sign for A&M Records in 1977?

9. Which Stranglers A-side of 1977 was banned by the BBC for its offensive lyrics?

10. Who sang 'Nice 'N' Sleazy' does it in 1978?

11. Whose top three album was titled 'Give 'Em Enough Rope'?

12. Bram Tchaikovsky and Ricky Slaughter were members of which band?

13. Who said that 1979 was the 'Time For Action'?

14. Which punk band originally had a drummer called Palmolive?

15. Which band had a hit with 'Hong Kong Garden'?

16. Which band took their name from a 1970 Vincent Price movie?

Answers to page 263
ALBUMS 10: **1.** Fleetwood Mac **2.** Paul Simon **3.** The Faces **4.** Swing Out Sister **5.** The Chemical Brothers **6.** Annie Lennox **7.** David Bowie **8.** Adam and The Ants **9.** Status Quo **10.** Bob Dylan **11.** Boney M **12.** Texas **13.** Cathy Dennis **14.** U2 **15.** Motorhead **16.** Rick Wakeman

Lyrics 10

Answers on page 268

From which songs are the following lyrics taken?

1. 'Why do birds suddenly appear every time you are near'

2. 'To insure yourself you've got to provide communication constantly'

3. 'But now there's nowhere to hide since you pushed my love aside'

4. 'I gave you my heart and my soul to keep'

5. 'Touch me now, I close my eyes and dream away'

6. 'But is her sweet expression worth more than my love and affection'

7. 'You can't start a fire without a spark'

8. 'I play my part and you play your game'

9. 'I wish I could fly right up to the sky but I can't'

10. 'When you're weary, feeling small, when tears are in your eyes I will dry them all'

11. 'When I was down, I was your clown'

12. 'People say I'm crazy and that I'm blind, risking it all in a glance'

13. 'And once again I'm thinking about taking the easy way out'

14. 'I need a man who'll take a chance on a love that burns hot enough to last'

15. 'Recreation is our destination so don't wait up for us tonight'

16. 'It's not how it used to be, you've taken my life away, ruining everything'

Answers to page 268
POT LUCK 31: **1.** Neil Tennant (The Pet Shop Boys) **2.** Little Anthony
3. Chuck Berry **4.** The Twist **5.** The Three Degrees **6.** Dexy's Midnight
Runners ('Jackie Wilson Said') **7.** He didn't exist **8.** Norman **9.** Candy
10. Bobby Goldsboro ('Honey') **11.** Wyclef Jean **12.** Peter Bardens
13. Jean Jacques **14.** José Feliciano **15.** Kate Bush **16.** 'Elstree'

Pink Floyd 1

Answers on page 269

1. How did Pink Floyd get their name?

2. Which radio station banned 'Arnold Layne' because of its transvestite subject matter?

3. Which *Juke Box Jury* panellist and Radio 1 DJ described Pink Floyd as a 'con'?

4. What was the title of Pink Floyd's first album?

5. Why was the Floyd's 1967 US tour cancelled?

6. Who replaced Syd Barrett in 1968?

7. Which album became a UK number one in 1970?

8. 'Obscured By Clouds' was the soundtrack to which film?

9. Who is Pink Floyd's drummer?

10. Which album never became a UK number one despite spending over 350 weeks in the charts?

11. Who guested to sing 'Shine On You Crazy Diamond' on the album 'Wish You Were Here'?

12. Which violinist made an uncredited contribution to 'Wish You Were Here'?

13. In which year was 'The Wall' released?

14. Who left the band in 1980?

15. Who starred in the film version of 'The Wall'?

16. Which Pink Floyd album was named after an item of parliamentary procedure?

Answers to page 269
SOLO ARTISTS 6: **1.** Geri Halliwell **2.** Clodagh Rodgers **3.** Leo Sayer **4.** Boz Scaggs **5.** Billy Preston **6.** Betty Boo **7.** Sandie Shaw **8.** 'When You Say Nothing At All' **9.** Sean Maguire **10.** Michelle Gayle **11.** Jona Lewie **12.** Red **13.** Ringo Starr **14.** 'Jarrow Song' **15.** Curtis Mayfield **16.** *Opportunity Knocks*

Pot Luck 31

Answers on page 266

1. Which half of a pop duo used to be British editor of *Marvel Comics*?
2. Who fronted The Imperials?
3. Who invented the Duck Walk?
4. Which Sixties dance craze was pioneered by Chubby Checker?
5. Who faced a 'Year Of Decision' in 1974?
6. Which band, appearing on *Top of the Pops*, were surprised to be playing in front of a blow-up picture of darts player Jocky Wilson instead of one of singer Jackie Wilson?
7. What was the twist about the Bonzo Dog Doo-Dah Band's Urban Spaceman?
8. What was the name of Marmalade's cousin?
9. According to Brian Hyland what was Ginny as sweet as?
10. Which grieving husband encouraged his friends to 'See the tree, how big it's grown'?
11. Who sampled The Bee Gees' 'Stayin' Alive' in his 1997 hit 'We Trying To Stay Alive'?
12. Which keyboard player fronted Camel?
13. What does the J.J. in J.J. Cale stand for?
14. Which Latin guitarist, who had a 1968 hit with 'Light My Fire', was born blind?
15. Who kept 'Running Up That Hill' in 1985?
16. About which film studios did Buggles sing?

Answers to page 266
LYRICS 10: 1. 'Close To You' (The Carpenters) 2. 'Tell Her About It' (Billy Joel) 3. 'Hopelessly Devoted To You' (Olivia Newton-John) 4. 'In Too Deep' (Belinda Carlisle) 5. 'It Must Have Been Love' (Roxette) 6. 'Stop In The Name Of Love' (The Supremes) 7. 'Dancing In The Dark' (Bruce Springsteen) 8. 'You Give Love A Bad Name' (Bon Jovi) 9. 'Orville's Song' (Keith Harris and Orville) 10. 'Bridge Over Troubled Water' (Simon and Garfunkel) 11. 'Don't Go Breaking My Heart' (Elton John and Kiki Dee) 12. 'As Long As You Love Me' (Backstreet Boys) 13. 'If I Let You Go' (Westlife) 14. 'I Wanna Dance With Somebody (Who Loves Me)' (Whitney Houston) 15. 'Respectable' (Mel and Kim) 16. 'What Do You Want From Me?' (Monaco)

Solo Artists 6

Answers on page 267

1. Who reached number one in 1999 with 'Lift Me Up'?

2. Which Irish singer had a 1969 hit with 'Goodnight Midnight'?

3. Which Seventies singer appeared in a clown's costume to promote his first hit?

4. Which Boz was 'Lowdown' in 1976?

5. In 1969 who maintained 'That's The Way God Planned It'?

6. Who appeared on *Top of the Pops* as a singer in 1990 a couple of years after she had been turned down by the BBC for a sound engineer's course?

7. Which Sixties singer married fashion designer Jeff Banks?

8. What was Ronan Keating's first solo hit?

9. Which ex-*EastEnder* recorded a cover version of Hamilton, Joe Frank and Reynolds's 1971 hit 'Don't Pull Your Love'?

10. Which ex-*EastEnder* had a top five hit with 'Sweetness' in 1994?

11. Who did you always find in the kitchen at parties?

12. What colour were roses for Bobby Vinton in 1962?

13. Who went solo and had hits with 'Back Off Boogaloo' and 'Photograph'?

14. Which Alan Price hit recalled a workers' march of 1926?

15. Who said 'Move On Up' in 1971?

16. For which TV talent show did Engelbert Humperdinck fail an audition?

Answers to page 267
PINK FLOYD 1: 1. Syd Barrett named the band after bluesmen Pink Anderson and Floyd Council 2. Radio London 3. Pete Murray 4. 'The Piper At The Gates Of Dawn' 5. Syd Barrett refused to mime properly on a US TV show 6. Dave Gilmour 7. 'Atom Heart Mother' 8. *La Vallée* 9. Nick Mason 10. 'The Dark Side Of The Moon' 11. Roy Harper 12. Stephane Grappelli 13. 1979 14. Rick Wright 15. Bob Geldof 16. 'The Division Bell'

Cover Versions 9

Answers on page 272

1. Which Beatles number one was covered by Ray Charles two years later?

2. Which one-time 'High Priestess of Punk' recorded a version of Martha and The Muffins' 'Echo Beach' in 1987?

3. Which song was a hit for both The Big Bopper in 1958 and Jerry Lee Lewis in 1972?

4. Which song links Elvis Presley, Andy Williams, The Stylistics and UB40?

5. Who first had a hit with Dave Edmunds's 'Born To Be With You'?

6. Which hit for Elvis in 1956 and for The Marcels in 1961 was revived by Showaddywaddy in 1980?

7. Which XTC song did The Crash Test Dummies cover in 1995 for the film *Dumb and Dumber*?

8. Who recorded the original hit version of Simply Red's 'Angel'?

9. Which song by Prince and the Revolution was covered by Art Of Noise featuring Tom Jones?

10. Which two groups charted with The Beatles' 'Ob-La-Di Ob-La-Da' in 1968?

11. Which Bee Gees song was revived by Adam Garcia in 1998?

12. Who first charted in the UK with 'Now That We've Found Love', a 1991 hit for Heavy D and The Boyz?

13. Which city song links Gary 'US' Bonds, Harley Quinne and Gillan?

14. Which Supremes hit did Bananarama cover in 1988?

15. Who covered Tommy James's 'Mony Mony' in 1987?

16. Who had a hit with 'Make The World Go Away' nine years before Donny and Marie Osmond?

Answers to page 272
SEVENTIES 8: **1.** Derek Longmuir **2.** Gilbert O'Sullivan **3.** Mud **4.** Paper Lace **5.** 'Billy Don't Be A Hero' **6.** Les Gray of Mud **7.** Bjorn Ulvaeus **8.** Donny Osmond **9.** The Four Seasons **10.** Midge Ure **11.** J. J. Barrie ('No Charge') **12.** Madeline Bell and Roger Cook **13.** Barry White **14.** Alice Cooper ('School's Out') **15.** Roxy Music **16.** 'Amoureuse'

Merseybeat 3

Answers on page 273

1. How far did 'A Little Loving' go for The Fourmost in 1964?

2. Who wrote Gerry and The Pacemakers' first two number ones?

3. Who was lead singer with The Mojos?

4. Which former member of The Merseybeats hit the charts again in 1976 with Liverpool Express?

5. Who replaced Tony Jackson as bass guitarist with The Searchers?

6. What was The Searchers' third UK number one?

7. Which band had a 1964 hit with 'You're No Good'?

8. Which artist destined for stardom co-wrote The Searchers' 'Needles And Pins'?

9. Who wrote the first three hits for Billy J. Kramer and The Dakotas?

10. Which Bacharach and David song did Billy J. Kramer cover in 1965?

11. Which infamous event took place on the same day in August 1963 that The Searchers had their first UK number one?

12. Who were the first act, apart from The Beatles, to top the charts with a Lennon and McCartney composition?

13. And what was the title of the song?

14. Who were the first Liverpool group to reach number one?

15. Which Merseybeat singer had previously worked for British Railways?

16. Which madcap comedian had his own Merseybeat group called The Midnighters?

Answers to page 273
THE WHO 1: **1.** The Ivy League **2.** *Ready, Steady, Go!* **3.** 'My Generation'
4. Miles **5.** 'You Better You Bet' **6.** 13 (his grandmother had complained about the noise) **7.** 'The Carnival Is Over' by The Seekers **8.** 1966
9. 'Pictures Of Lily' (the picture was of Lily Bayliss) **10.** Herman's
Hermits **11.** Tony Blackburn **12.** Pete Townshend **13.** Keith Moon
14. Keith Moon **15.** *Lisztomania* **16.** Kenny Jones

Seventies 8

Answers on page 270

1. Which member of The Bay City Rollers later worked as a nurse?

2. Whose 1971 album was titled 'Himself'?

3. 'The Cat Crept In' for which band in 1974?

4. Which band dressed as American Civil War soldiers to promote their 1974 number one?

5. And what was the title of the song?

6. Which singer was dubbed 'Leslie Presley' for his vocal impersonations of the 'king'?

7. Which member of Abba had previously been a member of The Hootenanny Singers?

8. Who was Britain's favourite Mormon in 1973?

9. Which New Jersey band, who topped the charts in 1976, named themselves after the cocktail lounge in a local bowling alley?

10. Which chart topper with Slik nearly joined The Sex Pistols but became one of The Rich Kids instead?

11. Which former comedian and manager of Blue Mink had a spoken number one in 1976?

12. Who were the two vocalists with Blue Mink?

13. Who had a bigger UK hit with 'Just The Way You Are' than its composer Billy Joel?

14. Which minister's son outraged parents with his 1972 number one?

15. Who released the 1979 album 'Manifesto'?

16. Veronique Sanson recorded the original version of which Kiki Dee hit?

Answers to page 270
COVER VERSIONS 9: 1. 'Eleanor Rigby' 2. Toyah 3. 'Chantilly Lace'
4. 'Can't Help Falling In Love' 5. The Chordettes 6. 'Blue Moon' 7. 'The Ballad Of Peter Pumpkinhead' 8. Aretha Franklin 9. 'Kiss' 10. Marmalade and The Bedrocks 11. 'Night Fever' 12. Third World 13. 'New Orleans'
14. 'Nathan Jones' 15. Billy Idol 16. Eddy Arnold

The Who 1

Answers on page 271

1. Which Sixties falsetto group did backing vocals on 'I Can't Explain'?

2. The Who's second hit, 'Anyway Anyhow Anywhere', was chosen as the new theme to which TV show?

3. Which was The Who's first top three hit?

4. For how far could The Who see in 1967?

5. What was The Who's last UK top ten single?

6. At what age did Pete Townshend smash his first guitar, and why?

7. Which song prevented 'My Generation' from reaching number one in the UK?

8. In which year was 'I'm A Boy' released?

9. Which Who single was inspired by a photo of an old vaudeville star hanging on a wall in Pete Townshend's girlfriend's house?

10. Which British band did The Who support on their first US tour?

11. Which Radio 1 DJ described the rock opera *Tommy* as 'sick'?

12. Which member of The Who produced Thunderclap Newman's 'Something In The Air'?

13. Which non-driving member of The Who accidentally ran over and killed his chauffeur while trying to escape from a gang of skinheads?

14. Which of The Who played J.D. Clover in the film *That'll Be The Day*?

15. In which 1975 Ken Russell film did Roger Daltrey star?

16. Who replaced Keith Moon as drummer in 1979?

Answers to page 271
MERSEYBEAT 3: 1. A long long way 2. Mitch Murray 3. Stu James 4. Billy Kinsley 5. Frank Allen 6. 'Don't Throw Your Love Away' 7. The Swinging Blue Jeans 8. Sonny Bono 9. Lennon and McCartney 10. 'Trains And Boats And Planes' 11. The Great Train Robbery 12. Billy J. Kramer and The Dakotas 13. 'Bad To Me' 14. Gerry and The Pacemakers 15. Billy J. Kramer 16. Freddie Starr

Pot Luck 32

Answers on page 276

1. Rob Pilatus and Fabrice Morvan were otherwise known as which disgraced duo?

2. Which Monkee used to be a jockey?

3. Rick Witter was the singer with which Nineties band?

4. Who was Dirk McQuickly?

5. Who was the lead singer with Free?

6. Which blue comedian joined Smokie for a 1995 version of 'Living Next Door To Alice'?

7. Who was 'Addicted To Love' in 1986?

8. Which former Australian soap star had a 1997 hit with 'Torn'?

9. Which Status Quo single was originally a country track recorded by Hank Thompson?

10. Who played bongos on The Shadows' 'Apache'?

11. What was the title of The Moody Blues' first UK number one album?

12. Which singing miners had a top twenty hit in 1973 with 'Vaya Con Dios (May God Be With You)'?

13. Ray Manzarek was keyboard player with which Sixties band?

14. What was Dr Hook's full name in the band's early years?

15. Which 1977 Barbara Dickson hit was taken from the musical *Evita*?

16. What nationality are The Cuban Boys?

Answers to page 276
CHART TOPPERS 12: 1. The Troggs 2. Floyd Cramer 3. Maya 4. The Goombay Dance Band 5. 'Town Called Malice' and 'Beat Surrender' 6. 'Karma Chameleon' 7. Johnny Kidd and The Pirates 8. 'Mouldy Old Dough' 9. 'Bad Moon Rising' 10. 'Devil Gate Drive' 11. Babylon Zoo 12. 'Never Gonna Give You Up' and 'China In Your Hand' 13. Livin' Joy 14. 'Hey Girl Don't Bother Me' 15. The Walker Brothers 16. Frank Ifield

Jazz 3

Answers on page 277

1. In which year did Dizzy Gillespie die?

2. What instrument is associated with James Moody?

3. Which jazz guitarist recorded the 1987 album 'Spontaneous Combustion'?

4. Which drummer's Big Band featured the vocals of Anita O'Day and the trumpet solos of Roy Eldridge during the early Forties?

5. Which jazzman's orchestra had a 1961 hit with 'African Waltz'?

6. Which 1976 track gave Acker Bilk his first UK hit for 13 years?

7. Which girl was the subject of a 1961 hit for Kenny Ball?

8. From which Bing Crosby/Frank Sinatra film was the tune taken?

9. With which instrument was Clyde Hart associated?

10. Which Big Band leader's first recording with Capitol in 1943 was 'Artistry In Rhythm'?

11. Which jazz singer teamed up with James Galway for the 1980 hit 'Sometimes When We Touch'?

12. Which Cleo Laine hit of 1961 was originally recorded by Patti Page?

13. Which British jazz band released the 1960 album 'Elite Syncopations'?

14. Which band leader had a 1962 hit with 'The Green Leaves Of Summer'?

15. From which John Wayne film was it taken?

16. What was Louis Armstrong's nickname?

Answers to page 277
BAY CITY ROLLERS 1: 1. Stuart Wood 2. 1973 3. 'Remember'
4. Tartan scarves 5. 1975 6. Six 7. 'Once Upon A Star' 8. Alan Longmuir
9. Ian Mitchell 10. Les McKeown 11. 'It's A Game' 12. 'Give A Little
Love' 13. 'You Made Me Believe In Magic' 14. Les McKeown
15. Jonathan King 16. Bill Martin and Phil Coulter

Chart Toppers 12

Answers on page 274

1. 'With A Girl Like You' was a 1966 number one for which group?

2. Who was 'On The Rebound' in 1961?

3. Who featured on Tamperer's 1998 number one 'Feel It'?

4. Who topped the charts in 1982 with 'Seven Tears'?

5. Which two tracks were UK number ones for The Jam in 1982?

6. What was the best-selling UK single of 1983?

7. Who were 'Shakin' All Over' in 1960?

8. Which 1972 number one was recorded in the front room of a Coventry semi?

9. Which 1969 number one was used 12 years later in the film *An American Werewolf in London*?

10. Which song gave Suzi Quatro a 1974 UK chart topper?

11. Who had a 1996 number one with 'Spaceman'?

12. Which two singles each spent five weeks at number one in 1987?

13. Who had a 1995 chart topper with 'Dreamer'?

14. What was the title of The Tams' number one from 1971?

15. 'Make It Easy On Yourself' was a 1965 hit for which American group?

16. Who had the 'Lovesick Blues' in 1962?

Answers to page 274
POT LUCK 32: **1.** Milli Vanilli **2.** Davy Jones **3.** Shed Seven **4.** The Rutles version of Paul McCartney **5.** Paul Rodgers **6.** Roy 'Chubby' Brown **7.** Robert Palmer **8.** Natalie Imbruglia **9.** 'Wild Side Of Life' **10.** Cliff Richard **11.** 'On The Threshold Of A Dream' **12.** Millican and Nesbitt **13.** The Doors **14.** Dr Hook and The Medicine Show **15.** 'Another Suitcase In Another Hall' **16.** British

Bay City Rollers 1

Answers on page 275

1. What was Woody's full name?

2. When did Les McKeown join the Rollers?

3. What was the first single to be released with McKeown as lead singer?

4. What did the Rollers' fans wrap around their wrists?

5. In which year did 'Bye Bye Baby' get to number one?

6. How many weeks did it stay at the top of the UK charts?

7. What was the title of the Rollers' second UK number one album?

8. Who quit the band in 1976, thinking he was too old?

9. Who replaced him?

10. In 1976, which band member was acquitted of shooting an air rifle at a girl fan?

11. Which Rollers hit was recorded originally by String Driven Thing?

12. What was the Rollers' second number one of 1975?

13. Which was the Rollers' last UK hit?

14. Who released the 1979 solo album 'All Washed Up'?

15. Who produced and sang on the Rollers' first single 'Keep On Dancing'?

16. Which pair wrote most of the Rollers' hits?

Answers to page 275
JAZZ 3: **1.** 1993 **2.** Saxophone **3.** Barney Kessel **4.** Gene Krupa
5. Johnny Dankworth **6.** 'Aria' **7.** 'Samantha' **8.** *High Society* **9.** Piano
10. Stan Kenton **11.** Cleo Laine **12.** 'You'll Answer To Me' **13.** Chris
Barber's Jazz Band **14.** Kenny Ball **15.** *The Alamo* **16.** 'Satchmo'

R & B 4

Answers on page 280

1. Under what name did Barry White perform in the early Sixties?

2. Which guitarist was the mainstay of Ten Years After?

3. Simon Kirke was drummer with which major R & B band?

4. Who recorded the posthumous 1971 album 'Pearl'?

5. Which member of Free was the son of a well-known actor?

6. Which replacement as drummer for Ringo Starr in Rory Storm and The Hurricanes went on to form his own R & B band?

7. Which R & B artist duetted with Celine Dion on the 1998 hit 'I'm Your Angel'?

8. Which Eric Clapton song was taken to number three in the charts by Damage in 1997?

9. Which band's debut album was titled 'Tons Of Sobs'?

10. Who featured on the Another Level hit 'Summertime'?

11. Who had the 'Love Of A Lifetime' in 1999?

12. Whose 1998 album was titled 'Anutha Zone'?

13. What was Barry White's only UK number one?

14. Which Barry White single reached number two in the UK charts in 1976?

15. Who featured on the Destiny's Child hit 'No No No'?

16. What was the title of the second album by Destiny's Child?

Answers to page 280
POT LUCK 33: **1.** Carl Douglas **2.** Ray Sawyer **3.** Drums **4.** Scotland
5. The Doobie Brothers **6.** Ruby Flipper **7.** Don **8.** Jesus Jones
9. Jefferson Airplane **10.** The Housemartins **11.** Jerome **12.** Jon Lord and
Nick Simper **13.** The Turtles **14.** Tim and Neil Finn **15.** A Mississippi
steamboat **16.** Bob Geldof

Number Twos 5

Answers on page 281

Which artists reached number two in the UK charts with the following singles?

1. 'Annie I'm Not Your Daddy' (1982)

2. 'Church Of The Poison Mind' (1983)

3. 'Then He Kissed Me' (1963)

4. 'Opposites Attract' (1990)

5. 'Night Of Fear' (1967)

6. 'The Bitterest Pill (I Ever Had To Swallow)'

7. 'A Man Without Love' (1968)

8. 'Someone Else's Baby' (1960)

9. 'Why Can't I Wake Up With You?' (1993)

10. 'Can't Get By Without You' (1976)

11. 'Morningtown Ride' (1966)

12. '(Dancing) On A Saturday Night' (1973)

13. 'Dreaming' (1979)

14. 'Private Investigations' (1982)

15. 'Save A Prayer' (1982)

16. 'Cindy Incidentally' (1973)

Answers to page 281
NAME CHANGES 11: **1.** Gene Vincent **2.** Rory Storm **3.** Ten Years After **4.** Engelbert Humperdinck **5.** James **6.** Warsaw **7.** Tom Jones **8.** Betty Boo **9.** Peter Smith **10.** Lieutenant Pigeon **11.** Jack Bruce **12.** J.J. Barrie **13.** Karl Denver **14.** The Grateful Dead **15.** The Dreamers **16.** The Four Tops

Pot Luck 33

Answers on page 278

1. Who was 'Kung Fu Fighting' in 1974?

2. Which member of Dr Hook wore an eye patch?

3. What instrument does Bill Bruford play?

4. In which country was Talking Heads' David Byrne born?

5. Which Seventies band took their name from the slang for a marijuana cigarette?

6. Who replaced Pan's People on *Top of the Pops*?

7. Who was the older of The Everly Brothers?

8. Which band's debut album was called 'Liquidizer'?

9. From which band did Jefferson Starship evolve?

10. Which Eighties chart band had a bass player named Stan Cullimore?

11. What did the J. in the J. Geils Band stand for?

12. Which two members of Deep Purple were previously in The Flowerpot Men?

13. Flo and Eddie were an off-shoot from which Sixties group?

14. Which brothers were members of Split Enz and Crowded House?

15. What was 'Proud Mary' in the 1969 hit for Creedence Clearwater Revival?

16. Which former punk has the middle names Frederick Zenon?

Answers to page 278
R & B 4: 1. Barry Lee 2. Alvin Lee 3. Free 4. Janis Joplin 5. Paul Kossoff (son of David) 6. Keef Hartley 7. R. Kelly 8. 'Wonderful Tonight' 9. Free 10. TQ 11. Honeyz 12. Dr John 13. 'You're The First, The Last, My Everything' 14. 'You See The Trouble With Me' 15. Wyclef Jean 16. 'The Writing's On The Wall'

Name Changes 11

Answers on page 279

1. Which rock 'n' roller was born Eugene Craddock?

2. Which Merseybeat band leader sought something more tempestuous than Alan Caldwell?

3. Which British R & B band changed their name from The Jaybirds?

4. Who is Gerry Dorsey better known as?

5. What is Midge Ure's real Christian name?

6. As what were Joy Division previously known?

7. Which international star was born Thomas Woodward?

8. Who changed her name from Alison Clarkson?

9. What was Crispian St Peters's less impressive real name?

10. Which band who had a novelty hit in the Seventies started out as Stavely Makepiece?

11. Which member of a key R & B threesome of the late Sixties was born John Asher Simon Bruce?

12. What name did Barrie Authors use to reach the top of the charts in 1976?

13. Which Sixties frontman of a trio Americanised his name from Angus McKenzie?

14. Which US acid rock band of the Sixties were formerly known as The Warlocks?

15. Which Sixties backing band used to be called The Kingfishers?

16. To what did The Four Aims change their name?

Answers to page 279
NUMBER TWOS 5: 1. Kid Creole and The Coconuts 2. Culture Club 3. The Crystals 4. Paula Abdul 5. The Move 6. The Jam 7. Engelbert Humperdinck 8. Adam Faith 9. Take That 10. The Real Thing 11. The Seekers 12. Barry Blue 13. Blondie 14. Dire Straits 15. Duran Duran 16. The Faces

Eighties 8

Answers on page 284

1. Which aunt of Whitney Houston had a US number with a song which become a UK number one in 1986 for The Communards?

2. Who had a 1986 number one with 'I Wanna Wake Up With You'?

3. Which five acts, all featuring female vocalists, filled the top five places in the UK singles chart in November 1986?

4. Who released the 1980 album 'Tears And Laughter'?

5. Who had a 1980 hit with 'I Am The Beat'?

6. In 1986, who became the second Swedish act to top the UK singles charts?

7. A spin-off group from which group recorded the original version of The Housemartins' 'Caravan Of Love'?

8. Which former Rubette was a member of The Firm who had a 1987 number one with 'Star Trekkin''?

9. Who was the singer with Berlin?

10. Who featured on Soul II Soul's 1989 hit 'Back To Life (However Do You Want Me)'?

11. Who was the singer with Transvision Vamp?

12. Which band, fronted by a present-day actress, had top ten hits with 'Happy Birthday' and 'I Could Be Happy'?

13. Who was the third member of Bros?

14. Which 1987 chart topper was the first since 'Je T'Aime…Moi Non Plus' to be sung entirely in a foreign language?

15. And in what language was it sung?

16. Which T'Pau single was originally titled 'Intimate Strangers'?

Answers to page 284
SINGER/SONGWRITERS 4: **1.** Alanis Morissette **2.** 'We Do What We Can' **3.** 'Songs Of Leonard Cohen' **4.** Brother Love **5.** Neil Sedaka **6.** Billy Joel **7.** 'True Love' **8.** 23 **9.** 'Rocky Mountain High' **10.** 'W-O-L-D' **11.** 'Cat's In The Cradle' **12.** Bobby Vee **13.** 'Run, Baby, Run' **14.** John Denver **15.** Don McLean **16.** 'Son Of My Father' by Chicory Tip

Bon Jovi 1

Answers on page 285

1. What did Jon Bon Jovi's mother used to be?

2. And what was his father?

3. Which 1986 single reached number 14 in the UK singles chart?

4. How many weeks did the album 'Slippery When Wet' spend at number one in the US?

5. In which year was 'Livin' On A Prayer' released?

6. Which Bon Jovi manager was convicted of drug offences in 1988?

7. Which 1988 Bon Jovi album became the first to reach the top spot in the UK?

8. The acoustic version of which Bon Jovi song, played at the 1989 MTV Video Music Awards, inspired the Unplugged series of the Nineties?

9. Which Bon Jovi song was the theme to the movie *Young Guns II*?

10. In which year was 'Keep The Faith' released?

11. Which actress did Bon Jovi guitarist Richie Sambora marry in 1994?

12. What is the name of Bon Jovi's drummer?

13. In which country did ticketless fans riot in 1995 after forcing their way into a Bon Jovi concert?

14. What was the title of Bon Jovi's debut album?

15. Which film gave Jon Bon Jovi his first acting role?

16. Which Bon Jovi track reached two in the UK charts in 1994?

Answers to page 285
POT LUCK 34: **1.** Tina Weymouth **2.** Billy Swan **3.** Mick Talbot **4.** 'The Very Best Of Slim Whitman' **5.** The Hollies **6.** The Stylistics **7.** American **8.** The Family Stone **9.** Shocking Blue ('Venus') **10.** Helen Shapiro **11.** Tom Robinson **12.** Saffron **13.** 1963 **14.** KC **15.** Evan Dando **16.** Sam Cooke

Singer/Songwriters 4

Answers on page 282

1. Which singer/songwriter once appeared in a short-lived US sitcom *Just One of the Girls*?

2. On which Sheryl Crow track from the 'Tuesday Night Music Club' album did her father Wendell play trumpet?

3. On which Leonard Cohen album did 'Suzanne' first appear?

4. Whose Travelling Salvation Show was created by Neil Diamond?

5. Apart from Led Zeppelin, which American artist penned a song called 'Stairway To Heaven'?

6. Who said 'We Didn't Start The Fire' in 1989?

7. Which Fifties song did Elton John revive with Kiki Dee in 1993?

8. How many singles had Chris De Burgh released before 'Lady In Red'?

9. What was John Denver's first US top ten album?

10. Which Harry Chapin song told the story of a morning DJ on a radio station?

11. And which Harry Chapin song that became a US number one was based on a poem by his wife about a neglectful father?

12. For which artist did Carole King write 'It Might As Well Rain Until September'?

13. What was Sheryl Crow's first single?

14. Which artist had 16 UK hit albums but only one hit single – a number one in 1974?

15. Who had his debut album 'Tapestry' rejected by 34 record labels?

16. Which song kept Don McLean's 'American Pie' from the top of the UK singles chart?

Answers to page 282
EIGHTIES 8: **1.** Thelma Houston ('Don't Leave Me This Way') **2.** Boris Gardiner **3.** Berlin, Kim Wilde, The Bangles, Mel and Kim and Swing Out Sister **4.** Johnny Mathis **5.** The Look **6.** Europe ('The Final Countdown') **7.** The Isley Brothers (Isley Jasper Isley) **8.** Tony Thorpe **9.** Terri Nunn **10.** Caron Wheeler **11.** Wendy James **12.** Altered Images (Clare Grogan) **13.** Craig Logan **14.** 'La Bamba' **15.** Spanish **16.** 'Sex Talk'

Pot Luck 34

Answers on page 283

1. What was the name of the only female in Talking Heads?

2. Who worked as a janitor at Columbia Studios before having a US number one with 'I Can Help'?

3. Who was Paul Weller's partner in Style Council?

4. Which country album spent six weeks at the top of the UK charts in 1976?

5. Who knew a 'Long Cool Woman In A Black Dress'?

6. Which Seventies group's hits included 'Betcha By Golly Wow' and 'I'm Stone In Love With You'?

7. What nationality are Smashing Pumpkins?

8. Who backed Sly?

9. Which Dutch group had a US number one in 1970?

10. Which teenage pop star of the Sixties ended up in the short-lived Eighties TV soap *Albion Market*?

11. Who had a 1983 UK top ten hit with 'War Baby'?

12. Who was recruited from being part of The Prodigy's stage act to singing with Republica?

13. In which year did *Ready, Steady, Go!* start?

14. Who was the leader of The Sunshine Band?

15. Who was the singer with The Lemonheads?

16. Who was 'Twistin' The Night Away' in 1962?

Answers to page 283
BON JOVI 1: **1.** Playboy bunny girl **2.** A hairdresser **3.** 'You Give Love A Bad Name' **4.** 15 **5.** 1986 **6.** Doc McGee **7.** 'New Jersey' **8.** 'Wanted Dead Or Alive' **9.** 'Blaze Of Glory' **10.** 1992 **11.** Heather Locklear **12.** Tico Torres **13.** Indonesia **14.** 'Bon Jovi' **15.** *Young Guns II* **16.** 'Always'

Lyrics 11

Answers on page 288

From which songs are the following lyrics are taken?

1. 'It's two hearts living in two separate worlds'
2. 'Don't say you're easy on me, you're about as easy as a nuclear war'
3. 'I've shivers down my spine and it feels divine'
4. 'Oh, look what has happened with just one kiss, I never knew that I could be in love like this'
5. 'Head over heels when toe to toe, this is the sound of my soul'
6. 'I love her, I'm hoping that I never recover'
7. 'Spirits move me every time I'm near you, whirling like a cyclone in my mind'
8. 'I'm a man without conviction, I'm a man who doesn't know how to sell a contradiction'
9. 'I blame you for the moonlit sky and the dream that died with the eagle's flight'
10. 'But then the sound of my desperate calls echoes off these dungeon walls'
11. 'And it's too late to wash my hands, caught in a trap set for a man'
12. 'I play it off but I'm dreamin' of you'
13. 'Showin' how funky and strong is your fight, it doesn't matter who's wrong or right'
14. 'When it seems all your hopes and dreams are a million miles away I will reassure you'
15. 'Hey baby, you really got my tail in a spin, hey baby, I don't even know where to begin'
16. 'What's love but a second-hand emotion'

Answers to page 288
RAP 3: **1.** Eve featuring Gwen Stefani **2.** Snoop Doggy Dogg **3.** *Beavis and Butthead Do America* **4.** Dr Dre **5.** Vanilla Ice **6.** 'U Can't Touch This'
7. 'Pray' **8.** 'Addams Groove' **9.** Notorious B.I.G. **10.** 'Can't Nobody Hold Me Down' **11.** 'I'll Be Missing You' **12.** 'No Way Out' **13.** JC001
14. Notorious B.I.G. **15.** Grandmaster Flash and Melle Mel **16.** 'It's Like That'

Home Towns 4

Answers on page 289

1. In which Scottish town were The Jesus and Mary Chain formed?

2. Which well-coiffeured Eighties band came from Beckenham, Kent?

3. Which firestarters hail from Braintree in Essex?

4. Which southern town was home to Cliff Bennett and The Rebel Rousers?

5. In which city did Ten Years After start their career?

6. Which city are The Stone Roses from?

7. From which city did The Specials hail?

8. Which Lancashire town was home to The Four Pennies?

9. Which mouldy old Seventies outfit came from Coventry?

10. From which city did Them originate?

11. In which seaside resort did Procul Harum have their roots?

12. They may have sounded American, but in reality The Nashville Teens came from which Surrey town?

13. Rockers King Crimson hailed from which genteel English resort?

14. Which city were The Sensational Alex Harvey Band from?

15. Which city did The Fortunes come from?

16. What was the home town of Simon Dupree and The Big Sound?

Answers to page 289
SIXTIES 8: **1.** The Rebel Rousers **2.** Neil Diamond **3.** Tom Jones **4.** Roy Orbison **5.** The Byrds **6.** Neil Sedaka **7.** Seven **8.** The Move **9.** 'The Good The Bad And The Ugly' **10.** Hugo Montenegro **11.** Johnny Keating **12.** The Four Seasons **13.** Frank Ifield ('I Remember You') **14.** Herman's Hermits **15.** 'Glad All Over' (The Dave Clark Five) **16.** Cat Stevens

Rap 3

Answers on page 286

1. Who had a 2001 hit with 'Let Me Blow Ya Mind'?
2. Whose debut album was titled 'Doggy Style'?
3. From which film was LL Cool J's 'Ain't Nobody' taken?
4. Who joined LL Cool J on the 1998 hit 'Zoom'?
5. Which rap artist covered Wild Cherry's 'Play That Funky Music' in 1991?
6. What was M.C. Hammer's first UK hit?
7. Which M.C. Hammer single was based around Prince's 'When Doves Cry'?
8. Which M.C. Hammer hit was taken from the film *The Addams Family*?
9. Which American rap artist, whose first album was called 'Ready To Die', was murdered in 1997?
10. Which Puff Daddy single sampled Grandmaster Flash and The Furious Five's 'The Message'?
11. Which Puff Daddy number one sampled The Police's 'Every Breath You Take'?
12. What was the title of Puff Daddy's debut album?
13. Which rap artist collaborated with The Beatmasters on 'Boulevard Of Broken Dreams'?
14. Which rapper's real name was Christopher Wallace?
15. Who had a 1984 hit with the anti-drug message 'White Lines (Don't Don't Do It)'?
16. What was the title of Run D.M.C.'s first UK number one?

Answers to page 286
LYRICS 11: 1. 'Sacrifice' (Elton John) 2. 'Is There Something I Should Know?' (Duran Duran) 3. 'Show Me Heaven' (Maria McKee) 4. 'I Only Want To Be With You' (Dusty Springfield) 5. 'True' (Spandau Ballet) 6. 'Never Let Her Slip Away' (Andrew Gold) 7. 'Could It Be Magic' (Barry Manilow) 8. 'Karma Chameleon' (Culture Club) 9. 'Sleeping Satellite' (Tasmin Archer) 10. 'Chains' (Tina Arena) 11. 'Forbidden City' (Electronic) 12. 'I Try' (Macy Gray) 13. 'Beat It' (Michael Jackson) 14. 'Reach' (S Club 7) 15. 'Life Is A Rollercoaster' (Ronan Keating) 16. 'What's Love Got To Do With It?' (Tina Turner)

Sixties 8

Answers on page 287

1. Which Sixties backing group took their name from a Duane Eddy track?

2. Who wrote The Monkees' 'I'm A Believer'?

3. Who experienced 'Funny Familiar Forgotten Feelings' in 1967?

4. Who had a 1963 hit with 'Blue Bayou'?

5. Which American band charted in 1965 with 'All I Really Want To Do' and 'Turn! Turn! Turn!'?

6. 'Happy Birthday Sweet Sixteen' was a number three hit for which artist in 1961?

7. How many members were there in Amen Corner?

8. Which band were successfully sued by Prime Minister Harold Wilson over a nude caricature of him on a promotional postcard?

9. Which 1968 theme from a spaghetti Western became the first instrumental for five years to top the UK charts?

10. And whose orchestra and chorus recorded it?

11. Which orchestra leader had a 1962 top ten hit with the theme from *Z Cars*?

12. Which band's first two UK hits were 'Sherry' and 'Big Girls Don't Cry'?

13. Which solo artist had the biggest-selling UK single of 1962?

14. Who ordered 'No Milk Today' in 1966?

15. Which song knocked 'I Want To Hold Your Hand' off the top of the UK charts?

16. 'Matthew And Son' was a 1967 top three hit for which artist?

Answers to page 287
HOME TOWNS 4: **1.** East Kilbride **2.** Haircut 100 **3.** The Prodigy
4. Slough **5.** Nottingham **6.** Manchester **7.** Coventry **8.** Blackburn
9. Lieutenant Pigeon **10.** Belfast **11.** Southend **12.** Weybridge
13. Bournemouth **14.** Glasgow **15.** Birmingham **16.** Portsmouth

Chart Toppers 13

Answers on page 292

1. Scott Engel, John Maus and Gary Leeds were better known as which 1966 chart toppers?

2. Which singer with a band who had a 1976 number one returned to the limelight in 1987 when his Afghan hound was Supreme Champion at Crufts?

3. What was the title of Tony Di Bart's 1994 chart topper?

4. What was The Prodigy's second number one of 1996?

5. Junior Campbell was a guitarist with which Scottish chart toppers of 1969?

6. Which member of The Mamas and The Papas wrote 'San Francisco (Be Sure To Wear Some Flowers In Your Hair)' for Scott McKenzie?

7. Which 1983 number one told the story of a fictitious woman who accused Michael Jackson of being the father of her illegitimate son?

8. Which 1984 single spent nine weeks at number one in the UK but lost out as the year's best-seller to Band Aid?

9. Who had a 1980 number one with 'The Tide Is High'?

10. Whose 1973 chart topper was titled 'Angel Fingers'?

11. Who were the only duo to reach number one in the UK in 1968?

12. In 1958, which American singer reached the top spot with 'On The Street Where You Live'?

13. Which two former Shadows knocked their old mates off the UK number one perch in 1963?

14. And with which tune did they do it?

15. Who wanted to 'Paint It Black' in 1966?

16. Which Australian band had a UK number one in 1983?

Answers to page 292
ALBUMS 11: 1. 'Animals' 2. Bob Dylan 3. 'Parallel Lines' 4. Donna Summer 5. The Smiths 6. 'We Can't Dance' 7. 'For Your Pleasure' 8. 'Urban Hymns' 9. 'Labour Of Love' 10. Prince 11. 'Bridge Over Troubled Water' 12. Kate Bush 13. Culture Club 14. Luther Vandross 15. 'Blue' 16. Hanson

Pot Luck 35

Answers on page 293

1. In 1986, who became the first band named after a European city to have a UK number one?

2. What does KLF stand for?

3. German music students Ralf Hutter and Florian Schneider-Esleben were the founders of which Seventies band?

4. What links Lenny Kravitz, Slash from Guns N' Roses and Maria McKee?

5. What is Dionne Warwick's first name?

6. Who backed Junior Walker?

7. Who is the bass player with U2?

8. What was the title of Spandau Ballet's debut single?

9. Which girl duo took their name from a Smiths' song?

10. In which country was Sade born?

11. Which DJ introduced the first edition of *Top of the Pops*?

12. Guitarist Phil Manzanera was a member of which Seventies band?

13. Who went 'Crazy' after leaving Adamski?

14. Which Seventies singer married her band's guitarist Len Tuckey?

15. Which rock star's sister was a member of the girl band Fanny?

16. Which Eighties band developed their New York docker image from Robert De Niro's film *Mean Streets*?

Answers to page 293
INDIE 6: 1. Swedish 2. 1998 3. Tom Jones 4. Catatonia 5. The Verve
6. 'Hush' 7. The Bluetones 8. Ash 9. Blur 10. Ian Broudie 11. Travis
12. Suede 13. Ocean Colour Scene 14. 'Moseley Shoals' 15. The
Stereophonics 16. Space

Albums 11

Answers on page 290

1. Which Pink Floyd album cover depicted an inflatable pig over Battersea Power Station?

2. Who released the 1968 album 'John Wesley Harding'?

3. Which Blondie album was the UK best-seller for 1979?

4. Which disco diva's 1977 album was titled 'I Remember Yesterday'?

5. 'The Queen Is Dead' was a 1986 album by which band?

6. What was the title of the 1992 number one album from Genesis?

7. What was Roxy Music's second album?

8. Which Verve album featured 'Bitter Sweet Symphony'?

9. Which was UB40's first UK number one album?

10. Who recorded the 1990 album 'Graffiti Bridge'?

11. 'The Boxer' was a track on which Simon and Garfunkel album?

12. 'Hounds Of Love' was the title of a 1985 album by which female artist?

13. Which band fronted by Boy George topped the album charts in 1983?

14. 'Give Me The Reason' was a top five album for which R & B artist in 1987?

15. What colour was the title of Simply Red's number one album in 1998?

16. Which US pop band were in the 'Middle Of Nowhere' in 1997?

Answers to page 290
CHART TOPPERS 13: **1.** The Walker Brothers **2.** Chris Amoo (The Real Thing) **3.** 'The Real Thing' **4.** 'Breathe' **5.** Marmalade **6.** John Phillips **7.** 'Billie Jean' **8.** 'Two Tribes' (Frankie Goes To Hollywood) **9.** Blondie **10.** Wizzard **11.** Esther and Abi Ofarim **12.** Vic Damone **13.** Jet Harris and Tony Meehan **14.** 'Diamonds' **15.** The Rolling Stones **16.** Men At Work ('Down Under')

Indie 6

Answers on page 291

1. What nationality are The Cardigans?

2. In which year did The Cardigans' 'My Favourite Game' first enter the UK charts?

3. Who teamed up with The Cardigans for the 1999 hit 'Burning Down The House'?

4. Who were 'Dead From The Waist Down' in 1999?

5. Which Indie band released the album 'A Northern Soul' in 1995?

6. Which cover of a Deep Purple track was a hit for Kula Shaker?

7. 'Return To The Last Chance Saloon' was a 1998 album by which Indie band?

8. Who released the 1998 album 'Nu-Clear Sounds'?

9. Who reckoned 'Modern Life Is Rubbish'?

10. Who composed 'Three Lions', England's football anthem at Euro 96?

11. Fran Healy is the frontman of which Indie band?

12. Who sang about a 'Filmstar' in 1997?

13. 'The Day We Caught The Train' was a top ten hit for which band?

14. And from which album was it taken?

15. Who encouraged us to 'Have A Nice Day' in 2001?

16. Tommy Scott is the lead singer with which band?

Film Tracks 7

Answers on page 296

1. Seal's 'Kiss From A Rose' was the theme from which film?

2. Who reached number one with 'Nothing's Gonna Stop Us Now' from the film *Mannequin*?

3. Which track from *Sister Act 2: Back in the Habit* was a 1994 hit for Aretha Franklin?

4. Which of the Monty Python team sang 'Always Look On The Bright Side Of Life'?

5. And which film did it close?

6. Who had a hit with 'Two Hearts' from the film *Buster*?

7. Natalie Cole's 1990 hit 'Wild Women Do' was from the soundtrack of which Julia Roberts film?

8. Which film featured the 1954 Dean Martin hit 'That's Amore'?

9. The 1961 hit 'Moon River' was taken from which film?

10. Which film spawned the Frank Sinatra song 'High Hopes'?

11. Who sang 'Step By Step' from the film *The Preacher's Wife*?

12. Who had a UK top five hit with 'Where Do I Begin', the theme from *Love Story*?

13. Who sang the theme from the 1967 film *The Valley of the Dolls*?

14. Which film featured 'Tonight', a hit for Shirley Bassey in 1962?

15. Madonna's number one single 'Into The Groove' was a track from which film?

16. The Brenda Lee hit 'Speak To Me Pretty' came from which film?

Answers to page 296
NOVELTY NUMBERS 5: **1.** Bob The Builder **2.** 'The Chicken Song'
3. Leapy Lee **4.** 1981 **5.** His Cast Of Idiots **6.** 'Disco Duck' **7.** Doc Cox
8. The Goons **9.** Lonnie Donegan **10.** Billy Howard **11.** Brown Sauce
12. 'I Wanna Be A Winner' **13.** Joy Sarney **14.** Mel Brooks **15.** Hale and
Pace **16.** Kevin the Gerbil

Pot Luck 36

Answers on page 297

1. Which Manchester band took their name from a New Order song?

2. 'Rich Girl' was a US number one in 1977 for which duo?

3. Mike Score was the lead singer with which Eighties band?

4. What is the surname of Morten from a-ha?

5. Which Seventies band got their name from the first letters of the four members' Christian names?

6. Before she became a singer, who used to choreograph the cheerleaders of the LA Lakers Basketball team?

7. Who had a 1985 hit with 'Every Time You Go Away'?

8. Shaun Ryder was the singer with which band?

9. Which musical knight used to work in a Peterborough pea factory?

10. Who sang 'I'll Be There For You', the theme from *Friends*?

11. In 1997, which song took over from 'White Christmas' as the biggest-selling single in the world?

12. In which year was 'White Christmas' first released?

13. Which sinister Caribbean mystery provided the title for a Barry Manilow hit in 1981?

14. With whom did Billy Paul have 'a thing going on' in 1973?

15. Which California foursome had a 1966 hit with 'I Saw Her Again'?

16. In 1986, which band were giving 'Lessons In Love'?

Answers to page 297
TINA TURNER 1: 1. 'We Don't Need Another Hero' 2. Bonnie Tyler
3. Bryan Adams 4. 1989 5. Tony Joe White 6. Jeff Beck 7. 'Nutbush City
Limits' 8. 'I Don't Wanna Fight' 9. Sting 10. 'Break Every Rule'
11. 'What's Love Got To Do With It' 12. Aunty Entity 13. Edgar Winter
14. Rod Stewart 15. 'Disco Inferno' 16. Phil Spector

Novelty Numbers 5

Answers on page 294

1. Which handyman covered 'Mambo No. 5' in 2001?

2. Which fowl number topped the charts for Spitting Image in 1986?

3. Who fired 'Little Arrows' in 1968?

4. In which year did The Tweets inflict 'The Birdie Song' on an unsuspecting nation?

5. Who backed Rick Dees on his 1976 hit single?

6. What was the title of the Rick Dees track that drove everyone quackers?

7. Which *That's Life* presenter charted under the name of Ivor Biggun?

8. Who were Walking Backwards For Christmas?

9. Who asked: 'Does Your Chewing Gum Lose Its Flavour On The Bedpost Overnight'?

10. Who did impressions of TV detectives on the Roger Miller parody 'King Of The Cops'?

11. Under what name did presenters from *Multi-Coloured Swap Shop*, led by Noel Edmonds, enter the charts in 1981?

12. And what was the inspirational title of their song?

13. Who did Punch and Judy impressions on 'Naughty Naughty Naughty'?

14. Which film producer charted with 'The Hitler Rap' in 1984?

15. Which pair had a Comic Relief number one with 'The Stonk'?

16. Which rodent covered Cliff Richard's 'Summer Holiday' in 1984?

Answers to page 294
FILM TRACKS 7: 1. *Batman Forever* 2. Starship 3. 'A Deeper Love'
4. Eric Idle 5. *The Life of Brian* 6. Phil Collins 7. *Pretty Woman* 8. *The Caddy* 9. *Breakfast At Tiffany's* 10. *A Hole in the Head* 11. Whitney Houston 12. Andy Williams 13. Dionne Warwick 14. *West Side Story*
15. *Desperately Seeking Susan* 16. *Two Little Bears*

Tina Turner 1

Answers on page 295

1. Which Tina Turner hit single was taken from the film *Mad Max: Beyond Thunderdome*?

2. Who originally recorded 'The Best'?

3. With whom did Tina Turner duet on 'It's Only Love'?

4. In which year was 'The Best' released?

5. Who recorded the original version of 'Steamy Windows'?

6. Who played guitar on 'Private Dancer'?

7. What was Tina Turner's last UK hit with husband Ike?

8. Lulu joined Tina Turner on which 1993 single?

9. Who contributed backing vocals for the 1996 hit 'On Silent Wings'?

10. What was the title of Tina Turner's second solo album?

11. Which Tina Turner single won Record Of The Year at the 1985 Grammy Awards?

12. Which part did Tina Turner play in *Mad Max: Beyond Thunderdome*?

13. Who played the saxophone solo on 'The Best'?

14. With whom did Turner duet on 'It Takes Two', an update of the Marvin Gaye/Tammi Terrell song?

15. Which Trammps song did Turner cover in 1993?

16. Who produced 'River Deep Mountain High'?

Answers to page 295
POT LUCK 36: **1.** Happy Mondays ('Blue Monday') **2.** Daryl Hall and John Oates **3.** A Flock Of Seagulls **4.** Harket **5.** Abba (Agnetha, Bjorn, Benny and Anni-Frid) **6.** Paula Abdul **7.** Paul Young **8.** Happy Mondays **9.** Sir Bob Geldof **10.** The Rembrandts **11.** 'Candle In The Wind' (Elton John) **12.** 1942 **13.** 'Bermuda Triangle' **14.** Mrs Jones ('Me And Mrs Jones') **15.** The Mamas and The Papas **16.** Level 42

Nineties 8

Answers on page 300

Which artists had top ten UK hits with the following tracks in the Nineties?

1. 'Slam Dunk (Da Funk)'

2. 'Smack My Bitch Up'

3. 'North Country Boy'

4. 'Not Over You Yet'

5. 'My Oh My'

6. 'Mary Had A Little Boy'

7. 'The Millennium Prayer'

8. 'If You Buy This Record Your Life Will Be Better'

9. 'Doodah!'

10. 'Shiny Happy People'

11. 'Satan'

12. 'Stupid Girl'

13. 'Sailing On The Seven Seas'

14. 'You Stole The Sun From My Heart'

15. 'Get The Message'

16. 'Get Get Down'

Answers to page 300
POT LUCK 37: 1. The Jackson Five (to honour Michael's 30 years in showbiz) 2. Orchestral Manoeuvres in the Dark 3. Australian 4. The Shades 5. Salt 'N' Pepa 6. Sailor 7. 10cc 8. Al Green 9. Frank Zappa 10. Benny and Graham 11. Staind 12. Freddie and The Dreamers 13. Because the title was seen as promoting the magazine 14. Jon Moss 15. One 16. 'Night Owl'

Heavy Metal 5

Answers on page 301

1. Who was lead singer with Whitesnake?

2. What was the name of the final Deep Purple studio album?

3. John Kay was the singer with which Sixties band?

4. Which band's debut album was 'Bleach'?

5. Which Guns 'N' Roses song is on the soundtrack to *End of Days*?

6. Which German band was founded by Rudolf and Michael Schenker in 1971?

7. Whose 1980 album was titled 'Strong Arm Of The Law'?

8. 'Since You Been Gone' was a 1979 hit for which band?

9. Who were 'Back In Black' in 1980?

10. Which former member of Deep Purple joined Rainbow in 1979?

11. Which ex-member of Deep Purple and Rainbow used to play in Screaming Lord Sutch's band?

12. Which Scorpions single reached number two in the UK charts in 1991?

13. Which Guns N' Roses album contained a song written by Charles Manson?

14. Which Whitesnake album got to number two in the UK charts in 1981?

15. Which band were formed in 1976 by bass guitarist Steve Harris?

16. Who joined Deep Purple as vocalist in 1969?

Answers to page 301
ONE-HIT WONDERS 9: **1.** Renaissance **2.** The Rattles **3.** Nana Mouskouri **4.** *Full Metal Jacket* **5.** Al Matthews **6.** Keith Marshall **7.** McFadden and Whitehead **8.** Maureen McGovern **9.** Mary McGregor **10.** Gino Latino **11.** Rodney Franklin **12.** 'Peppermint Twist' **13.** Anne-Marie David **14.** Johnny Cymbal **15.** Louise Cordet **16.** Bimbo Jet

Pot Luck 37

Answers on page 298

1. Which group reunited in September 2001 for the first time since 1984?

2. What does OMD stand for?

3. What nationality is Helen Reddy?

4. With which group did Lou Reed make his recording debut in 1957?

5. Cheryl James and Sandra Denton were better known as which American duo?

6. Which nautical band enthused about 'Girls Girls Girls' in 1976?

7. Hotlegs were the forerunners of which Seventies supergroup?

8. Who had hits with 'Tired Of Being Alone' and 'Let's Stay Together'?

9. Who was leader of the Mothers Of Invention?

10. What are the Christian names of Seventies duo Gallagher and Lyle?

11. Who had a number one album in 2001 with 'Break The Cycle'?

12. Who encouraged us to 'Do The Freddie'?

13. Why did the BBC ban Dr Hook's 'The Cover Of Rolling Stone'?

14. Who was drummer with Culture Club?

15. How old was Marti Pellow when 'Love Is All Around' was a hit for The Troggs?

16. What was Gerry Rafferty's follow-up to 'Baker Street'?

Answers to page 298
NINETIES 8: **1.** Five **2.** The Prodigy **3.** The Charlatans **4.** Diana Ross **5.** Aqua **6.** Snap! **7.** Cliff Richard **8.** Tamperer featuring Maya **9.** Cartoons **10.** R.E.M. **11.** Orbital **12.** Garbage **13.** OMD **14.** Manic Street Preachers **15.** Electronic **16.** Paul Johnson

One-Hit Wonders 9

Answers on page 299

1. Which band's only UK hit was 'Northern Lights' in 1978?

2. Which German group charted with 'The Witch' in 1970?

3. Which Greek singer's only UK hit single was 'Only Love'?

4. The title track from which film gave Abigail Mead and Nigel Goulding a number two hit in 1987?

5. In 1975, 'Fool' gave which American singer his only UK chart action?

6. Who was 'Only Crying' in 1981?

7. Which duo were wrong when they said 'Ain't No Stoppin' Us Now' in 1979?

8. Who was doing 'The Continental' in 1976?

9. Who was 'Torn Between Two Lovers' in 1977?

10. Which Italian artist reached the UK top twenty with 'Welcome' in 1990?

11. Who got to number seven with 'The Groove' in 1980?

12. Joey Dee and The Starliters had a hit with which dance record in 1962?

13. Which 1973 Eurovision Song Contest winner had a 'Wonderful Dream'?

14. Which singer, also named after a musical instrument, extolled the virtues of 'Mr Bass Man' in 1963?

15. Which French artist said 'I'm Just A Baby' in 1962?

16. And French act had a 1975 hit with 'El Bimbo'?

Name Changes 12

Answers on page 304

1. Which Australian rock band were previously called The Farriss Brothers?

2. As which rap artist is Sean Combs better known?

3. Which Sixties group started out as The Howlin' Wolves?

4. What is Jet Harris's real name?

5. Which international band were previously known as Feedback?

6. Which jazz singer was born Clementina Dinah Campbell?

7. What stage name did Lee Brilleaux adopt?

8. What is Fats Domino's real name?

9. Which singer with a Scottish band changed his name from Mark McLoughlin?

10. As which rapper is Andre Young better known?

11. Which Sixties group who were into something good were previously known as The Heartbeats?

12. Which head of the family was born Sylvester Stewart?

13. Which member of Roxy Music changed his name from Philip Targett Adams?

14. To what did The Dalton Brothers change their name?

15. Which singer started out as a member of Café Society?

16. Which Eighties chart-toppers were previously called Caviar?

Answers to page 304
NUMBER TWOS 6: **1.** 1975 **2.** 1982 **3.** 1982 **4.** 1969 **5.** 1974 **6.** 1997 **7.** 1984 **8.** 1964 **9.** 1969 **10.** 1975 **11.** 1961 **12.** 1980 **13.** 1995 **14.** 1983 **15.** 1979 **16.** 1983

Cover Versions 10

Answers on page 305

1. In 1974, whose eyes did smoke get in, 15 years after it had first affected The Platters?

2. Who first had a UK hit in 1971 with 'Softly Whispering I Love You', revived by Paul Young in 1990?

3. Which Jonathan King project covered The Archies' 'Sugar Sugar'?

4. What song links Bobby Hebb, Georgie Fame and Boney M?

5. Who originally had a hit with Glamma Kid's 'The Sweetest Taboo'?

6. Which Searchers number one was taken to number three by C.J. Lewis in 1994?

7. Which group covered Billie Davis's 'Tell Him' in 1974?

8. Which Isaac Hayes track was revived by Eddy and The Soulband in 1985?

9. What did both The Carpenters in 1970 and Gwen Guthrie in 1986 long to be?

10. Who first had success with 'The Three Bells', a hit for Brian Poole and The Tremeloes in 1965?

11. What did both R. Dean Taylor and The Fall discover 13 years apart?

12. Who had the original hit with 'This Old Heart Of Mine', covered by Rod Stewart in 1989?

13. What identical message was sent out by The Four Tops, Gloria Gaynor and Michael Bolton?

14. Which Andrew Gold song did Undercover turn their attention to?

15. In 1971, who covered the aptly named 'It's The Same Old Song' by The Four Tops?

16. Which park was frequented by both The Small Faces and M People?

Answers to page 305
SEVENTIES 9: **1.** Gary Numan (his uncle, Jeff Lidyard was the drummer with Tubeway Army) **2.** Led Zeppelin **3.** David Cassidy **4.** Denny Laine **5.** Dr Hook **6.** Abba, Demis Roussos and Pussycat **7.** Tony Orlando **8.** Jeff **9.** Ray Dorset (Mungo Jerry) **10.** Andrea True **11.** The Ramones **12.** Paul Nicholas (*Just Good Friends*) **13.** Nazareth **14.** 'Julie Ann' **15.** Andrew Gold **16.** Creedence Clearwater Revival

Number Twos 6

Answers on page 302

In which years did the following tracks reach number two in the UK charts?

1. 'Glass Of Champagne' (Sailor)

2. 'Mirror Man' (Human League)

3. 'Just An Illusion' (Imagination)

4. 'Goodbye' (Mary Hopkin)

5. 'Never Can Say Goodbye' (Gloria Gaynor)

6. 'Stand By Me' (Oasis)

7. 'Wild Boys' (Duran Duran)

8. 'Bits And Pieces' (Dave Clark Five)

9. 'I'm Gonna Make You Mine' (Lou Christie)

10. 'There's A Whole Lot Of Loving' (Guys and Dolls)

11. 'Wild Wind' (John Leyton)

12. 'Dance Yourself Dizzy' (Liquid Gold)

13. 'Hold Me, Thrill Me, Kiss Me, Kill Me' (U2)

14. 'Wings Of A Dove' (Madness)

15. 'Pop Muzik' (M)

16. 'They Don't Know' (Tracey Ullman)

Answers to page 302
NAME CHANGES 12: **1.** INXS **2.** P Diddy **3.** Simon Dupree and The Big Sound **4.** Terence **5.** U2 **6.** Cleo Laine **7.** Dr Feelgood **8.** Antoine Domino **9.** Marti Pellow **10.** Dr Dre **11.** Herman's Hermits **12.** Sly Stone **13.** Phil Manzanera **14.** The Walker Brothers **15.** Tom Robinson **16.** Bros

Seventies 9

Answers on page 303

1. Whose uncle played in his band on their 1979 chart topper?

2. Who released the 1976 album 'Presence'?

3. Which teen idol was just a 'Daydreamer' in 1973?

4. Which Moody Blue became one of Wings?

5. Dennis Locorriere was one of the singers with which band?

6. Which three European acts had number one singles in the UK in 1976?

7. Who was the lead singer with Dawn?

8. What was the first name of Christie who had a 1970 number one with 'Yellow River'?

9. Who was working as a laboratory researcher when his song reached number one in 1970 and had to ask for time off to appear on *Top of The Pops*?

10. Whose Connection wanted 'More More More' in 1976?

11. Who told us in 1977: 'Sheena Is A Punk Rocker'?

12. Which actor who appeared in a long-running Eighties sit-com had three top twenty singles in 1976?

13. 'My White Bicycle' was a 1975 hit for which band?

14. Which girl gave Kenny a top ten hit in 1975?

15. Who was a 'Lonely Boy' in 1977?

16. 'Up Around The Bend' was a 1970 hit for which US band?

Answers to page 303
COVER VERSIONS 10: **1.** Bryan Ferry **2.** The Congregation **3.** Sakkarin **4.** 'Sunny' **5.** Sade **6.** 'Sweets For My Sweet' **7.** Hello **8.** 'Theme From *Shaft*' **9.** 'Close To You' **10.** The Browns **11.** 'There's A Ghost In My House' **12.** The Isley Brothers **13.** 'Reach Out I'll Be There' **14.** 'Never Let Her Slip Away' **15.** The Weathermen **16.** Itchycoo Park

Pot Luck 38

Answers on page 308

1. What do Otis Redding, Jim Reeves, Laurel and Hardy, and Jimi Hendrix have in common?

2. Which Scottish band took their name from a line in a Scritti Politti song?

3. Which heavy metal frontman has a B.A. and can speak four languages?

4. What was the original title of The Beatles' 'Hey Jude'?

5. Which TV presenters enjoyed chart success as PJ and Duncan?

6. Which group backed Peter Jay?

7. Which band knocked Band Aid's 'Do They Know It's Christmas' off the top of the UK charts?

8. Which self-promoting star of the late Eighties was once a regional Golden Gloves boxing champion in Florida?

9. Who is the singer with The Cure?

10. Which future chart toppers played their first gig in Liverpool in 1980 as support act to Hambi and The Dance?

11. Roger Chapman was lead singer with which Seventies band?

12. Who was 'Mr Soft' in 1974?

13. Which American state did Ernie Ford put before his name?

14. Who backed Reparata?

15. What nationality was Edmund Hockridge?

16. What was the name of Bruce Hornsby's backing band?

Answers to page 308
FOLK 5: 1. Tommy Makem 2. 'Catch The Wind' 3. Jimmy Page 4. Bob Dylan 5. The Band 6. Ewan MacColl 7. Don McLean 8. 'Letter From America' 9. Three 10. 'Silver Threads And Golden Needles' 11. 'All Around My Hat' was produced by chief Womble Mike Batt 12. Dave Swarbrick 13. 'You've Got A Friend' 14. Donovan 15. James Taylor 16. Suzanne Vega

The Sex Pistols 1

Answers on page 309

1. Who was the drummer with The Sex Pistols?

2. How did Johnny Rotten get his name?

3. Who joined the band in 1976?

4. What milestone in The Sex Pistols history occurred on 1 December 1976?

5. Out of 19 scheduled dates for the 'Anarchy In The UK' tour, how many went ahead?

6. Which record label dropped The Pistols at the start of 1977?

7. How many days did The Sex Pistols stay with the A & M label?

8. Why did A & M sack The Sex Pistols?

9. Workers at a record factory refused to press copies of which Pistols' single?

10. Outside which buildings did The Pistols perform 'Anarchy In The UK' in June 1977 in a boat travelling along the Thames?

11. Which track did the band perform on their *Top of the Pops* debut?

12. Who was the Pistols' manager?

13. What was the title of the planned Sex Pistols film?

14. In which city did the Pistols play their last-ever gig?

15. Which band did Johnny Rotten form after The Sex Pistols split up?

16. Which Sex Pistol covered 'My Way'?

Answers to page 309
DUOS 4: 1. Jaki Graham 2. Bobbie Gentry 3. 'Back Together Again'
4. Phil Collins and Philip Bailey 5. Lennie Peters (Peters and Lee) 6. 'We Close Our Eyes' 7. 'King Of Wishful Thinking' 8. Alisha's Attic 9. 1969
10. 'West End Girls' 11. Liza Minnelli ('Losing My Mind') 12. Yazoo
13. Sonny and Cher 14. Chris Norman 15. Sarah Brightman 16. 'Deep Purple'

Folk 5

Answers on page 306

1. Which whistle player joined The Clancy Brothers?

2. What was the title of Donovan's first UK hit single?

3. Which guitar legend played on Donovan's 'Sunshine Superman'?

4. Who had a hit with 'Subterranean Homesick Blues' in 1965?

5. Who originally recorded 'The Night They Drove Old Dixie Down', a 1971 hit for Joan Baez?

6. Which folk singer wrote 'The First Time Ever I Saw Your Face'?

7. Which American folk singer wrote 'And I Love You So', which became an international success for Perry Como?

8. What was The Proclaimers' first hit?

9. How many members of The Springfields were there?

10. Which country standard gave The Springfields their biggest US hit?

11. What is the link between Steeleye Span and The Wombles?

12. Which violinist joined Fairport Convention in 1972?

13. Which song from Carole King's 'Tapestry' album became a hit for James Taylor?

14. Who had a 1969 hit with 'Goo Goo Barabajagal?

15. Who released the album 'Sweet Baby James'?

16. 'Luka' was a 1987 hit for which female singer?

Answers to page 306
POT LUCK 38: 1. They all had their biggest hits after they had died
2. Wet Wet Wet 3. Gene Simmons 4. 'Hey Jules' (after Julian Lennon)
5. Ant and Dec 6. The Jaywalkers 7. Foreigner 8. Terence Trent D'Arby
9. Robert Smith 10. Frankie Goes To Hollywood 11. Family 12. Steve
Harley (and Cockney Rebel) 13. Tennessee 14. The Delrons
15. Canadian 16. The Range

Duos 4

Answers on page 307

1. Who joined David Grant on a 1985 version of The Detroit Spinners' 'Could It Be I'm Falling In Love'?

2. Which artist combined with Glen Campbell for a 1969 cover of 'All I Have To Is Dream'?

3. Which song did Roberta Flack and Donny Hathaway take to number three in the UK charts in 1980?

4. Which two Phils joined forces on the 1985 number one 'Easy Lover'?

5. The Kray Twins were said to be old friends of which half of a successful Seventies duo?

6. What was Go West's first UK hit?

7. Which Go West single appeared in the film *Pretty Woman*?

8. 'I Am, I Feel' was a hit for which Nineties duo?

9. In which year did Simon and Garfunkel chart with 'The Boxer'?

10. Which Pet Shop Boys song was named Best Single Of The Year at the 1987 Brit Awards?

11. Which American diva gained her UK chart debut in 1989 courtesy of a song produced by The Pet Shop Boys?

12. 'Only You' and 'Don't Go' were Eighties hits for which duo?

13. Which duo topped the UK charts in 1965?

14. Which Smokie singer was Suzi Quatro 'Stumblin' In' with in 1978?

15. Which star of musicals linked with Cliff Richard on the 1986 hit 'All I Ask Of You'?

16. Which colour was a hit for Nino Tempo and April Stevens in 1963?

Answers to page 307
THE SEX PISTOLS 1: **1.** Paul Cook **2.** His catchphrase was 'You're rotten, you are' **3.** Sid Vicious **4.** They were interviewed by Bill Grundy on *Today* **5.** Three **6.** EMI **7.** Six **8.** Other A & M artists complained about signing them **9.** 'God Save The Queen' **10.** The Houses of Parliament **11.** 'Pretty Vacant' **12.** Malcolm McLaren **13.** *Who Killed Bambi?* **14.** San Francisco **15.** Public Image Ltd **16.** Sid Vicious

Eighties 9

Answers on page 312

1. Which band's debut album was titled 'Bridge Of Spies'?

2. In 1987, which band had their fifth UK number one in total, but their first for eight years?

3. Who were 'Showing Out' in 1986?

4. Which Asian trouble spot was the title of a Kim Wilde hit of 1981?

5. Steve Grant was the male singer in which chart-topping Eighties trio?

6. In which year did 'The Land Of Make Believe' reach number one for Bucks Fizz?

7. Which city links Eighties hits for Elvis Costello and Kajagoogoo?

8. Who wanted to 'Kiss The Bride' in 1983?

9. Which solo artist had hits with 'New Song' and 'What Is Love'?

10. What was Barry Manilow's only UK top ten hit of the decade?

11. Who thought of herself as a 'Modern Girl' in 1980?

12. 'Wide Boy' was a 1985 hit for which diminutive UK artist?

13. What is the Christian name of the Bronski in Bronski Beat?

14. Which band were Dave Stewart and Annie Lennox in before The Eurythmics?

15. Who is vocalist with Erasure?

16. Who had a 1986 number one before deciding to join the police force six years later?

Answers to page 312
POT LUCK 39: 1. Edwyn Collins 2. The Emerald Express 3. The Aces 4. Del Amitri 5. 'Look Away' 6. The Beverley Sisters 7. Mick Jones 8. Curved Air 9. The Crystals 10. Randy Crawford 11. Sam Cooke 12. Welsh 13. Bobby Brown 14. The Beat 15. The Bangles 16. Mia Farrow

Elvis 2

Answers on page 313

1. 'Teddy Bear' was on the soundtrack of which film?

2. In which year was 'King Creole' released as a single?

3. Which Elvis number one was recorded originally by Vaughn Deleath in 1927?

4. How many UK number ones did Elvis have in 1961?

5. How many UK number ones did Elvis have in total?

6. What was his last UK number one before his death?

7. Which mansion did Elvis buy in 1957?

8. In which city is it located?

9. Which unique event took place on 2 March 1960?

10. Who recorded the original version of 'Crying In The Chapel'?

11. On a cold and grey Chicago morning where was another little baby child born?

12. Which 1969 single gave Elvis his first US number one for seven years?

13. In which year was Elvis's marriage to Priscilla dissolved?

14. Besides English, in which language did Elvis sing on 'Wooden Heart'?

15. Who sold Elvis from Sun for $35,000?

16. How many weeks did 'Heartbreak Hotel' remain at number one in the US charts?

Answers to page 313
GLAM ROCK 3: **1.** Alvin Stardust **2.** Frank Torpey **3.** 'Wig Wam Bam'
4. Nicky Chinn and Mike Chapman **5.** David Bowie **6.** The US moon
launch **7.** 'My Coo Ca Choo' **8.** 'Jealous Mind' **9.** Gary Glitter **10.** Mark
McManus (*Taggart*) **11.** The Glitter Band **12.** Alvin Stardust **13.** T. Rex
14. 1973 **15.** 'The Groover' **16.** Alvin Stardust

Pot Luck 39

Answers on page 310

1. Which singer/guitarist was with Orange Juice before going solo?

2. Which fiddle section joined Dexy's Midnight Runners in 1982?

3. What was the name of Desmond Dekker's backing group?

4. Which Glaswegian band were formed by Justin Currie and Iain Harvie?

5. What was Big Country's last UK top ten hit?

6. Which British female trio saw Mommy kissing Santa Claus in 1953?

7. Which member of The Clash formed Big Audio Dynamite?

8. Sonja Kristina was the singer with which Seventies band?

9. Dee Dee Kennibrew and La La Brooks were part of which girl group of the Sixties?

10. Who reached number two in the charts in 1980 with 'One Day I'll Fly Away'?

11. Who was lead singer with The Soul Stirrers between 1951 and 1956 before going solo?

12. What nationality were Budgie?

13. Which singer married Whitney Houston in 1992?

14. Which two-tone band had a rapper by the name of Ranking Roger?

15. 'All Over The Place' was the debut album from which girl band?

16. Which actress's sister was the subject of The Beatles' 'Dear Prudence'?

Answers to page 310
EIGHTIES 9: **1.** T'Pau **2.** The Bee Gees **3.** Mel and Kim **4.** 'Cambodia' **5.** Tight Fit **6.** 1981 **7.** New York (Elvis Costello sang about 'New Amsterdam' (New York's former name) and Kajagoogoo had a hit titled 'Big Apple') **8.** Elton John **9.** Howard Jones **10.** 'I Wanna Do It With You' **11.** Sheena Easton **12.** Nik Kershaw **13.** Steve **14.** The Tourists **15.** Andy Bell **16.** Nick Berry (who went on to star in *Heartbeat*)

Glam Rock 3

Answers on page 311

1. Which glam rocker's previous incarnations included Bernard Jewry and Shane Fenton?

2. Who did Andy Scott replace as guitarist in Sweet?

3. For which song did Sweet dress up as Native American Indians?

4. Which glam rock writers were commonly known as Chinnichap?

5. Whose early backing groups included The King Bees, The Lower Third and The Buzz?

6. Which real-life event was Bowie's 'Space Oddity' released to coincide with?

7. What was Alvin Stardust's first hit?

8. And which was his first UK number one?

9. Who pleaded 'Remember Me This Way'?

10. Sweet singer Brian Connolly was later revealed to be the half-brother of which actor who played a TV cop?

11. Pete Phipps was one of the drummers in which band?

12. Which glam rock star went on to advise youngsters of the importance of road safety?

13. 'Solid Gold Easy Action' was a 1972 hit for which band?

14. In which year was Marc Bolan/T. Rex's last UK top ten hit?

15. What was the title of the track?

16. Who ended up playing a pub landlord in *Hollyoaks*?

Answers to page 311
ELVIS 2: **1.** *Loving You* **2.** 1958 **3.** 'Are You Lonesome Tonight?' **4.** Four **5.** 17 **6.** 'The Wonder Of You' **7.** Graceland **8.** Memphis **9.** Elvis set foot on British soil for the only time, during his plane's refuelling stop at Prestwick Airport in Scotland **10.** Sonny Til and The Orioles **11.** 'In The Ghetto' **12.** 'Suspicious Minds' **13.** 1973 **14.** German **15.** Sam Phillips **16.** Eight

Classical Gas 4

Answers on page 316

1. In which Italian province was Verdi born?

2. What nationality was Bruckner?

3. Who used to pour jugs of iced water over his head to stimulate his brain while composing?

4. Who composed a piano piece that required a player to use two hands and a nose to hit the right notes?

5. Who composed the choral work *St Matthew Passion?*

6. Who wrote *The Trout Quintet?*

7. What was the Christian name of Berlioz?

8. *The Damnation Of Faust* was a concert opera by which composer?

9. Who composed the 'Pathetique Symphony'?

10. What is Beethoven's Fifth Piano Concerto more commonly known as?

11. Who wrote *The Marriage Of Figaro?*

12. Who composed 'The Moonlight Sonata'?

13. The *William Tell* overture was the work of which composer?

14. Which Claudio was born in 1567 in the Italian town of Cremona?

15. What was the Christian name of Vaughan Williams?

16. What nationality was Carl Nielsen?

Answers to page 316
REGGAE 3: **1.** Greyhound **2.** Glamma Kid **3.** The Specials **4.** '007'
5. 'The Israelites' **6.** Dave and Ansil Collins **7.** Brinsley Forde **8.** 'Don't Turn Around' **9.** Tina Turner **10.** 'Give A Little Love' **11.** Pato Banton
12. Bob Marley and The Wailers **13.** Chrissie Hynde **14.** Dusty Springfield **15.** 'Signing Off' **16.** Peter Tosh

Sixties 9

Answers on page 317

Which artists recorded the following UK hits of the Sixties?

1. 'The Wind Cries Mary'

2. 'Take Good Care Of My Baby'

3. 'Strawberry Fair'

4. 'Swiss Maid'

5. 'Reflections Of My Life'

6. 'Little Man'

7. 'Everybody Knows'

8. 'Games People Play'

9. 'From The Underworld'

10. 'If The Whole World Stopped Loving'

11. 'Hello Mary Lou'

12. 'Wonderful World Beautiful People'

13. 'Too Soon To Know'

14. 'Sorry Suzanne'

15. 'Sleepy Joe'

16. 'Little Green Apples'

Answers to page 317
LYRICS 12: 1. 'Homeward Bound' (Simon and Garfunkel) 2. 'Dreadlock Holiday' (10cc) 3. 'One Man Band' (Leo Sayer) 4. 'Sorry Seems To Be The Hardest Word' (Elton John) 5. 'Rotterdam' (The Beautiful South) 6. 'Oh You Pretty Things' (David Bowie) 7. 'Private Investigations' (Dire Straits) 8. 'Miss You Nights' (Cliff Richard) 9. 'Disco 2000' (Pulp) 10. 'River Deep Mountain High' (Ike and Tina Turner) 11. 'For Your Babies' (Simply Red) 12. 'You've Got A Friend' (James Taylor) 13. 'Wherever I Lay My Hat' (Paul Young) 14. 'Light My Fire' (The Doors) 15. 'Go Your Own Way' (Fleetwood Mac) 16. 'Money For Nothing' (Dire Straits)

Reggae 3

Answers on page 314

1. Which band who had a 1971 hit with 'Black And White' evolved from The Rudies?

2. As whom is Iyael Constable better known?

3. Who sent a 'Message To You Rudy'?

4. What was the title of Desmond Dekker's first UK hit?

5. Which was the first reggae song to top the UK singles charts?

6. And which pair had the second UK reggae number one, in 1971?

7. Which member of Aswad used to be the children's TV show presenter on *Double Deckers*?

8. Which song gave Aswad their first UK number one?

9. And who recorded the track originally?

10. Which cover of a Bucks Fizz song gave Aswad a 1988 hit?

11. As whom is Patrick Murray better known?

12. Whose albums included 'Natty Dread' and 'Rastaman Vibration'?

13. With which previous collaborator did UB40 duet on the 1988 hit 'Breakfast In Bed'?

14. Which Sixties artist recorded the song originally?

15. What was the title of UB40's debut album?

16. Which Wailer's full name was Winston Hubert McIntosh?

Answers to page 314
CLASSICAL GAS 4: **1.** Parma **2.** Austrian **3.** Beethoven **4.** Mozart **5.** Bach **6.** Schubert **7.** Hector **8.** Berlioz **9.** Tchaikovsky **10.** 'The Emperor' **11.** Mozart **12.** Beethoven **13.** Rossini **14.** Monteverdi **15.** Ralph **16.** Danish

Lyrics 12

Answers on page 315

From which songs are the following lyrics taken?

1. 'I'm sitting on a railway station, got a ticket for my destination'
2. 'I don't like cricket – I love it'
3. 'Everybody knows down Ladbroke Grove you have to leap across the street'
4. 'What do I do when lightning strikes me and I wake to find that you're not there'
5. 'The whole place is pickled, the people are pickles for sure'
6. 'Wake up you sleepy head, put on some clothes, shake up your bed'
7. 'It's a mystery to me, the game commences for the usual fee – plus expenses'
8. 'I've had many times I can tell you, times when innocence I'd trade for company'
9. 'Oh Deborah do you recall, your house was very small with wood-chip on the wall'
10. 'When I was a little girl I had a rag doll'
11. 'You've got that look again, the one I hoped I had when I was a lad'
12. 'When you're down and troubled and you need a helping hand'
13. 'By the look in your eyes I can tell you're gonna cry, is it over me?'
14. 'You know that it would be untrue, you know that I would be a liar, if I was to say to you, girl, we couldn't get much higher'
15. 'Loving you isn't the right thing to do, how can I ever change things that I feel'
16. 'Now look at them yo-yo's that's the way you do it, you play the guitar on the MTV'

Answers to page 315
SIXTIES 9: **1.** The Jimi Hendrix Experience **2.** Bobby Vee **3.** Anthony Newley **4.** Del Shannon **5.** Marmalade **6.** Sonny and Cher **7.** Dave Clark Five **8.** Joe South **9.** The Herd **10.** Val Doonican **11.** Rick Nelson **12.** Jimmy Cliff **13.** Roy Orbison **14.** The Hollies **15.** Herman's Hermits **16.** Roger Miller

Pot Luck 40

Answers on page 320

1. Which hit song came to Tommy James while he was sitting in a hotel room watching the flashing neon sign of the Mutual of New York building?

2. Which band had a 'Perfect Skin' in 1984?

3. Which Sixties band's compilation album was called '25 Thumping Great Hits'?

4. Peter Cetera was the singer with which band named after a US city?

5. Which US band who were invariably on the road included Bob 'The Bear' Hite and Al 'Blind Owl' Wilson?

6. In what gear was King Midas according to a 1967 Hollies hit?

7. Who sang the first solo part on USA For Africa's 'We Are The World'?

8. Which of the Jackson Five married the daughter of Motown boss Berry Gordy?

9. Which UK number one hit of 1966 was recorded originally as a TV commercial jingle for petrol?

10. What is Missy short for, as in Missy Elliott?

11. From what cartoon character did Stephen Duffy take his nickname?

12. What was the title of Dire Straits' fourth UK number one album?

13. Which Uncle had a 2001 top five hit with 'Follow Me'?

14. On which Kinks album did 'Waterloo Sunset' first appear?

15. What is Santana's first name?

16. Which Prince was a profound influence on Madness?

Answers to page 320
DISCO 2: **1.** Amii Stewart **2.** Six **3.** 'In The Navy' **4.** *Can't Stop The Music*
5. Donna Summer **6.** The Bee Gees **7.** Tina Charles **8.** Baccara
9. 'Son Of My Father' (Chicory Tip) **10.** The Village People **11.** Chic
12. *Thank God It's Friday* **13.** Chic **14.** B. Devotion **15.** French
16. Hamilton Bohannon

Chart Toppers 14

Answers on page 321

1. Which 1965 UK number one by an Australian foursome was written and produced by Tom Springfield, brother of Dusty?

2. Who went all the way with a 'Sailor' in 1961?

3. Which American female artist had two number ones in 1958?

4. Who featured on Eternal's 1997 chart topper, 'I Wanna Be The Only One'?

5. 'Professional Widow (It's Got To Be Big)' was a 1997 hit for which Cornflake Girl?

6. Who played the 'Pipes Of Peace' to the top spot in 1984?

7. Which disco favourite was the best-selling UK single of 1979?

8. Which group spent eight weeks at number one in 1969 even though they didn't exist in the flesh?

9. Which 1961 hit from The Shadows was named after Thor Heyerdahl's raft?

10. Which band originally recorded 'If', a 1975 number one for Telly Savalas?

11. Two Philadelphia groups, The Percussions and The Monarchs, merged to form which 1975 chart toppers?

12. And what was the title of their number one?

13. Which number one had the chorus, 'Heathcliff, it's me, I'm Cathy come home again'?

14. Who had a 1968 UK number one with a Lennon and McCartney song but had to wait another 15 years before getting as high as number seven again?

15. Which trio reached the top in 1965 with 'Make It Easy On Yourself'?

16. Who had a 1999 number one with 'If I Let You Go'?

Answers to page 321
BACKSTREET BOYS 2: **1.** Brian and Nick **2.** Gene **3.** Four **4.** 'Black And Blue' **5.** 'Millennium' **6.** A.J. **7.** Nick **8.** Two **9.** 'Black And Blue' **10.** Brian **11.** Kevin **12.** 'Millennium' **13.** 'Answer To Our Life' and 'Time' **14.** Nick **15.** 1999 **16.** Four

Disco 2

Answers on page 318

1. Who decided to 'Knock On Wood' in 1979?

2. How many Village People were there?

3. What was The Village People's follow-up to 'Y.M.C.A.'?

4. In which 1980 movie did The Village People appear?

5. Who had a 1977 top ten hit with 'Love's Unkind'?

6. 'Too Much Heaven' was a 1978 top three hit for which band?

7. Whose second UK top ten hit was titled 'Dance Little Lady Dance'?

8. Which disco divas were the first female duo to have a UK number one?

9. Donna Summer's 'I Feel Love' was the second Giorgio Moroder composition to reach number one in the UK, but what was the first?

10. Which group's second album was titled 'Macho Man'?

11. Nile Rodgers was the leader of which US disco group?

12. In which film did Donna Summer make her acting debut?

13. 'Le Freak' sold over four million copies for which band?

14. Who backed Sheila?

15. And what nationality was she?

16. Who did the 'Disco Stomp'?

Answers to page 318
POT LUCK 40: **1.** 'Mony Mony' **2.** Lloyd Cole and The Commotions **3.** The Dave Clark Five **4.** Chicago **5.** Canned Heat **6.** Reverse ('King Midas In Reverse') **7.** Lionel Richie **8.** Jermaine **9.** 'Get Away' **10.** Misdemeanor **11.** 'Tin Tin' **12.** 'On Every Street' **13.** Uncle Kracker **14.** 'Something Else' **15.** Carlos **16.** Prince Buster

Backstreet Boys 2

Answers on page 319

1. Which two Backstreet Boys wrote 'Ain't That Cute' for Aaron Carter's debut album?

2. What is Nick Carter's middle name?

3. How many siblings does Nick Carter have?

4. 'More Than That', 'Get Another Boyfriend' and 'It's True' are tracks off which album?

5. Which Backstreet Boys album went diamond?

6. Which member of the group is nicknamed 'Bone Daddy'?

7. Which Backstreet Boy is a licensed scuba diver?

8. What number in the UK charts did 'Quit Playing Games (With My Heart)' reach in 1997?

9. Which album features an a cappella version of 'All I Have To Give'?

10. Which band member's nickname is 'B-Rok'?

11. Which member co-wrote 'Back To Your Heart'?

12. And on which album did it appear?

13. Which two tracks on 'Black And Blue' were written by the whole group?

14. Who sang lead vocals on 'I Need You Tonight'?

15. In which year were The Backstreet Boys 'Larger Than Life'?

16. How many UK top ten hits did the band have in 1997?

Answers to page 319
CHART TOPPERS 14: **1.** 'I'll Never Find Another You' (The Seekers) **2.** Petula Clark **3.** Connie Francis **4.** Bebe Winans **5.** Tori Amos **6.** Paul McCartney **7.** 'Y.M.C.A.' **8.** The Archies **9.** 'Kon-Tiki' **10.** Bread **11.** The Stylistics **12.** 'Can't Give You Anything (But My Love)' **13.** 'Wuthering Heights' **14.** Joe Cocker **15.** The Walker Brothers **16.** Westlife

Fifties 6

Answers on page 324

1. Which three singers had UK charts hits in 1955 with 'Yellow Rose Of Texas'?

2. Who had a 1958 hit with 'Deck Of Cards'?

3. Although Ronnie Hilton recorded a UK version, which American singer had the number one with 'Magic Moments'?

4. The theme from which TV Western gave Frankie Laine a UK top ten hit in 1959?

5. Lita Roza and Patti Page both had hits with which tender tale in 1953?

6. About what did Doris Day tell the golden daffodils in 1954?

7. Which Pat Boone song was the UK's biggest-selling single of 1956?

8. Who recorded the theme from the film *April Love*?

9. Who warned in 1955: 'Never Do A Tango With An Eskimo'?

10. Which British singer said 'Arrivederci Darling' in 1955?

11. Who were the resident band on the TV pop show *Oh Boy!*?

12. Whose appearance on *Oh Boy!* brought a flood of criticism over his 'crude exhibitionism'?

13. Which pair of brothers replaced another pair of brothers at the top of the UK charts in 1958?

14. Where was Emile Ford born?

15. Which was the biggest-selling UK single of 1954?

16. How many UK top twenty hits did Russ Conway have in 1959?

Answers to page 324
INDIE 7: 1. U2 2. Soul Asylum 3. Space 4. Travis 5. Cerys Matthews
6. Train 7. 'Girls And Boys' 8. Dodgy 9. Cast 10. 'Goldfinger' 11. Ocean
Colour Scene 12. The Verve 13. After a long dispute with Verve Records
14. The Lightning Seeds 15. Ash 16. 'You Showed Me'

Motown 4

Answers on page 325

1. Which Temptations hit bemoaned the disintegrating fabric of American society?

2. Who did Diana Ross oust as The Supremes' lead singer?

3. Which group's 1970 debut single became the fastest-selling record in Motown history?

4. What was Mary Wells's only UK top ten hit?

5. Where were The Miracles going in 1966?

6. In 1967, who replaced Florence Ballard in The Supremes?

7. With which fellow Motown band did The Supremes record 'I'm Gonna Make You Love Me'?

8. Who had the 1965 hit 'Uptight (Everything's Alright)'?

9. What was Marvin Gaye's first solo hit in the UK?

10. Who were stuck in 'Seven Rooms Of Gloom' in 1967?

11. Who was too busy thinking about his baby in 1969?

12. What was The Four Tops' last UK top ten hit before quitting Motown in 1972?

13. What was the first UK hit for Gladys Knight and The Pips?

14. Who told what life was like 'Behind A Painted Smile' in 1969?

15. Who had a 1967 hit with 'The Happening'?

16. What lesson in the alphabet did The Jackson Five provide?

Answers to page 325
POT LUCK 41: **1.** The Kinks **2.** Darius Rucker **3.** J. Geils Band **4.** Squeeze **5.** Bobby G **6.** Kirsty MacColl **7.** Nadinia **8.** Van Morrison **9.** Bob Seger **10.** *All You Need Is Cash* **11.** Dean Friedman **12.** Neil Sedaka **13.** John Parr **14.** Dandy Livingstone **15.** 'Raindrops Keep Falling On My Head' **16.** Tuesday

Indie 7

Answers on page 322

1. Who released the album 'Achtung Baby'?

2. Which American band caught a 'Runaway Train' in 1993?

3. Who sang about their beautiful 'Neighbourhood' in 1996?

4. Whose 1997 album was titled 'Good Feeling'?

5. Who is the singer with Catatonia?

6. Who had a 2001 album called 'Drops Of Jupiter'?

7. Which was the first single to be taken from Blur's 'Parklife'?

8. Who were 'Staying Out For The Summer' in 1994?

9. Whose second album was titled 'Mother Nature Calls'?

10. Which hit for Ash was also the title of a Bond film?

11. Simon Fowler is the vocalist with which Indie band?

12. Whose 1993 album was titled 'A Storm In Heaven'?

13. Why were Verve renamed The Verve?

14. 'Sugar Coated Iceberg' was a 1997 hit for which band?

15. Which Indie band's first chart single was 'Kung Fu'?

16. Which Lightning Seeds hit was previously recorded back in the Sixties by both The Byrds and The Turtles?

Answers to page 322
FIFTIES 6: 1. Mitch Miller, Gary Miller and Ronnie Hilton 2. Wink Martindale 3. Perry Como 4. *Rawhide* 5. '(How Much Is) That Doggie In The Window?' 6. 'Secret Love' 7. 'I'll Be Home' 8. Pat Boone 9. Alma Cogan 10. Anne Shelton 11. Lord Rockingham's XI 12. Cliff Richard 13. The Kalin Twins replaced The Everly Brothers 14. The Bahamas 15. 'Secret Love' 16. Five

Pot Luck 41

Answers on page 323

1. The 1972 single 'Supersonic Rocket Ship' was which band's last UK hit for nine years?

2. Who is the lead singer of Hootie and the Blowfish?

3. Whose baby was on the 'Centerfold' in 1982?

4. Chris Difford and Glenn Tilbrook were the songwriting partnership of which band?

5. Which member of Bucks Fizz recorded the theme from the TV series *Big Deal*?

6. Who joined The Pogues in a 'Fairytale Of New York'?

7. What is Alanis Morissette's real Christian name?

8. Which Irish singer released the 1970 album 'Moondance'?

9. Who fronted The Silver Bullet Band?

10. George Harrison, Mick Jagger and Paul Simon all appeared in which Rutles film?

11. Which American singer/songwriter had a number three hit in 1978 with 'Lucky Stars'?

12. Who sang about 'Laughter In The Rain' in 1974?

13. 'St Elmo's Fire' was a 1986 hit for which artist?

14. Who warned 'Suzanne Beware Of The Devil'?

15. What identical meteorological sensation was experienced by Bobbie Gentry, Sacha Distel and B.J. Thomas in 1970?

16. What day was everything for Chairmen Of The Board in 1971?

Answers to page 323
MOTOWN 4: 1. 'Ball Of Confusion' 2. Florence Ballard 3. The Jackson Five ('I Want You Back') 4. 'My Guy' 5. To A Go-Go 6. Cindy Birdsong 7. The Temptations 8. Stevie Wonder 9. 'How Sweet It Is' 10. The Four Tops 11. Marvin Gaye 12. 'Simple Game' 13. 'Take Me In Your Arms And Love Me' 14. The Isley Brothers 15. The Supremes 16. 'ABC'

Tom Jones 1

Answers on page 328

1. Who recorded the original version of 'Green Green Grass Home'?

2. In which year was 'Delilah' released?

3. Who wrote 'She's A Lady'?

4. From which film was the single 'A Boy From Nowhere' taken?

5. What was Tom Jones's first UK number one?

6. Who managed both Tom Jones and Engelbert Humperdinck?

7. What was the name of Jones's backing band in the mid-Sixties?

8. What was the title of his debut album?

9. Which Tom Jones hit was written and originally recorded by Lonnie Donegan?

10. Which three successive Tom Jones singles all got stuck at number two in the UK charts?

11. Which 1987 song gave Jones his first UK top ten success for 15 years?

12. What was the title of Jones's first single?

13. On which Prince song did he collaborate with Art Of Noise?

14. What did 27-year-old Katherine Berkery do to Jones in 1989?

15. Which Bond theme did Jones record in 1966?

16. Which 1971 single was recorded originally by Roger Williams in 1957?

Answers to page 328
NAME CHANGES 13: **1.** Bag Of Blues **2.** Mungo Jerry **3.** Gene Simmons **4.** Culture Club **5.** Johnny Rotten **6.** Doris Day **7.** Kool (And The Gang) **8.** Paul and Barry Ryan **9.** Family **10.** Ranking Roger **11.** Bobby Rydell **12.** The Sex Pistols **13.** Tom Jones **14.** The Cure **15.** Dr Hook **16.** Devo

Number Twos 7

Answers on page 329

Which artists reached number two in the UK singles charts with the following tracks?

1. 'Are You Sure' (1961)

2. 'True Love Ways' (1965)

3. 'The Most Beautiful Girl' (1974)

4. 'Going In With My Eyes Open' (1977)

5. 'Up The Junction' (1979)

6. 'What You're Proposing' (1980)

7. 'You Drive Me Crazy' (1981)

8. 'Every Beat Of My Heart' (1986)

9. 'Golden Brown' (1982)

10. 'Part Of The Union' (1973)

11. 'Heart Full Of Soul' (1965)

12. 'Let's Hear It For The Boy' (1984)

13. 'Heartbreaker' (1982)

14. 'Holding Out For A Hero' (1985)

15. 'You Can Get It If You Really Want' (1970)

16. 'I Did What I Did For Maria' (1971)

Answers to page 329
ALBUMS 12: 1. The Bay City Rollers 2. Queen 3. Style Council
4. Boyzone 5. 'True Blue' 6. 10cc 7. Curiosity Killed The Cat 8. Spandau
Ballet 9. The Cure 10. 'The Great Escape' 11. 'Steptacular' 12. Elton
John 13. Wet Wet Wet 14. It was circular 15. Paris 16. 'Abbey Road'

Name Changes 13

Answers on page 326

1. What were Jethro Tull previously known as?

2. Which Sixties band changed their name from The Good Earth?

3. Which heavy rock frontman was born Chaim Witz?

4. Which flamboyant Eighties band started out as In Praise Of Lemmings?

5. Who changed his name from John Lydon and then adopted it again later?

6. Which singer looked for something easier to pronounce than Doris Kappelhoff?

7. Which gang leader did Robert Bell become?

8. Who began their lives as Paul and Barry Sapherson?

9. Which Seventies band were previously called The Farinas?

10. What stage name did Roger Charlery adopt when joining the two-tone movement?

11. What shorter name did Robert Ridarelli choose for himself?

12. Which band used to be called The Swankers?

13. Who did 'Tommy' of Tommy Scott and The Senators go on to become?

14. Which band were once known as The Goat Band?

15. Who started their career as The Chocolate Papers?

16. Which American band was reduced from the De-Evolution Band?

Answers to page 326
TOM JONES 1: 1. Johnny Darrell 2. 1968 3. Paul Anka 4. *Matador* 5. 'It's Not Unusual' 6. Gordon Mills 7. The Squires 8. 'Along Came Jones' 9. 'I'll Never Fall In Love Again' 10. 'I'll Never Fall In Love Again', 'I'm Coming Home' and 'Delilah' 11. 'A Boy From Nowhere' 12. 'Chills And Fever' 13. 'Kiss' 14. She successfully filed a paternity suit against him 15. 'Thunderball' 16. 'Till'

Albums 12

Answers on page 327

1. Which tartan horde released the 1975 album 'Once Upon A Star'?

2. Whose 1980 number one album was titled 'The Game'?

3. 'Our Favourite Shop' was a 1985 album by which band?

4. Whose debut album in 1995 was 'Said And Done'?

5. Which Madonna album was the UK best-seller for 1986?

6. Which band recorded the 1974 album 'Sheet Music'?

7. 'Keep Your Distance' was a 1987 number one album for which band?

8. Who released a 1986 album titled 'Through The Barricades' which bore a single of the same name?

9. Whose 1992 chart-topping album was called 'Wish'?

10. Which Blur album contained 'Stereotypes' and 'Country House'?

11. What was the title of Steps' UK number one album of 1999?

12. Who was 'Sleeping With The Past' in 1990?

13. Who had 'Popped In Souled Out' in 1988?

14. What was revolutionary about the cover of The Small Faces' album 'Ogden's Nut Gone Flake'?

15. In which city was Simple Minds' 'Live In The City Of Light' recorded?

16. Which album was the UK best-seller of 1969?

Answers to page 327
NUMBER TWOS 7: 1. The Allisons 2. Peter and Gordon 3. Charlie Rich 4. David Soul 5. Squeeze 6. Status Quo 7. Shakin' Stevens 8. Rod Stewart 9. The Stranglers 10. The Strawbs 11. The Yardbirds 12. Deniece Williams 13. Dionne Warwick 14. Bonnie Tyler 15. Desmond Dekker and The Aces 16. Tony Christie

Seventies 10

Answers on page 332

1. 'Five Minutes' and 'Duchess' were hits for which punk band?

2. Which two members of Showaddywaddy are fathers of noted sportsmen?

3. How many sisters were there in Pussycat?

4. Jeffrey Calvert and Max West were better known as which 1975 chart-topping act?

5. Who requested 'Don't Play Your Rock 'N' Roll To Me' in 1975?

6. Which Australian winners of *Opportunity Knocks*, who had a 1971 hit with 'Tom Tom Turnaround', were at the centre of a vote-rigging storm?

7. Which band's first UK hit was 'Only You Can' in 1975?

8. Which island did The Gibson Brothers sing about in 1979?

9. 'You Don't Have To Be In The Army To Fight In The War' was a 1971 hit for which band?

10. 'Dyna-Mite' was which band's UK top ten debut?

11. Who played the violin with Slade?

12. Which bopping bird was a 1972 hit for Michael Jackson?

13. Which British R & B band had a 1972 hit with 'Burlesque'?

14. Which member of *The Partridge Family* did David Cassidy play?

15. How many UK top ten hits did Abba have in 1979?

16. Which Yorkshire brass band found themselves at number two in the charts in 1977 with their version of 'The Floral Dance'?

Answers to page 332
POT LUCK 42: **1.** Everything But The Girl **2.** The Shondells **3.** 1964
4. Curiosity Killed The Cat **5.** Carousel ('On A Carousel') **6.** Wings
7. Red Hot Chili Peppers **8.** The Strokes **9.** Tom Jones **10.** Jeremy Clyde
(Chad and Jeremy) **11.** Jon Anderson (Yes) **12.** Deacon Blue **13.** Dollar
14. Edison Lighthouse **15.** Dexy's Midnight Runners **16.** Huey Lewis and
The News

Girl Bands 6

Answers on page 333

1. What family trait links The Ronettes and Eternal?

2. Which girl group had a 1963 hit with 'One Fine Day'?

3. What was All Saints' first UK number one?

4. Which member of Bananarama left in 1987 and married Dave Stewart of The Eurythmics?

5. Who replaced her in Bananarama?

6. The Ganser sisters were members of which Sixties girl group?

7. Bernie, Linda and Ann were members of which Seventies singing sisters?

8. Which Sixties singer wrote 'He's A Rebel' for The Crystals?

9. Which girl band split up in 1989, months after having a number one single on both sides of the Atlantic?

10. Which Ronette married Phil Spector?

11. Which artist, now an international star, sang backing vocals on The Ronettes' 1963 hit 'Be My Baby'?

12. Which girl band had a 1999 hit with 'So Long'?

13. Which pet is Atomic in a current girl band?

14. Who wanted to know when 'Jimmy Mack' was coming back in 1967?

15. Which Steam hit charted for Bananarama in 1983?

16. 'Deep Sea Skiving' was the title of which girl band's first hit album?

Answers to page 333
SINATRA 1: **1.** 'Three Coins In The Fountain' **2.** Albert **3.** Nelson Riddle **4.** Sammy Davis Jnr **5.** Whispering Jack Smith **6.** 'Strangers In The Night' **7.** 1969 **8.** 'Love's Been Good To Me' **9.** 'Songs For Swinging Lovers' **10.** The Wine ('I Will Drink The Wine') **11.** 'My Way' **12.** Bono **13.** 'Granada' **14.** New York **15.** 'Chicago' **16.** 'My Way'

Pot Luck 42

Answers on page 330

1. Which duo took their name from a second-hand furniture shop in Hull?

2. What was the name of Tommy James's backing group?

3. In which year was *Top of the Pops* first broadcast?

4. Ben Volpeliere-Pierrot was lead singer with which band?

5. Which fairground ride was a big hit with The Hollies in 1967?

6. Who had a 1974 hit with 'Band On The Run'?

7. 'Antwan The Swan' and 'Flea' are members of which US band?

8. Whose 2001 album was titled 'Is This It'?

9. Which international singing star made his professional debut at the Treforest Non-Political Working Men's Club in 1957?

10. Which member of a Sixties duo is now a TV actor?

11. Which singer with a progressive rock group once went solo under the name of Hans Christian Anderson?

12. Which Scottish band got their name from a Steely Dan song?

13. Who asked 'Who Were You With In The Moonlight'?

14. 'It's Up To You Petula' was which band's follow-up to a number one?

15. Violinist Helen O'Hara joined which band in 1982?

16. Who was 'Stuck With You' in 1986?

Answers to page 330

SEVENTIES 10: 1. The Stranglers 2. Romeo Challenger (father of international athlete Ben) and Trevor Oakes (father of professional footballer Scott) 3. Three 4. Typically Tropical 5. Smokie 6. New World 7. Fox 8. 'Cuba' 9. Mungo Jerry 10. Mud 11. Jim Lea 12. 'Rockin' Robin' 13. Family 14. Keith 15. Five 16. Brighouse and Rastrick

Sinatra 1

Answers on page 331

1. Which title song from a 1954 film gave Sinatra his first UK number one?

2. What was Sinatra's middle name?

3. Whose orchestra backed Sinatra on his 1955 hit 'Learnin' The Blues'?

4. With whom did Sinatra duet on the 1962 hit 'Me And My Shadow'?

5. Who recorded the original version of 'Me And My Shadow' back in 1927?

6. Which 1966 UK chart topper was taken from the film *A Man Could Get Killed*?

7. In which year did Sinatra release 'My Way'?

8. Which 1969 hit for Sinatra was first recorded by Rod McKuen?

9. What was the title of Sinatra's landmark album from 1958?

10. What did Sinatra say he would drink in 1971?

11. Which Sinatra track spent a record 124 weeks on the UK singles chart?

12. Which Irish rock star joined Sinatra for a 1993 version of 'I've Got You Under My Skin'?

13. Which Sinatra hit from 1961 was originally recorded by Frankie Laine?

14. According to Sinatra, which city is so good they named it twice?

15. Where did Sinatra say was 'My Kind Of Town'?

16. Claude Francois recorded the original version of which Sinatra classic?

Answers to page 331
GIRL BANDS 6: **1.** Both had pairs of Bennett sisters **2.** The Chiffons
3. 'Never Ever' **4.** Siobhan Fahey **5.** Jacqui Sullivan **6.** The Shangri-Las
7. The Nolans **8.** Gene Pitney **9.** The Bangles **10.** Veronica 'Ronnie'
Bennett **11.** Cher **12.** Fierce **13.** Kitten **14.** Martha Reeves and The
Vandellas **15.** 'Na Na Hey Hey Kiss Him Goodbye' **16.** Bananarama

Chart Toppers 15

Answers on page 336

1. Which was the first UK number one to have the number 'two' in the title?

2. Which was the first UK number one to have a boy's name in the title?

3. Which was the first UK number one to feature a girl's name in the title?

4. Which was the first UK number one to mention the word 'Christmas' in the title?

5. Which was the first UK number one to include a capital city in the title?

6. Which was the first UK number one with the colour 'blue' in the title?

7. Which was the first UK number one to include the name of a breed of bird?

8. Which was the first UK number one with the name of a musical instrument in the title?

9. Excluding 'Maggie May', which was the first UK number one with a month in the title?

10. Which was the first UK number one with a reptile in the title?

11. Which was the first UK number one to include the colour 'red' in the title?

12. Which was the first UK number one with 'gold' in the title?

13. Which was the first UK number one with 'black' in the title?

14. Which was the first UK number one with the name of an insect in the title?

15. Which was the first UK number one to include the name of a mammal in the title?

16. Which was the first UK number one to include a rodent in the title?

Answers to page 336
BLUES 2: **1.** John Lee Hooker **2.** B.B. King **3.** 'The Kid' **4.** Muddy Waters
5. Memphis Slim **6.** John Mayall **7.** Magic Slim **8.** CCS **9.** Freddie King
10. Elmore James **11.** Etta James **12.** 1995 **13.** 'Champion Jack' **14.** Fats
Domino **15.** Chicago **16.** Ray Charles

Cover Versions 11

Answers on page 337

1. Which US singer covered Wings' 'Let 'Em In' in 1977?

2. Coast To Coast had a 1981 hit with 'Let's Jump The Broomstick', but which female singer had a UK hit with it 20 years earlier?

3. Which Scottish duo revived P.J. Proby's 'Hold Me' in 1981?

4. Which song has been a hit for both The Chi-Lites and M.C. Hammer?

5. Who originally had a hit with the Rolling Stones' 1986 chartbuster 'Harlem Shuffle'?

6. Which Mamas and The Papas song did Bitty McLean cover in 1994?

7. Lee Lawrence had the original hit with which Elvis number one?

8. Which Beach Boys song did David Cassidy take to number 16 in the UK charts in 1975?

9. Who recorded the original version of Don McLean's 1980 number one 'Cryin''?

10. Which two artists have had number ones with 'Baby Come Back'?

11. Who had a 1987 hit with Tommy James's 'Mony Mony'?

12. Who had a 1965 UK hit with 'The Promised Land', ten years before Elvis?

13. Which song links Maurice Williams and The Zodiacs, The Hollies and Jackson Browne?

14. Which Fun Boy Three hit of 1982 was recorded by Al Martino 22 years previously?

15. Which Beach Boys song was covered by Aaron Carter in 1998?

16. In 1986, which band found a Chi-Lites song 'Too Good To Be Forgotten'?

Answers to page 337
NINETIES 9: 1. 'Stars' 2. Santana 3. 'Love Is The Drug' 4. R.E.M.
5. Dr Dre 6. Shaggy 7. Prince Naseem 8. Gabrielle 9. 'Train In Vain'
10. *The Butcher's Wife* 11. Madonna 12. M People 13. George Michael
14. 'I Will Always Love You' 15. 'World In Motion' 16. 'Fantasy'

Blues 2

Answers on page 334

1. Which blues guitarist had a UK hit with 'Boom Boom' when it was featured in a 1992 TV commercial for jeans nearly 30 years after its original release?

2. Which blues singer teamed up with U2 in 1989 for 'When Love Comes To Town'?

3. What was young blues pianist Billy Emerson's nickname?

4. Which guitarist's 1981 album was titled 'King Bee'?

5. Who was boogie-woogie piano player Peter Chatman better known as?

6. Which British blues king headed the Bluesbreakers?

7. Guitarist Morris Holt adopted which stage name?

8. Which band did Alexis Korner form initially?

9. Who released the 1974 album 'Burglar'?

10. Which slide guitarist's debut release was 'Dust My Broom'?

11. Which blues singer was born Jamesetta Hawkins?

12. In which year did Rory Gallagher die?

13. What was William Thomas Dupree's nickname?

14. Which blues giant reached number six in the UK charts in 1956 with his version of 'Blueberry Hill'?

15. Which city did The Climax Blues Band drop from their name?

16. Who had a 1961 hit with 'Hit The Road Jack'?

Answers to page 334
CHART TOPPERS 15: **1.** 'Two Little Boys' **2.** 'Hey Joe' (Frankie Laine) **3.** 'Rose Marie' (Slim Whitman) **4.** 'Christmas Alphabet' (Dickie Valentine) **5.** 'Poor People Of Paris' (Winifred Atwell) **6.** 'Singing The Blues' **7.** 'Little Red Rooster' **8.** 'Mr Tambourine Man' **9.** 'January' **10.** 'Turtle Power' **11.** 'She Wears Red Feathers' (Guy Mitchell) **12.** 'Silence Is Golden' **13.** 'Paint It Black' **14.** 'Butterfly' (Andy Williams) **15.** 'Running Bear' (Johnny Preston) **16.** 'Rat Trap'

Nineties 9

Answers on page 335

1. 'Something Got Me Started' was taken from which Simply Red album?

2. Whose 1999 hit 'Smooth' was his first UK chart entry for 19 years?

3. Which Roxy Music song was remixed by Rollo and Sister Bliss in 1996?

4. 'Bang And Blame' was a hit for which band?

5. Who featured on Eminem's 'Guilty Conscience'?

6. Whose 1995 number one was 'Boombastic'?

7. Which boxer teamed up with Kaliphz for the 1996 single 'Walk Like A Champion'?

8. Which solo artist joined East 17 on 'If You Ever'?

9. Which Clash single was sampled on Garbage's 'Stupid Girl'?

10. From which film was Julia Fordham's 'Love Moves (In Mysterious Ways)' taken?

11. Who released the 1992 album 'Erotica'?

12. Who conducted a 'Search For The Hero' in 1995?

13. Who had a number two hit in 1998 with 'Outside'?

14. Which film track was the best-selling UK single of 1992?

15. Which soccer song reached number one in 1990?

16. Which Mariah Carey single sampled Tom Tom Club's 'Genius Of Love'?

Answers to page 335
COVER VERSIONS 11: **1.** Billy Paul **2.** Brenda Lee **3.** B.A. Robertson and Maggie Bell **4.** 'Have You Seen Her' **5.** Bob and Earl **6.** 'Dedicated To The One I Love' **7.** 'Crying In The Chapel' **8.** 'Darlin'' **9.** Roy Orbison **10.** The Equals and Pato Banton **11.** Billy Idol **12.** Chuck Berry **13.** 'Stay' **14.** 'Summertime' **15.** 'Surfin' USA' **16.** Amazulu

Solo Artists 7

Answers on page 340

1. Which Eagle aired his 'Dirty Laundry' after going solo?

2. Which member of the Jackson family had a number one album with 'Control'?

3. 'Steppin' Out' was a track from which Joe Jackson album?

4. What is Cyndi Lauper's real first name?

5. Who wrote 'Step Inside Love', a 1968 hit for Cilla Black?

6. What nationality is Bjork?

7. Which hit band did Bjork used to be a member of?

8. Which Texan singer's biggest chart success was 'It Must Be Him' in 1967?

9. Whose debut solo album was the 1972 offering 'Cherish'?

10. Which Gloria Gaynor anthem was remixed to chart again 14 years on in 1993?

11. Who sang about 'Games Without Frontiers' in 1980?

12. And which female singer provided supporting vocals for 'Games Without Frontiers'?

13. Which Richie opened the Woodstock Festival in 1969?

14. Who took Billie Holliday's 'That Ole Devil Called Love' to number two in the UK in 1985?

15. Which 1990 UK number one for a solo artist was written by Prince and originally recorded by The Family?

16. Who could see clearly now in 1972?

Answers to page 340
POT LUCK 43: 1. Pilot 2. The Cruisers 3. David Clayton-Thomas
4. 'Parallel Lines' 5. Sloopy ('Hang On Sloopy') 6. 'Jennifer Eccles'
7. Peter Shelley 8. Prince 9. A grocery store 10. Kate Bush 11. Lilac
12. The Cufflinks 13. Foreigner 14. Africa 15. 2 16. 'Breakout'

Sixties 10

Answers on page 341

Which artists had UK hits with the following tracks in the Sixties?

1. 'Still I'm Sad'

2. 'To Whom It Concerns'

3. 'Time For Living'

4. 'Little Town Flirt'

5. 'Just Like Eddie'

6. 'Gimme A Little Sign'

7. 'Gimme Some Loving'

8. 'Baby Make It Soon'

9. 'Am I That Easy To Forget'

10. 'Barbara Ann'

11. 'Early In The Morning'

12. 'Dick-A-Dum-Dum'

13. 'Multiplication'

14. 'My Little Lady'

15. 'My Mind's Eye'

16. 'The Wedding'

Answers to page 341
COUNTRY AND WESTERN 5: **1.** His collie dog **2.** The Oak Ridge Boys **3.** Shania Twain **4.** Dolly Parton **5.** Kenny Rogers ('Ruby, Don't Take Your Love To Town') **6.** Donegal **7.** Willie Nelson **8.** Waylon Jennings **9.** 'Lucille' **10.** 'Man! I Feel Like A Woman!' **11.** John Denver **12.** Charlie Rich **13.** Kenny O'Dell **14.** Marty Robbins **15.** LeAnn Rimes **16.** 'The Wayward Wind'

Pot Luck 43

Answers on page 338

1. David Paton was the singer with which Seventies band?

2. What was the name of Dave Berry's backing group?

3. Who is the lead vocalist with Blood, Sweat and Tears?

4. Which Blondie album contained 'Hanging On The Telephone'?

5. Who did The McCoys say 'lives in a very bad part of town'?

6. Whose satchel did The Hollies used to carry?

7. Who issued the ultimatum: 'Love Me Love My Dog'?

8. Who sang about '1999' in 1985?

9. Where did Anthony work in Billy Joel's 'Movin' Out'?

10. Who had a 1980 hit with 'Babooshka'?

11. What colour wine was on Elkie Brooks's lips in 1978?

12. Which US group of the late Sixties scored hits with 'Tracy' and 'When Julie Comes Around'?

13. Which American band were 'Waiting For A Girl Like You' in 1981?

14. Which continent was a hit with Toto in 1983?

15. What position in the UK charts did The Tremeloes' '(Call Me) Number One' reach?

16. What was Swing Out Sister's first UK hit?

Answers to page 338
SOLO ARTISTS 7: **1.** Don Henley **2.** Janet Jackson **3.** 'Night And Day **4.** Cynthia **5.** Paul McCartney **6.** Icelandic **7.** The Sugarcubes **8.** Vikki Carr **9.** David Cassidy **10.** 'I Will Survive' **11.** Peter Gabriel **12.** Kate Bush **13.** Richie Havens **14.** Alison Moyet **15.** 'Nothing Compares 2 U' (Sinead O'Connor) **16.** Johnny Nash

Country and Western 5

Answers on page 339

1. Three years after Jim Reeves died, what was buried at his feet?

2. Wally Fowler was leader of which American country band?

3. Whose 1995 album was titled 'The Woman In Me'?

4. Who had a country hit with a song called 'Dumb Blonde'?

5. Who lamented: 'It's hard to love a man whose legs are bent and paralysed'?

6. In which Irish county was Daniel O'Donnell born?

7. Which veteran country star teamed up with Julio Iglesias for the 1984 hit 'To All The Girls I've Loved Before'?

8. Whose theme for the TV series *The Dukes of Hazzard* made the US top thirty?

9. Who picked a fine time to leave Kenny Rogers?

10. In which song did Shania Twain want to 'go totally crazy, forget I'm a lady'?

11. Who said 'Thank God I'm A Country Boy' in 1975?

12. Who had a 1974 UK hit with 'Behind Closed Doors'?

13. But who recorded the song originally?

14. Which country singer had hits in the early Sixties with 'El Paso' and 'Devil Woman'?

15. Which American singer went 'Crazy' in 1999?

16. Which Tex Ritter hit of 1956 later became a number one for Frank Ifield?

Answers to page 339
SIXTIES 10: **1.** The Yardbirds **2.** Chris Andrews **3.** The Association **4.** Del Shannon **5.** Heinz **6.** Brenton Wood **7.** Spencer Davis Group **8.** Marmalade **9.** Engelbert Humperdinck **10.** The Beach Boys **11.** Vanity Fare **12.** Des O'Connor **13.** Bobby Darin **14.** The Tremeloes **15.** The Small Faces **16.** Julie Rogers

Boyzone 1

Answers on page 344

1. On whose Irish TV show did Boyzone make their debut?

2. Which Louis was Boyzone's manager?

3. Which member of Boyzone took part in *Celebrity Big Brother*?

4. Which two members of the band used to be garage mechanics?

5. What was Shane Lynch studying before he joined Boyzone?

6. 'Love Me For A Reason' and 'Father And Son' were both tracks on which Boyzone album?

7. Which song gave Boyzone their second UK number one?

8. Which Boyzone single came from the musical *Whistle Down The Wind*?

9. Which was Boyzone's second cover version to reach number one in 1999?

10. What was the title of the band's third album?

11. Which member of Boyzone had his first solo number one in 1999?

12. What was the title of the track?

13. In which year did Boyzone release their debut single?

14. What did 'No Matter What' achieve that none of the band's three previous number ones had managed?

15. In which year did Boyzone release the album 'Where We Belong'?

16. Which former number one was removed from circulation at the request of Polydor while still in the charts at number 34?

Answers to page 344
EIGHTIES 10: 1. 'Eat To The Beat' 2. Bruce Foxton 3. Dexy's Midnight Runners 4. Olivia Newton-John 5. Odyssey 6. Major Tom 7. Jason Donovan 8. Fleetwood Mac 9. 'January February' 10. Katrina and The Waves 11. ZZ Top 12. 'Joan Of Arc' 13. DeBarge 14. Hazell Dean 15. Aswad 16. Tiffany

One-Hit Wonders 10

Answers on page 345

1. Whose only UK top twenty hit was 'That's Nice' in 1966?

2. Whose only hit was the 1972 instrumental 'Popcorn'?

3. Which UK band's one chart entry came with 'Making Up Again' in 1978?

4. What was the title of Crazy Elephant's 1969 hit?

5. Which South African girl band reached number two in 1978 with 'Substitute'?

6. Which French group had a number two hit in 1977 with 'Magic Fly'?

7. 'We Do It' was a 1976 hit for which duo?

8. Who asked 'Why Did You Do It?' in 1975?

9. Which Dutch group had a UK hit with 'Ding-A-Dong', their 1975 Eurovision Song Contest winner?

10. Which Jamaican artist had a 1970 top ten hit with his version of 'Love Of The Common People'?

11. Which cover of a Jerry Lee Lewis song gave Tiny Tim his only UK hit?

12. Which much-covered song gave The Tokens their only chart success in 1961?

13. Who ate cannibals in 1982 and never figured again in the UK top 50?

14. Which kiddies' classic soared to number four in the charts in 1984 for The Toy Dolls?

15. America's Toxic Two had a 1992 hit with which track?

16. Which star of *Bonanza* charted in 1964 with 'Ringo'?

Answers to page 345
NOVELTY NUMBERS 6: 1. *Tiswas* 2. 'Eh-Oh!' 3. 'Margate' 4. Adge Cutler 5. The Wombles 6. A dustman 7. The Barron Knights 8. Dick Emery 9. 'Monster Mash' 10. Bobby 'Boris' Pickett and The Crypt-Kickers 11. 'In The Brownies' 12. 'Black Pudding Bertha' 13. 'D.I.V.O.R.C.E.' 14. 1975 15. 'The Ying Tong Song' 16. 'Bloodnok's Rock 'n' Roll Call'

Eighties 10

Answers on page 342

1. The number one single 'Atomic' was taken from which Blondie album?

2. Who was the bassist with The Jam?

3. Big Jim Paterson played trombone with which Eighties band?

4. Who joined the Electric Light Orchestra on the 1980 number one 'Xanadu'?

5. Which disco band topped the charts with 'Use It Up And Wear It Out'?

6. In 'Ashes To Ashes', who was revealed as 'a junkie...hitting an all-time low'?

7. 'Every Day (I Love You More)' was a 1989 hit for which soap star?

8. 'Oh Diane' and 'Big Love' were hits for which band in the Eighties?

9. Which two months did Barbara Dickson sing about in 1980?

10. Who were 'Walking On Sunshine' in 1985?

11. 'Gimme All Your Lovin'' and 'Sharp Dressed Man' were hits for which US rockers?

12. Which 15th-century French maid provided Orchestral Manoeuvres In The Dark with a 1981 top five hit?

13. Who had a 1985 hit with 'Rhythm Of The Night'?

14. Who was 'Searchin'' in 1984?

15. Which band's name means 'black' in Arabic?

16. As whom was American teenager Ms Darwisch better known?

Answers to page 342
BOYZONE 1: **1.** Gay Byrne **2.** Louis Walsh **3.** Keith Duffy **4.** Mikey Graham and Keith Duffy **5.** Architecture **6.** 'Said And Done' **7.** 'A Different Beat' **8.** 'No Matter What' **9.** 'You Needed Me' **10.** 'Where We Belong' **11.** Ronan Keating **12.** 'When You Say Nothing At All' **13.** 1994 **14.** It stayed at number one in the UK for more than a week **15.** 1998 **16.** 'No Matter What'

Novelty Numbers 6

Answers on page 343

1. The presenters of which Saturday morning TV show unleashed 'The Bucket Of Water Song'?

2. What did Teletubbies say in 1997?

3. About which seaside resort did Chas and Dave wax lyrical in 1982?

4. Who led The Wurzels on their 1967 hit 'Drink Up Thy Zider'?

5. 'Minuetto Allegretto' was a 1974 hit for which furry creatures?

6. What was Lonnie Donegan's old man by profession?

7. 'Call Up The Groups' and 'Pop Go The Workers' were Sixties hits for which comedy band?

8. Who used his catchphrase 'You Are Awful' in a 1973 hit?

9. Which monster hit began: 'I was working in the lab late one night'?

10. And which group sang it?

11. What was Billy Connolly's answer to The Village People's 'In The Navy'?

12. According to The Goodies, who was the Queen of Northern Soul?

13. Which Billy Connolly parody achieved a higher chart placing than the original?

14. In which year did Jasper Carrott ride into town on his 'Funky Moped'?

15. Which song gave The Goons top ten hits in 1956 and 1973?

16. Which track formed a double A-side on the Goons' hit of 1956?

Answers to page 343
ONE-HIT WONDERS 10: **1.** Neil Christian **2.** Hot Butter **3.** Goldie
4. 'Gimme Gimme Good Lovin'' **5.** Clout **6.** Space **7.** R and J Stone
8. Stretch **9.** Teach-In **10.** Nicky Thomas **11.** 'Great Balls Of Fire'
12. 'The Lion Sleeps Tonight' **13.** Toto Coelo **14.** 'Nellie The Elephant'
15. 'Rave Generator' **16.** Lorne Greene

Pot Luck 44

Answers on page 348

In which years were the following tracks top ten hits in the UK?

1. 'Far Far Away' (Slade)

2. 'Best Years Of Our Lives' (Modern Romance)

3. 'Material Girl' (Madonna)

4. 'As Tears Go By' (Marianne Faithfull)

5. 'Elected' (Alice Cooper)

6. 'The Universal' (Blur)

7. 'Zabadak!' (Dave Dee, Dozy, Beaky, Mick and Tich)

8. 'Whole Lotta Shakin' Goin' On' (Jerry Lee Lewis)

9. 'Rio' (Duran Duran)

10. 'Like Clockwork' (The Boomtown Rats)

11. 'Blue Eyes' (Elton John)

12. 'Daydream Believer' (The Monkees)

13. 'Old Before I Die' (Robbie Williams)

14. 'My Eyes Adored You' (Frankie Valli)

15. 'Happy Jack' (The Who)

16. 'Calendar Girl' (Neil Sedaka)

Answers to page 348
LYRICS 13: 1. 'You're So Vain' (Carly Simon) 2. 'Maggie May' (Rod Stewart) 3. 'Green Green Grass Of Home' (Tom Jones) 4. 'Substitute' (The Who) 5. 'Wishing Well' (Free) 6. 'Vincent' (Don McLean) 7. 'Chance' (Big Country) 8. 'Crocodile Rock' (Elton John) 9. 'Life On Mars' (David Bowie) 10. 'Radio Ga Ga' (Queen) 11. 'Breakfast In America' (Supertramp) 12. 'Don't Look Back In Anger' (Oasis) 13. 'Love Is All Around' (Wet Wet Wet) 14. 'Let It Be' (The Beatles) 15. 'You Keep It All In' (The Beautiful South) 16. 'Australia' (Manic Street Preachers)

Soul 3

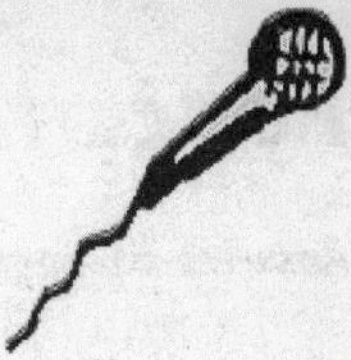

Answers on page 349

1. Which duo had a 1969 hit with 'Soul Sister Brown Sugar'?
2. Who boarded the 'Love Train' in 1973?
3. Which group released 'Doctor My Eyes' as a single in 1973?
4. Which northern soul band were 'Skiing In The Snow' in 1975?
5. For which group was 'Na-Na The Saddest Word'?
6. 'You Little Trustmaker' was a 1974 hit for which group?
7. Which soul singer was invited to dinner at the White House after appealing on TV for calm in the wake of the assassination of Martin Luther King?
8. Which female singer enjoyed 31 US chart singles in the Sixties?
9. For whom was Michael Jackson's hit 'Ben' originally written?
10. Which event shook the soul world on 1 April 1984?
11. Eddie Levert, Walter Williams and William Powell made up which group?
12. Who had a 1970 hit with 'Farewell Is A Lonely Sound'?
13. In 1964, which soul star was shot dead by the manageress of a Los Angeles motel he had just booked into?
14. Who wanted to 'Blame It On The Boogie' in 1978?
15. Which Jimmy Ruffin song was a UK top ten record twice in the space of eight years?
16. In which year did Aretha Franklin record 'I Say A Little Prayer'?

Answers to page 349

CHER 1: **1.** 'All I Really Want To Do' **2.** 'Bang Bang (My Baby Shot Me Down)' **3.** *Chastity* **4.** 'Gypsies, Tramps And Thieves' **5.** 1974 **6.** Gregg Allman **7.** David Bowie **8.** *Silkwood* **9.** 'I Found Someone' **10.** Time ('If I Could Turn Back Time') **11.** 'Believe' **12.** All the tracks were written and performed originally by men **13.** Memphis **14.** Bonnie Jo Mason **15.** He was elected Mayor of Palm Springs **16.** 'Sonny Side Of Cher'

Lyrics 13

Answers on page 346

From which songs are the following lyrics taken?

1. 'You walked into the party like you were walking on to a yacht'

2. 'It's late September and you really should be back at school'

3. 'The old home town looks the same as I step down from the train'

4. 'I was born with a plastic spoon in my mouth'

5. 'You've always been a good friend of mine but you're always saying farewell'

6. 'Starry starry night, paint your palette blue and grey'

7. 'All the rain came down on a cold new town as he carried you away'

8. 'I remember when rock was young, me and Susie had so much fun'

9. 'It's a god-awful small affair to the girl with the mousy hair'

10. 'So don't become some background noise, a backdrop for the girls and boys'

11. 'Take a look at my girlfriend she's the only one I got'

12. 'Slip inside the eye of your mind, don't you know you might find a better place to play'

13. 'I feel it in my fingers, I feel it in my toes'

14. 'When I find myself in time of trouble Mother Mary comes to me'

15. 'Just like that murder in '73, just like that robbery in '62'

16. 'I want to fly and run till it hurts, sleep for a while and speak no words'

Answers to page 346
POT LUCK 44: 1. 1974 2. 1982 3. 1985 4. 1964 5. 1972 6. 1995
7. 1967 8. 1957 9. 1982 10. 1978 11. 1982 12. 1967 13. 1997 14. 1975
15. 1966 16. 1961

Cher 1

Answers on page 347

1. Which Bob Dylan song gave Cher her first solo success?

2. Which track, produced by husband Sonny, reached number three in the UK in 1966?

3. Cher appeared in which 1969 film named after her and Sonny's daughter?

4. What was Cher's first US solo number one?

5. In which year did Sonny and Cher get divorced?

6. From whom did Cher seek a divorce in 1975, just ten days after their wedding?

7. Which UK artist made his US TV debut on Cher's show in 1975, singing a duet with her?

8. For which film was Cher nominated for an Oscar as Best Supporting Actress in 1984?

9. Which 1987 single was Cher's first UK chart entry for nearly 14 years?

10. What did Cher wish she could turn back in 1989?

11. In 1998, which song gave Cher her second UK number one?

12. Why was her album 'It's A Man's World' aptly titled?

13. Where was Cher walking in the title of a 1995 hit?

14. Under what pseudonym did Cher sing on the 1964 Phil Spector novelty number 'Ringo I Love You'?

15. What happened to Sonny in the same week in April 1988 that Cher won an Oscar for *Moonstruck*?

16. What was the corny title of Cher's second solo album?

Answers to page 347
SOUL 3: 1. Sam and Dave 2. The O'Jays 3. The Jackson Five 4. Wigan's Ovation 5. The Stylistics 6. The Tymes 7. James Brown 8. Aretha Franklin 9. Donny Osmond 10. Marvin Gaye was shot dead by his father 11. The O'Jays 12. Jimmy Ruffin 13. Sam Cooke 14. The Jacksons 15. 'What Becomes Of The Broken Hearted' 16. 1968

Film Tracks 8

Answers on page 352

1. Geri Halliwell's 'It's Raining Men' came from which film?
2. Which film featured The Cranberries' 1995 hit 'Ridiculous Thoughts'?
3. Which singer's daughter reached number 11 in the UK charts in 1967 with the theme from the Bond film *You Only Live Twice*?
4. Which group sang the title track from *Car Wash*?
5. Doris Day's 'Secret Love' was from the soundtrack of which Western?
6. 'Moon River' from *Breakfast at Tiffany's* provided which singer with his only UK number one?
7. 'A Certain Smile' from the film of the same name was a top five UK hit for which American singer in 1958?
8. Johnny Ray's 1955 hit 'If You Believe' came from which film?
9. Queen's 'Another One Bites The Dust' was re-released in 1998 following its inclusion in which film?
10. Part of which Queen track featured memorably in *Wayne's World*?
11. Paul McCartney's 'No More Lonely Nights' featured in which film?
12. 'Will You?' from *Breaking Glass* was a 1981 hit for which female artist?
13. 'I'm Every Woman' and 'I Have Nothing' were Whitney Houston tracks from which movie?
14. Which number from *Carousel* has been sung on football grounds across the land?
15. Adam Faith's top five hit 'The Time Has Come' featured in which film?
16. Who had a 1973 hit with the title track from *Take Me High*?

Answers to page 352
POT LUCK 45: **1.** Paul Anka ('I Confess' and 'Diana') **2.** Bjork **3.** Perry Como **4.** Take That had just announced their split **5.** Andy Fairweather-Low **6.** Georgie Fame and Alan Price **7.** 'Bridget The Midget' **8.** The Young Rascals **9.** Neil Young **10.** Blue **11.** The Smiths **12.** 'Money For Nothing' (Dire Straits) **13.** Phil Collins **14.** The Eagles **15.** Paul Carrack **16.** Mickie Most

Albums 13

Answers on page 353

Who released the following albums?

1. 'The Raven' (1979)

2. 'Captain Fantastic And The Brown Dirt Cowboy' (1975)

3. 'Heroes' (1977)

4. 'Calling All Stations' (1997)

5. 'Touch' (1984)

6. 'A New Flame' (1989)

7. 'Human Touch' (1992)

8. 'Pop' (1997)

9. 'Rock 'n' Roll Juvenile (1979)

10. 'Dancing On The Ceiling' (1986)

11. 'Ommadawn' (1975)

12. 'Get Ready' (2001)

13. 'Close To The Edge' (1972)

14. 'Ironfist' (1982)

15. 'Time' (1981)

16. 'Shepherd Moons' (1991)

Answers to page 353
PUNK 5: **1.** Johnnie Fingers **2.** The Buzzcocks (*Never Mind the Buzzcocks*)
3. Dave Vanian **4.** Jon Moss **5.** Sham 69 **6.** The Skids **7.** Tenpole Tudor
8. The Clash **9.** 'Something Better Change' **10.** The Boomtown Rats
11. The Adverts **12.** Tony James **13.** 'Kiss Me Deadly' **14.** X-Ray Spex
15. X-Ray Spex **16.** 'Dear Prudence'

Pot Luck 45

Answers on page 350

1. Whose first single in the Fifties sold 3,000 copies and his second over nine million?

2. Which singer used to be in an Icelandic band called Tappi Takarrass which translates as 'cork that bitch's arse'?

3. Which crooner was often known as 'The Singing Barber'?

4. Why were Childline and the Samaritans besieged with calls from distraught teenage girls on 13 February 1996?

5. Which former Amen Corner singer was 'Wide Eyed And Legless' in 1975?

6. Which two pop pianists joined forces in 1971 for 'Rosetta'?

7. Who was The Queen of the Blues according to Ray Stevens?

8. Who were 'Groovin'' in 1967?

9. A lyric from one of whose songs did Kurt Cobain quote in his suicide note?

10. Who reached number one in 2001 with their single 'Too Close'?

11. Which band played their farewell gig at Wolverhampton Civic Hall on 22 December 1988?

12. Which was the first music video to be broadcast on MTV Europe?

13. Who played drums in place of the late John Bonham when Led Zeppelin reunited for the US branch of Live Aid?

14. After an acrimonious split, which band vowed not to work together until 'hell freezes over'?

15. Who links Ace, Roxy Music, Squeeze, and Mike and The Mechanics?

16. Which record producer was born Michael Hayes?

Answers to page 350
FILM TRACKS 8: **1.** *Bridget Jones's Diary* **2.** *Butterfly Kiss* **3.** Frank Sinatra (Nancy Sinatra) **4.** Rose Royce **5.** *Calamity Jane* **6.** Danny Williams **7.** Johnny Mathis **8.** *There's No Business Like Show Business* **9.** *Small Soldiers* **10.** 'Bohemian Rhapsody' **11.** *Give My Regards To Broad Street* **12.** Hazel O'Connor **13.** *The Bodyguard* **14.** 'You''ll Never Walk Alone' **15.** *What a Whopper!* **16.** Cliff Richard

Punk 5

Answers on page 351

1. What did John Moylett change his name to when joining The Boomtown Rats?

2. Which punk band lent their name to a BBC rock quiz?

3. Who was working as a gravedigger in Hemel Hempstead when he was asked to join The Damned?

4. Which future member of Culture Club temporarily replaced Rat Scabies in The Damned during 1977?

5. Which band's first hit single was 'Angels With Dirty Faces'?

6. 'Masquerade' was a 1979 hit for which Scottish band?

7. Who had a 1981 hit with 'Wunderbar'?

8. 'Tommy Gun' and 'I Fought The Law' were hits for which band?

9. What was The Stranglers' second UK top ten record?

10. For which band was everything going 'Like Clockwork' in 1978?

11. Who reckoned it was 'No Time To Be 21' in 1978?

12. Who was in Generation X before setting up Sigue Sigue Sputnik?

13. What was the title of Generation X's final album?

14. Poly Styrene was the singer with which punk band?

15. Which punk band recorded 'Germ Free Adolescents'?

16. Which Beatles song gave Siouxsie and The Banshees their biggest hit?

Answers to page 351
ALBUMS 13: **1.** The Stranglers **2.** Elton John **3.** David Bowie **4.** Genesis **5.** The Eurythmics **6.** Simply Red **7.** Bruce Springsteen **8.** U2 **9.** Cliff Richard **10.** Lionel Richie **11.** Mike Oldfield **12.** New Order **13.** Yes **14.** Motorhead **15.** Electric Light Orchestra **16.** Enya

Chart Toppers 16

Answers on page 356

1. Which workman kept Eminem off the top of the UK singles chart in 2000?

2. On what date in 1975 did Pilot's 'January' reach number one?

3. Which 1966 number one was inspired by the Fifties film *The Asphalt Jungle* in which a gangster dreams of returning home to his farm?

4. Which 1968 hit was 'most efficacious in every way'?

5. Which single was UK number one from 13 July to 2 November 1991?

6. What was The Kinks' second UK number one?

7. Who was 'Starry Eyed' in 1960?

8. Which 1977 song from a musical was the 400th UK number one?

9. Who backed Ian Dury on his 1979 chart topper?

10. What nationality were 1982 chart toppers The Goombay Dance Band?

11. '99 Luftballons' was the German title of which 1984 UK number one?

12. How many weeks did Lionel Richie spend at number one in 1984 with 'Hello'?

13. With which act had Lionel Richie previously topped the chart?

14. What is Lionel Richie's middle name?

15. Gabriele Kerner was the singer with which number one band of the Eighties?

16. Which Seventies number one had just two letters in the title?

Answers to page 356
NUMBER TWOS 8: 1. Frankie Vaughan 2. Four Non-Blondes 3. 'When A Man Loves A Woman' 4. 'What's Love Got To Do With It' 5. Will Smith 6. 1966 7. Terrorvision 8. 'Streets Of Philadelphia' 9. 'Stayin' Alive' 10. Nat King Cole 11. 'Perfect 10' 12. Duane Eddy 13. Donny and Marie Osmond 14. MN8 15. The Pet Shop Boys 16. Steps

Seventies 11

Answers on page 357

1. In 1978, which young band won a talent contest sponsored by Guinness Harp Lager at Limerick Civic Week?

2. What role did Sven-Olof Walldoff play in the story of Abba?

3. In what year was 'Tiger Feet' a UK number one for Mud?

4. Who had two successive number ones ending in 'O'?

5. In 1972, which singer couldn't keep it in?

6. John Coghlan was the drummer with which band?

7. 'When', 'You Got What It Takes' and 'Dancin' Party' were all top five hits for Showaddywaddy in which year?

8. How many UK top ten hits did Showaddywaddy have in the Seventies?

9. Which two female solo singers topped the UK charts in 1970?

10. For whom did nothing rhyme in 1970?

11. Which brother and sister had a 1974 hit with 'Morning Side Of The Mountain'?

12. 'With A Little Luck' charted in 1978 for which band?

13. Who released the album 'The Six Wives Of Henry VIII'?

14. What was Robin Scott better known as?

15. And what was his biggest hit in that guise?

16. Which theme from *The Sting* was a hit for Marvin Hamlisch?

Answers to page 357
DANCE 5: **1.** Kosheen **2.** Lionrock **3.** *The X Files* **4.** Dutch **5.** 'The Launch' **6.** Louise Gard **7.** DJ Misjah and DJ Tim **8.** Tricky **9.** DJ Shadow **10.** Fatboy Slim **11.** DJ Krush **12.** Farley Jackmaster Funk **13.** Nester **14.** Turkish **15.** 'For The Love Of A Princess' **16.** DJ Luck and MC Neat

Number Twos 8

Answers on page 354

1. Whose 1956 number two with 'Green Door' was bettered by Shakin' Stevens 25 years later?

2. Which band of brunettes got to number two in 1993 with 'What's Up'?

3. Which Percy Sledge classic got to number two on its re-release in 1987?

4. Warren G took which Tina Turner hit to number two in 1996?

5. 'Wild Wild West' stopped short at number two for which artist in 1999?

6. In which year did The Troggs' 'Wild Thing' miss out on the top spot?

7. Who got to number two in 1999 with 'Tequila'?

8. Which Bruce Springsteen track made it to number two in 1994?

9. N-Trance made it second spot in 1995 with their revival of which Bee Gees song?

10. Who had to 'Pretend' in 1953?

11. Which 1998 song from The Beautiful South received top marks even though it only got to number two?

12. 'Pepe' was a 1961 runner-up for which guitarist?

13. Who both said 'I'm Leaving It All Up To You' in 1974?

14. Who promised in 1995: 'I've Got A Little Something For You'?

15. Who were eager to 'Go West' in 1993?

16. Which band got to number two in 2001 with 'Chain Reaction'?

Answers to page 354
CHART TOPPERS 16: **1.** Bob The Builder **2.** 1 February **3.** 'Green Green Grass Of Home' **4.** 'Lily The Pink' **5.** '(Everything I Do) I Do It For You' **6.** 'Tired Of Waiting For You' **7.** Michael Holliday **8.** 'Don't Cry For Me Argentina' **9.** The Blockheads **10.** German **11.** '99 Red Balloons' **12.** Six **13.** The Commodores **14.** Brockman **15.** Nena **16.** 'If'

Dance 5

Answers on page 355

1. Who wanted to 'Hide U' in 2001?

2. As whom is Manchester DJ/remixer Justin Robertson better known?

3. DJ Dado got into the charts in 1996 with a dance version of the theme to which TV sci-fi series?

4. What nationality are DJ Jean and Alice Deejay?

5. And which dance track did he take to number two in the UK charts in 1999?

6. Who was the vocalist on DJ Miko's 1994 hit 'What's Up'?

7. Which two DJs combined on 'Access' in 1996?

8. Who released 'The Hell' EP in 1995?

9. Josh Davis is more usually known as which Californian DJ who scored a 1997 hit with 'High Noon'?

10. Who was 'Gangsta Trippin'' in 1998?

11. Which Japanese hip-hop artist released the album 'Strictly Turntablized' in 1994?

12. Which Chicago DJ had a hit in 1986 with a cover version of 'Love Can't Turn Around'?

13. What is Haddaway's first name?

14. What nationality is DJ Quicksilver, resident of 'Planet Love' in 1998?

15. Which track from the film *Braveheart* was sampled on 'Protect Your Mind', a 1999 hit for DJ Sakin and Friends?

16. Which pair had a 1999 dance hit with 'A Little Bit Of Luck'?

Answers to page 355
SEVENTIES 11: **1.** U2 **2.** He was the conductor who dressed as Napoleon when the group performed 'Waterloo' at the 1974 Eurovision Song Contest **3.** 1974 **4.** The Brotherhood Of Man ('Angelo' and 'Figaro') **5.** Cat Stevens ('I Can't Keep It In') **6.** Status Quo **7.** 1977 **8.** Ten **9.** Dana and Freda Payne **10.** Gilbert O'Sullivan ('Nothing Rhymed') **11.** Donny and Marie Osmond **12.** Wings **13.** Rick Wakeman **14.** M **15.** 'Pop Muzik' **16.** 'The Entertainer'

Pot Luck 46

Answers on page 360

1. Police in which Canadian city offered to 'review' Madonna's SkyDome show in 1990 following complaints about lewdness?

2. On which birthday did Prince announce that he was changing his name to a symbol?

3. Which legendary band took their name from a Muddy Waters song?

4. Who played his own version of 'The Star Spangled Banner' at Woodstock?

5. Which Eighties fashion icon was the son of a boxing club manager?

6. Which Sixties trio comprised sisters Barbara Ann and Rosa Lee Hawkins and their cousin Joan Johnson?

7. What was the name of Adam Faith's backing group?

8. Which Sixties R & B singer was 6ft 7in tall?

9. What was deceptive about the Canadian band Barenaked Ladies?

10. What is the real Christian name of Pink Floyd recluse Syd Barrett?

11. The theme from which BBC series about a boating family gave the Simon May Orchestra a 1985 hit?

12. Which tragic fate befell both singers of Badfinger?

13. Alice Nutter was a member of which anarchic group which had a number two hit in 1997?

14. Who wrote 'Downtown' for Petula Clark?

15. How many Fine Young Cannibals were there?

16. Which Beatle released the solo album 'All Things Must Pass'?

Answers to page 360
CLASSICAL GAS 5: 1. 'The Military' 2. Vivaldi 3. Mendelssohn 4. French 5. Hamburg 6. 'Brahms' Lullaby' 7. Worcestershire 8. Sibelius 9. Puccini 10. Liszt 11. Dmitri 12. Elgar 13. 'The Clock' 14. 'All women are the same' 15. Beethoven 16. Berlioz

The Rolling Stones 2

Answers on page 361

1. Which future Kinks drummer played with the Stones on their live debut in 1962?

2. In 1962, which Stone advertised in *Jazz News* under the name of Elmo Lewis for R & B musicians to form a band?

3. Which song did the Stones perform when making their TV debut on ITV's *Thank Your Lucky Stars*?

4. In which Gloucestershire town was Brian Jones born?

5. In which year did '(I Can't Get No) Satisfaction' top both the UK and US singles charts?

6. Which song kept '19th Nervous Breakdown' off the top of the UK charts after five successive number ones?

7. To promote which single did the Stones appear in drag?

8. Which song's lyrics did the Stones have to change when singing on America's *Ed Sullivan Show* in 1967?

9. What did the Stones refuse to do when appearing on *Sunday Night at the London Palladium* in 1967?

10. Which 1968 track gave the Stones their first UK number one for two years?

11. Which Stones album of 1972 was called 'obscene' by Mary Whitehouse?

12. In which year was 'Fool To Cry' released as a single?

13. What was the title of the Stones' number one album of 1980?

14. Which Stone bought a part-share in US soccer team Philadelphia Furies?

15. Which Bob and Earl song did the Stones cover in 1986?

16. Which Mick Jagger solo album featured 'Let's Work'?

Answers to page 361
ROCK 'N' ROLL 4: **1.** Johnny Cash **2.** Cliff Richard **3.** He was pilot of the plane in which Buddy Holly, Ritchie Valens and The Big Bopper were killed **4.** The Valiants **5.** 'Long Tall Sally' **6.** Jerry Lee Lewis **7.** Adam Faith **8.** 1956 **9.** Five **10.** 30 **11.** He had been involved in a car crash **12.** 'Tutti Frutti' **13.** Lionel Bart **14.** 'Mr Parnes Shillings and Pence' **15.** 'Maybe Tomorrow' **16.** Jerry Lee Lewis

Classical Gas 5

Answers on page 358

1. What is the nickname of Haydn's Symphony No 100?

2. Which Italian composer became a priest for a year in 1703?

3. Who composed *A Midsummer Night's Dream*?

4. What nationality was Chopin's father?

5. In which German city was Brahms born?

6. As what is the song 'Wiegenlied' better known?

7. In which English county was Sir Edward Elgar born?

8. Who composed *Finlandia*?

9. *La Bohème* was an operatic work by which composer?

10. Who composed the *Faust Symphony*?

11. What was Shostakovich's first name?

12. Who wrote the *Enigma Variations*?

13. What is Haydn's Symphony No 101 more commonly known as?

14. What does the title of Mozart's opera *Cosi Fan Tutte* mean in English?

15. Which composer was born in Bonn on 15 December 1770?

16. Who composed the symphony *Harold In Italy*?

Answers to page 358
POT LUCK 46: **1.** Toronto **2.** 35th **3.** The Rolling Stones **4.** Jimi Hendrix **5.** Boy George **6.** The Dixie Cups **7.** The Roulettes **8.** Long John Baldry **9.** They were all men **10.** Roger **11.** *Howards Way* **12.** Both committed suicide **13.** Chumbawamba **14.** Tony Hatch **15.** Three **16.** George Harrison

Rock 'n' Roll 4

Answers on page 359

1. Who had to leave Elvis Presley, Jerry Lee Lewis and Carl Perkins at their famous impromptu Sun recording session in 1956 because his wife wanted to go shopping?

2. Which 18-year-old singing hopeful began a four-week residency at Butlins Holiday Camp, Clacton, in 1958?

3. What role did Roger Peterson play in the history of rock 'n' roll?

4. Who recorded the original version of 'Good Golly Miss Molly'?

5. Which statuesque girl gave Little Richard a number three hit in the UK in 1957?

6. Who recorded the title track from the film *High School Confidential*?

7. Which rock 'n' roller acquired his stage name from a book of boys' and girls' names?

8. In which year did 'Don't Be Cruel' become a US number one for Elvis?

9. At what age did Buddy Holly make his stage debut?

10. How old was Bill Haley when 'Rock Around The Clock' first became number one?

11. Why was Carl Perkins unable to promote 'Blue Suede Shoes'?

12. Which rock classic gave Little Richard his first mainstream hit in the USA?

13. Which songwriter discovered Marty Wilde?

14. What was manager Larry Parnes's nickname?

15. What was Billy Fury's debut single?

16. Which rock 'n' roller was arrested in 1976 for waving a gun outside Elvis's home?

Answers to page 359
THE ROLLING STONES 2: **1.** Mick Avory **2.** Brian Jones **3.** 'Come On' **4.** Cheltenham **5.** 1965 **6.** 'These Boots Are Made for Walkin'' **7.** 'Have You Seen Your Mother, Baby, Standing In The Shadow'? **8.** 'Let's Spend The Night Together' became 'Let's Spend Some Time Together' **9.** They refused to stand and wave on the famous revolving stage at the end of the show **10.** 'Jumpin' Jack Flash' **11.** 'Exile On Main Street' **12.** 1976 **13.** 'Emotional Rescue' **14.** Mick Jagger **15.** 'Harlem Shuffle' **16.** 'Primitive Cool'

Nineties 10

Answers on page 364

1. Who covered Harry Chapin's 'Cat's In The Cradle' in 1993?

2. Which TV presenter revived his 1962 hit 'Sun Arise' in 1997?

3. Who was peering through 'Steamy Windows' in 1990?

4. Brothers Chris and Rich Robinson founded which US R & B band?

5. Who charted in 1990 with 'Step On'?

6. Who boasted in 1996: 'The Only Thing That Looks Good On Me Is You'?

7. Which Lightning Seeds track was used in its instrumental form to accompany the Football League tables at the end of BBC's *Grandstand*?

8. What are the names of the three sisters in The Corrs?

9. And who is The Corrs' performing brother?

10. Who had a 1992 top ten hit with 'It's A Fine Day'?

11. In 1992, who reflected: 'This Used To Be My Playground'?

12. 'Blue Savannah' was a 1990 hit for which duo?

13. Which band could see a 'Distant Sun' in 1993?

14. What was the title of Wet Wet Wet's second UK number one?

15. Who followed the 1990 World Cup with 'Regret'?

16. Which band had a 1997 top three hit with the theme from *The Saint*?

Answers to page 364
SIXTIES 11: **1.** The Bee Gees **2.** Donovan **3.** Herb Alpert **4.** Mark Wynter **5.** The Supremes **6.** The Animals **7.** Cliff Richard **8.** Des O'Connor **9.** Andy Williams **10.** The Small Faces **11.** Wilson Pickett **12.** Marty Wilde **13.** Kathy Kirby **14.** Marianne Faithfull **15.** The Kinks **16.** Manfred Mann

New Romantics 2

Answers on page 365

1. Who was pianist with Duran Duran?

2. Who made the risqué video for Duran Duran's 'Girls On Film'?

3. Which 1993 single gave Duran Duran their biggest hit for eight years?

4. In which year did Duran Duran have their first UK number one?

5. On what day of the week was there a new moon, according to the title of Duran Duran's 1984 hit?

6. What colour did Visage fade to?

7. Which band of New Romantics began with a guitarist called Lester Square?

8. Who was a dandy highwayman in 1981?

9. Which band had a 1983 hit with 'Communication'?

10. Who were 'Walking In The Rain' in 1983?

11. Who released a 1982 album titled 'The Anvil'?

12. Who was guest vocalist on Culture Club's 'Church Of The Poison Mind'?

13. Whose 1984 album was called 'Waking Up With The House On Fire'?

14. What was Marilyn's only UK top ten hit?

15. In which year did 'Do You Really Want To Hurt Me' reach number one for Culture Club?

16. Whose first hit album was 'Journey To Glory'?

Answers to page 365
POT LUCK 47: 1. Led Zeppelin 2. It was deemed degrading to Catholics 3. Luciano Pavarotti 4. Del Shannon's cover of 'From Me To You' 5. Cliff Richard 6. 'Pleasure And Pain' 7. Foreigner 8. Jake ('My Brother Jake') 9. Carl Palmer 10. Ashford and Simpson 11. Art Of Noise 12. Demis Roussos and Vangelis 13. Joan Armatrading 14. The Pharaohs 15. Chris Andrews 16. Annabella Lu Win

Sixties 11

Answers on page 362

The following singles were UK hits for which artists in the Sixties?

1. 'World'

2. 'There Is A Mountain'

3. 'Tijuana Taxi'

4. 'Venus In Blue Jeans'

5. 'In And Out Of Love'

6. 'Don't Let Me Be Misunderstood'

7. 'Big Ship'

8. 'Careless Hands'

9. 'Can't Get Used To Losing You'

10. 'My Mind's Eye'

11. 'In The Midnight Hour'

12. 'Jezebel'

13. 'Let Me Go Lover'

14. 'Come And Stay With Me'

15. 'Dead End Street'

16. 'Ha Ha Said The Clown'

Answers to page 362
NINETIES 10: **1.** Ugly Kid Joe **2.** Rolf Harris **3.** Tina Turner **4.** The Black Crowes **5.** The Happy Mondays **6.** Bryan Adams **7.** 'The Life Of Riley' **8.** Andrea, Sharon and Caroline **9.** Jim **10.** Opus III **11.** Madonna **12.** Erasure **13.** Crowded House **14.** 'Goodnight Girl' **15.** New Order **16.** Orbital

Pot Luck 47

Answers on page 363

1. Which band had to wait 28 years and five months between their first appearance in the UK album chart and their debut in the singles chart?

2. Why was The Singing Nun's 'Dominique' banned by a Massachusetts radio station?

3. Who once received 165 curtain calls and was applauded for an hour and seven minutes by an appreciative German audience?

4. Which was the first Lennon and McCartney composition to chart in the US?

5. Who is the only UK solo artist to have had hits in five decades?

6. Which Dr Hook album contained 'When You're In Love With A Beautiful Woman'?

7. Which band charted with 'Feels Like The First Time' and 'Cold As Ice'?

8. What was the name of Free's brother in a 1971 hit?

9. Who went to Asia after leaving Emerson, Lake and Palmer?

10. Which songwriting duo penned such Motown classics as 'Ain't No Mountain High Enough' and 'Reach Out And Touch Somebody's Hand'?

11. With which Eighties band was Anne Dudley one of the keyboard players?

12. Which two members of Aphrodite's Child enjoyed successful solo careers?

13. Whose first UK hit was 'Love And Affection' in 1976?

14. Who backed Sam The Sham?

15. Who wrote Sixties hits for Adam Faith and Sandie Shaw before getting into the top ten himself with 'Yesterday's Man'?

16. Who was the 14-year-old singer with Bow Wow Wow?

Answers to page 363
NEW ROMANTICS 2: **1.** Nick Rhodes **2.** Godley and Creme
3. 'Ordinary World' **4.** 1983 **5.** Monday ('New Moon On Monday')
6. Grey **7.** Adam and The Ants **8.** Adam Ant **9.** Spandau Ballet
10. Modern Romance **11.** Visage **12.** Helen Terry **13.** Culture Club
14. 'Calling Your Name' **15.** 1982 **16.** Spandau Ballet

Boy Bands 4

Answers on page 368

1. Bryan, Mark, Nicky, Shane and Kian are better known as which boy band?

2. Who were 'Bodyshakin'' in 1997?

3. The title of which boy band's debut hit is a term in basketball?

4. JC, Lance and Justin are members of which American boy band?

5. Which boy band took their name from the emergency telephone number in the USA?

6. Which member of New Kids On The Block was head chorister in the local church choir?

7. Who did New Kids On The Block support on their first US tour?

8. In which year did 'Keep On Movin'' reach number one for Five?

9. What was the title of Westlife's second UK number one?

10. Who wanted to 'Be The First To Believe' in 1999?

11. What was the title of Donny Osmond's first solo album?

12. Who wrote Donny Osmond's 'Puppy Love'?

13. Which Osmonds single featured in a Virgin Atlantic TV commercial 27 years after its original release?

14. Which member of New Kids On The Block was arrested after setting fire to the carpet outside his Louisville hotel room?

15. 'Private Number' was a top three hit for which boy band in 1999?

16. Whose 2001 album was 'Kingsize'?

Answers to page 368
EUROVISION 4: **1.** Sandie Shaw ('Puppet On A String') **2.** Black Lace
3. Norway **4.** Finland **5.** Monaco **6.** Luxembourg **7.** 11 **8.** The Shadows
9. 'Let Me Be The One' **10.** 1976 **11.** Live Report **12.** Yugoslavia
13. Linda Martin **14.** 'Why Me?' **15.** 'Love Shine A Light' **16.** 'Hold Me Now'

Heavy Metal 6

Answers on page 369

1. Which Mötley Crüe member advertised his services as: 'Loud, rude, aggressive guitarist available'?

2. How did the band get the name Motörhead?

3. 'Knockin' On Heaven's Door' by Guns N' Roses was a live recording taken from which 1992 tribute concert?

4. Which band's first UK number one was 'Bring Your Daughter...To The Slaughter'?

5. Which band had a 1982 album called 'Saints 'N' Sinners'?

6. Which heavy metal band recorded the title track for the film *Eat The Rich*?

7. 'Machine Head' was a 1972 chart-topping album by which band?

8. Who considered the consequences of 'When Love And Hate Collide'?

9. Who broke four bones in his foot during his 1992 farewell tour?

10. What was the title of Led Zeppelin's in-concert film of 1976?

11. Which singer was unable to join Led Zeppelin because of a contract dispute and recommended Robert Plant instead?

12. Vincent Crane was the leader of which Seventies band?

13. Tony Iommi is guitarist with which band?

14. Which Seventies Hawkwind single was hastily withdrawn after terrorist bombs exploded in London?

15. Whose drummer was nicknamed 'Philthy'?

16. Which band scored hits with 'Wheels Of Steel' and '747(Strangers In The Night)'?

Answers to page 369
INDIE 8: 1. Suede 2. By the motorway 3. Ash 4. 'Blue Is The Colour'
5. The Happy Mondays 6. Kermit 7. The Teardrop Explodes 8. Dodgy
9. Supernaturals 10. 'Richard III' 11. The Levellers 12. Charmless
13. 'Parklife' 14. Strawberry 15. Super Furry Animals 16. 'This Is My Truth Tell Me Yours'

Eurovision 4

Answers on page 366

1. Who was the first Eurovision Song Contest winner to top the UK chart?

2. Five years before 'Agadoo', who came seventh for the UK at the 1979 Eurovision?

3. Which country's 1973 entry included the contrived rhyme: 'Come and join us! In the game of girl and boyness!'

4. 'Pump Pump' was the 1976 entry from which Scandinavian nation?

5. And who came up with 'Boum Badaboum' in 1967?

6. Who pulled out of the 1995 contest because, as that year's European City of Culture, they considered it too tacky?

7. How old was Nathalie Paque, the French singer at the 1989 Eurovision?

8. Which UK act, not renowned for their singing, finished second in 1975?

9. And what was the title of their number?

10. In which year did Brotherhood Of Man win for the UK?

11. Who finished runners-up for the UK in 1989 with 'Why Do I Always Get It Wrong'?

12. Which country won that year for the first time?

13. Which Linda was Ireland's triumphant singer of 1992?

14. And what was the title of her winning song?

15. With which song did Katrina and The Waves win?

16. What was the title of Johnny Logan's second Eurovision winner?

Answers to page 366
BOY BANDS 4: **1.** Westlife **2.** 911 **3.** Five ('Slam Dunk (Da Funk)')
4. *NSync **5.** 911 **6.** Jordan Knight **7.** Tiffany **8.** 1999 **9.** 'If I Let You Go'
10. a1 **11.** 'Portrait Of Donny' **12.** Paul Anka **13.** 'Crazy Horses'
14. Donnie Wahlberg **15.** 911 **16.** Five

Indie 8

Answers on page 367

1. Which Indie band was Justine Frischmann with before fronting Elastica?

2. Where did Suede enjoy a picnic on their album 'Coming Up'?

3. Which Northern Ireland band did guitarist Charlotte Hatherley join in 1997?

4. Which Beautiful South album featured 'Rotterdam' and 'Don't Marry Her'?

5. The seeds of Black Grape were sown in which band?

6. What was the stage name of Black Grape's Paul Leveridge?

7. Food Records boss David Balfe used to be the keyboard player in which Eighties band?

8. Which band's 1996 album was titled 'Free Peace Sweet'?

9. Which band had hits with 'The Day Before Yesterday's Man' and 'Smile'?

10. Which English king provided Supergrass with a top two placing in 1997?

11. 'What A Beautiful Day' was a 1997 hit for which British Indie band?

12. What type of man did Blur sing about on a 1996 single?

13. Which Blur album shows greyhound racing on the cover?

14. What fruit is on the cover of The Lightning Seeds' 'Jollification'?

15. Which band's first hit album was 'Fuzzy Logic'?

16. 'If You Tolerate This Your Children Will Be Next' came from which Manic Street Preachers album?

Answers to page 367
HEAVY METAL 6: **1.** Mick Mars **2.** 'Motorhead' was the last song Lemmy wrote before being sacked from Hawkwind **3.** The Freddie Mercury Tribute Concert **4.** Iron Maiden **5.** Whitesnake **6.** Aersomith **7.** Deep Purple **8.** Def Leppard **9.** Ozzy Osbourne **10.** *The Song Remains The Same* **11.** Terry Reid **12.** Atomic Rooster **13.** Black Sabbath **14.** 'Urban Guerrilla' **15.** Motorhead (Phil Taylor) **16.** Saxon

Home Towns 5

Answers on page 372

1. From which English city did Eighties band ABC come?

2. The Climax Blues Band started out in which town?

3. Which Yorkshire town was home to Smokie?

4. Which city do Scritti Politti come from?

5. From which European city are Ace Of Base?

6. In which North Wales town did The Alarm begin their punk career?

7. From which city did Altered Images hail?

8. What location links America and Wham!?

9. In which district of London did Aswad form?

10. At which university did Tracey Thorn and Ben Watt meet before forming Everything But The Girl?

11. Badfinger started out in which Welsh town?

12. In which town in Greater Manchester were Barclay James Harvest formed?

13. Which south Midlands town was home to Bauhaus?

14. From which area of Merseyside do The Boo Radleys hail?

15. Which Seventies US rock band, fronted by Brad Delp, took their name from their home city?

16. Which London borough did Bros come from?

Answers to page 372
R & B 5: **1.** R. Kelly **2.** Nelly Furtado **3.** Damage **4.** 'From The Heart' **5.** The Thunderbirds **6.** Cream **7.** 'Whoa Nelly!' **8.** 'The Duchess' **9.** The Pretty Things **10.** Chicken Shack **11.** Dane Bowers **12.** Joe Cocker **13.** Eric Clapton **14.** Steampacket **15.** Bob Dylan **16.** Free

Pot Luck 48

Answers on page 373

1. Bachman-Turner Overdrive were an off-shoot from which Canadian band?

2. Thanks to comedians Harry Enfield and Paul Whitehouse, which Bachman-Turner Overdrive received renewed attention in the Nineties?

3. Who was singer with The Alarm?

4. Who were the first British group to top the US singles chart?

5. Which member of the Manic Street Preachers often wears a dress on stage?

6. Which rock star sang backing vocals on Carly Simon's 'You're So Vain'?

7. Which number one artist of the Seventies got his big break in New York wearing a paper bag over his head?

8. Which opera singer was once arrested for pinching a lady's bottom in the monkey house of New York Zoo?

9. In which country were the bagpipes first played?

10. Who sang backing vocals on Steve Winwood's 'Higher Love'?

11. Who was the world's biggest-selling recording artist of the Nineties?

12. Jeff 'Skunk' Baxter was lead guitarist with which US band?

13. Which Canadian rocker reached number two in the UK in 1993 with 'Please Forgive Me'?

14. What nationality were Focus?

15. What was the title of Focus's first hit?

16. Which astrologically minded Seventies group comprised a Libran, a Cancerian, an Aquarian and a Leo?

Answers to page 373
EIGHTIES 11: **1.** Carol Kenyon **2.** Rockwell ('Somebody's Watching Me') **3.** The Communards **4.** 'Sexual Healing' **5.** Black Coffee **6.** Siedah Garrett **7.** Erasure **8.** Paul Young **9.** 'Senses Working Overtime' **10.** Bagpipes **11.** Five **12.** Brother Beyond **13.** The Gap Band **14.** 'Oops Up Side Your Head' **15.** Big Country **16.** The Eurythmics

R & B 5

Answers on page 370

1. 'She's Got That Vibe' and 'Bump 'N Grind' were Nineties hits for which R & B artist?

2. Who had a hit in 2001 with 'Turn Off The Light'?

3. 'Love II Love' and 'Forever' were 1996 hits for which band?

4. Which Another Level single was taken from the film *Notting Hill*?

5. What was the name of Chris Farlowe's backing band?

6. Who charted in 1967 with 'Strange Brew'?

7. What was the title of Nelly Furtado's 2001 album?

8. Which female guitarist backed Bo Diddley on his 1963 UK tour?

9. Which British R & B band of the Sixties named themselves after a Bo Diddley song?

10. 'I'd Rather Go Blind' was a hit for which Sixties R & B outfit?

11. Who has become a successful solo artist after the demise of Another Level?

12. Which singer started out in 1961 with a Sheffield band called The Cavaliers?

13. Which guitar great's first band was The Roosters?

14. Which band featured the combined talents of Rod Stewart, Long John Baldry, Brian Auger and Julie Driscoll?

15. Who wrote 'This Wheel's On Fire', a 1968 top five hit for Julie Driscoll, Brian Auger and The Trinity?

16. 'Heartbreaker' was a 1973 album by which band?

Answers to page 370
HOME TOWNS 5: 1. Sheffield 2. Stafford 3. Bradford 4. Leeds
5. Gothenburg 6. Rhyl 7. Glasgow 8. Both bands met at school in
Bushey, Hertfordshire 9. Notting Hill 10. Hull 11. Swansea 12. Oldham
13. Northampton 14. Wallasey 15. Boston 16. Lewisham

Eighties 11

Answers on page 371

1. Who was the female vocalist on 'Temptation' by Heaven 17?

2. Who reckoned somebody was watching him in 1984?

3. Who had a 1986 hit with 'So Cold The Night'?

4. What was Marvin Gaye's last UK top ten hit before his death?

5. What were Squeeze drinking in bed in 1982?

6. With whom did Michael Jackson duet on his 1987 number one 'I Just Can't Stop Loving You'?

7. Whose 1989 album was titled 'The Innocents'?

8. 'The Secret Of Association' was a 1985 album by which singer?

9. In which XTC song was all the world football-shaped?

10. What instrument did Big Country make their guitars sound like?

11. How many UK top ten singles did Bros have in 1988?

12. Which band had a 1988 hit with 'The Harder I Try'?

13. Which band took their name from the initials of three streets in their home town of Tulsa – Greenwood, Archer and Pine?

14. And what was the title of their first hit single in the UK?

15. Tony Butler was bass guitarist with which Eighties band?

16. Aretha Franklin joined which band on the 1985 hit 'Sisters Are Doin' It For Themselves'?

Answers to page 371
POT LUCK 48: **1.** Guess Who **2.** 'You Ain't Seen Nothing Yet' **3.** Mike Peters **4.** The Tornados **5.** Nicky Wire **6.** Mick Jagger **7.** David Soul **8.** Enrico Caruso **9.** Persia **10.** Chaka Khan **11.** Garth Brooks **2.** Steely Dan **13.** Bryan Adams **14.** Dutch **15.** 'Hocus Pocus' **16.** The Floaters

Albums 14

Answers on page 376

1. Which band parodied The Beatles' 'Abbey Road' album with a cover in which they were totally naked except for strategically placed socks?

2. In which year did The Beatles release 'Rubber Soul'?

3. Which US band topped the UK album charts in 1970 with 'Cosmo's Factory'?

4. Whose 1994 album was titled 'Starry Eyed And Bollock Naked'?

5. Which Irish singer's Greatest Hits Album of 1997 was called 'Paint The Sky With Stars'?

6. Whose 1978 album was 'The Man With The Golden Flute'?

7. 'Here Come The Warm Jets' was a solo album by which ex-member of Roxy Music?

8. 'Holding Back The River' was a number two album for which band in 1989?

9. Who recorded 'Have Twangy Guitar Will Travel' in 1959?

10. Who had the 'Fishermen's Blues' in 1988?

11. Whose 1983 number one album was titled 'Colour By Numbers'?

12. Who released 'New Adventures In Hi-Fi' in 1996?

13. 'Crash Boom Bang' was a 1994 album from which Swedish band?

14. Which band recorded the 1991 album 'The Beast Inside'?

15. Which Irish folk band offered 'A Drop Of The Hard Stuff' in 1967?

16. Which band's 1994 album was titled 'God Shuffled His Feet'?

Answers to page 376
POT LUCK 49: 1. Phil Collins 2. Eric Clapton 3. Meat Loaf 4. 'It's Still Rock 'N' Roll To Me' 5. Joan Jett 6. Manfred Mann 7. Katrina (and The Waves) 8. KC and The Sunshine Band 9. Ian Dury 10. Colin Blunstone 11. 'Love Will Tear Us Apart' 12. Chris Squire 13. Elvis Costello 14. Eddie and Alex 15. The Four Seasons 16. George Michael

Madonna 2

Answers on page 377

1. Which instrument did Madonna play in her early band The Breakfast Club?

2. Which two singers rejected 'Holiday' before it was accepted by Madonna?

3. In which 1984 film did Madonna star with Rosanna Arquette?

4. Which Rose Royce ballad was covered by Madonna on the album 'Like A Virgin'?

5. How many weeks did the single 'Like A Virgin' remain at number one in the US?

6. Which UK number one for Madonna didn't make the Billboard Hot 100 in the US as it was on the B-side of the 12-inch 'Angel'?

7. On which birthday did Madonna marry Sean Penn?

8. Which female singer's 30-year-old record did Madonna equal by having three discs in the UK top 15 in December 1985?

9. Which was Madonna's fourth UK number one single?

10. In which year did Madonna top the UK charts with 'Like A Prayer'?

11. What is Madonna's full name?

12. What links Madonna with The Carpenters?

13. What was the name of Madonna's 1990 tour?

14. In which film did Madonna star in 1996?

15. In which London park did Madonna go jogging in 1990?

16. Which bedroom-shot, black and white Madonna video of 1990 was banned by MTV?

Answers to page 377
GIRL BANDS 7: **1.** The Dixie Cups **2.** The Supremes **3.** The Nolans **4.** The Bangles **5.** The Righteous Brothers **6.** Floy **7.** 'The Happening' **8.** Bananarama **9.** All Saints **10.** Dee Dee Kennibrew **11.** Sarah Dallin **12.** Vicki **13.** All Saints **14.** Nicole and Natalie **15.** 'Remember (Walkin' In The Sand)' **16.** Florence Ballard

Pot Luck 49

Answers on page 374

1. Which singer/drummer flew to America on Concorde and thus appeared in the Live Aid concerts on both sides of the Atlantic?

2. Who guested on guitar for The Beatles' 'While My Guitar Gently Weeps'?

3. In 1994, who released the 52-letter single 'Objects In The Rear View Mirror May Appear Closer Than They Are'?

4. What was Billy Joel's first US number one single?

5. Which US rocker was born Joan Larkin?

6. Mike Hugg and Tom McGuinness were members of which Sixties band?

7. Which UK Eurovision Song Contest winner had the surname Leskanich?

8. Which band had a 1974 hit with 'Queen Of Clubs'?

9. Who formed Kilburn and The High Roads before branching out with The Blockheads?

10. Which former Zombie charted in 1972 with 'Say You Don't Mind'?

11. Which Joy Division track did Paul Young cover on his album 'No Parlez'?

12. Which Squire was the bassist with Yes?

13. Who wrote 'Shipbuilding' for Robert Wyatt?

14. What are the names of the two Van Halen brothers?

15. Which US band were called The Variatones and The Four Lovers before settling on their final name?

16. Which singer was born Georgios Kyriacos Panayiotou?

Answers to page 374
ALBUMS 14: **1.** Red Hot Chili Peppers **2.** 1965 **3.** Creedence Clearwater Revival **4.** Carter – The Unstoppable Sex Machine **5.** Enya **6.** James Galway **7.** Brian Eno **8.** Wet Wet Wet **9.** Duane Eddy **10.** The Waterboys **11.** Culture Club **12.** R.E.M. **13.** Roxette **14.** Inspiral Carpets **15.** The Dubliners **16.** Crash Test Dummies

Girl Bands 7

Answers on page 375

1. Whose first UK hit was 'Chapel Of Love' in 1964?

2. Who were the first girl band to top the UK singles chart?

3. Which girl group said collectively in 1980: 'Gotta Pull Myself Together'?

4. Which band released the 1986 album 'Different Light'?

5. Who originally recorded 'Substitute', a 1978 hit for girl band Clout?

6. Who brought Joy to The Supremes in 1972?

7. Which film title track gave Diana Ross and The Supremes a UK top ten hit in 1967?

8. Who encountered a 'Shy Boy' in 1982?

9. Who were involved in a 'War Of Nerves' in 1998?

10. Which Crystals singer was born Dolores Henry?

11. Which member of Bananarama previously attended the London College of Fashion?

12. Which was the elder of the two Peterson sisters in The Bangles?

13. The Appleton sisters were members of which band?

14. What are the Christian names of the Appleton sisters?

15. Which Shangri-Las single featured the sound of seagulls in the background?

16. Which former Supreme died in 1976, aged 32?

Answers to page 375
MADONNA 2: **1.** Drums **2.** Phyllis Hyman and Mary Wilson
3. *Desperately Seeking Susan* **4.** 'Love Don't Live Here Anymore' **5.** Six
6. 'Into The Groove' **7.** Her 26th **8.** Ruby Murray **9.** 'La Isla Bonita'
10. 1989 **11.** Madonna Louise Veronica Ciccone **12.** John Bettis, who penned songs for The Carpenters, co-wrote 'Crazy For You' **13.** Blonde Ambition **14.** *Evita* **15.** Hyde Park **16.** 'Justify My Love'

Seventies 12

Answers on page 380

Which artists had UK hits with the following tracks in the Seventies?

1. 'Wonderous Stories'

2. 'Standing In The Road'

3. 'Superstition'

4. 'Really Free'

5. 'Little Piece Of Leather'

6. 'Everything Is Beautiful'

7. 'Freedom Come Freedom Go'

8. 'Art For Art's Sake'

9. '20th Century Boy'

10. 'Only Yesterday'

11. 'Pretty Little Angel Eyes'

12. 'Ball Park Incident'

13. 'Apeman'

14. 'Juke Box Jive'

15. 'Judy Teen'

16. 'I'm On Fire'

Answers to page 382
POT LUCK 50: **1.** Jim Steinman **2.** Lone Justice **3.** O'Dowd **4.** Eight
5. Roger McGuinn **6.** Mama Cass **7.** Jimmy McCulloch **8.** Curtis Mayfield
9. George Martin **10.** The Lighthouse Family **11.** Gordon Lightfoot
12. Lisa Loeb **13.** A spider's web **14.** The Heartbreakers **15.** Patti
LaBelle **16.** Focus

Cover Versions 12

Answers on page 381

1. Who originally recorded 'Walking In Memphis', a hit for Cher in 1995?
2. Which Rose Royce song was covered by Jimmy Nail?
3. Which Stylistics hit achieved similar success three years later in the hands of Johnny Mathis?
4. In 2001 who covered Stealers Wheel's 'Stuck In The Middle With You'?
5. Who reached number nine in 1987 with a cover of The Buzzcocks' 'Ever Fallen In Love (With Someone You Shouldn't've)'?
6. Which Crystals song did Gary Glitter resurrect with a change of sex in 1981?
7. Who covered The Four Seasons 'Walk Like A Man' in 1985?
8. Which song links Brian Poole and The Tremeloes, Salt 'N' Pepa and Chaka Demus and Pliers?
9. Who originally had a hit with 'This Is It', covered by Dannii Minogue in 1993?
10. Marillion's 1992 song 'Sympathy' was a UK chart entry in 1970 for which one-hit wonders?
11. Which Beatles track did Candy Flip take to number three in the charts in 1990?
12. Louchie Lou and Michie One covered which Lulu and The Luvvers hit in 1993?
13. Who first had a hit with 'Shotgun Wedding' 17 years before Rod Stewart?
14. Which song links Christopher Cross, Saxon and East Side Beat?
15. Which U2 track was covered by Mica Paris in 1995?
16. On which farm did both Bob Dylan and The Specials work?

Answers to page 383
CHART TOPPERS 17: **1.** 11 **2.** 'The Power Of Love' (Jennifer Rush) **3.** 'Eye Of The Tiger' (Survivor) **4.** '....Baby One More Time' **5.** 'Bohemian Rhapsody' **6.** Johnny Tillotson **7.** Jennifer Eccles **8.** The Crazy World Of Arthur Brown ('Fire') **9.** 'I've Gotta Get A Message To You' **10.** Scott McKenzie **11.** 'Cathy's Clown' **12.** Paul MacDowall **13.** 'Your Woman' **14.** 'It's Now Or Never', 'The Young Ones' and 'Get Back' **15.** Frankie Laine **16.** American

Lyrics 14

Answers on page 382

From which songs are the following lyrics taken?

1. 'You're lying again – you say you don't but then you do'
2. 'Check ignition and may God's love be with you'
3. 'I paid all my dues so I picked up my shoes, I got up and walked away'
4. 'What you gonna do when things go wrong, what you gonna do when it all cracks up'
5. 'There's a lady who's sure all that glitters is gold'
6. 'She came from Greece she had a thirst for knowledge, she studied sculpture at St Martin's College'
7. 'The mist across the window hides the lines but nothing hides the colour of the lights that shine'
8. 'Mama, just killed a man, put a gun against his head, pulled my trigger, now he's dead'
9. 'Sorry to disturb you, but I was in the neighbourhood, about a friend I've her picture, could you take a look'
10. 'I like a good beer buzz early in the morning and Billy likes to peel the labels'
11. 'I'm in the phone booth it's the one across the hall, if you don't answer I'll just ring it off the wall'
12. 'Standing in line marking time – waiting for the welfare dime'
13. 'Even when you died the press still hounded you'
14. 'I can't operate on this failure when all I want to be is completely in command'
15. 'She wears a low cut T-shirt, runs a little B & B, he's most accommodating when she's in her lingerie'
16. 'First I was afraid, I was petrified'

Answers to page 378
SEVENTIES 12: **1.** Yes **2.** Blackfoot Sue **3.** Stevie Wonder **4.** John Otway and Wild Willie Barrett **5.** Donnie Elbert **6.** Ray Stevens **7.** The Fortunes **8.** 10cc **9.** T. Rex **10.** The Carpenters **11.** Showaddywaddy **12.** Wizzard **13.** The Kinks **14.** The Rubettes **15.** Steve Harley and Cockney Rebel **16.** 5000 Volts

Name Changes 14

Answers on page 383

1. Which progressive rock band used to be known as Mabel Greer's Toyshop?

2. Which Seventies soul band, who were dangled on a string, started out as The Gentlemen?

3. Which Fifties singer who specialised in Western themes was born Frank Lovecchio?

4. Which punk band leader changed her name from Marion Elliott?

5. As whom was Peter Robinson better known in the Eighties?

6. Who simplified his name from Michael Bolotin?

7. Which punk band used to call themselves The Toilets?

8. Which Seventies group were previously called Blues Keepers?

9. What was Tammy Wynette's real name?

10. Which Eighties band, famous for their drive, were once known as Cap'n Swing?

11. Which member of The Stranglers was born Brian Duffy?

12. Which band changed their name from Salvation Forever and Ever?

13. Which arty Eighties band were previously called 1919?

14. Which American singer of the Fifties was born Clara Ann Fowler?

15. The Iveys changed their name to which ill-fated Seventies band?

16. What did The Black Crowes used to be known as?

Answers to page 379
COVER VERSIONS 12: **1.** Marc Cohn **2.** 'Love Don't Live Here Anymore'
3. 'I'm Stone In Love With You' **4.** Louise **5.** Fine Young Cannibals
6. 'Then He Kissed Me' **7.** Divine **8.** 'Twist And Shout' **9.** Melba Moore
10. Rare Bird **11.** 'Strawberry Fields Forever' **12.** 'Shout' **13.** Roy 'C'
14. 'Ride Like The Wind' **15.** 'One' **16.** 'Maggie's Farm'

Pot Luck 50

Answers on page 378

1. Who wrote Meat Leaf's epic 'Bat Out Of Hell'?

2. With which band was Maria McKee the singer before going solo?

3. What is Boy George's surname?

4. How many members of Showaddywaddy were there?

5. By 1968, who was the only original member of The Byrds still with the band?

6. Who was the only one getting fat in 'Creeque Alley'?

7. Which guitarist joined Wings from Thunderclap Newman?

8. Whose hits included 'Move On Up' and 'Freddie's Dead'?

9. Which Beatles producer was knighted in 1996?

10. Which family were 'Lifted' in 1996?

11. Which Candian singer/songwriter had a 1970 hit with 'If You Could Read My Mind'?

12. Whose 1994 song 'Stay (I Missed You)' was used as the theme of the film *Reality Bites*?

13. In 'Trouble', what were Coldplay caught in the middle of?

14. What was the name of Tom Petty's backing band?

15. To what did Patricia Holt change her name?

16. Jan Akkerman and Thijs Van Leer were members of which Seventies instrumental band?

Answers to page 378
LYRICS 14: 1. 'Lucky You' (The Lightning Seeds) 2. 'Space Oddity' (David Bowie) 3. 'Giving It All Away' (Leo Sayer) 4. 'Alive And Kicking' (Simple Minds) 5. 'Stairway To Heaven' (Led Zeppelin) 6. 'Common People' (Pulp) 7. 'Steppin' Out' (Joe Jackson) 8. 'Bohemian Rhapsody' (Queen) 9. 'Carrie' (Cliff Richard) 10. 'All I Wanna Do' (Sheryl Crow) 11. 'Hanging On The Telephone' (Blondie) 12. 'The Way It Is' (Bruce Hornsby) 13. 'Candle In The Wind' (Elton John) 14. 'Pale Shelter' (Tears For Fears) 15. 'Stereotypes' (Blur) 16. 'I Will Survive' (Gloria Gaynor)

Chart Toppers 17

Answers on page 379

1. How many consecutive UK number ones did The Beatles have in the Sixties?

2. Which was the only million-selling UK record of 1985?

3. David Bicker was the singer on which UK number one of 1982?

4. Which was the best-selling UK single of 1999 despite spending just two weeks at number one?

5. Which single was at number one in the UK from 29 November 1975 to 31 January 1976?

6. Who was 'Poetry In Motion' in 1961?

7. Who had terrible freckles in The Scaffold's 'Lily The Pink'?

8. Who appeared on *Top of the Pops* in a burning hat to perform his 1968 number one?

9. Which 1968 chart topper told the story of a killer waiting to be executed?

10. Which artist who had a number one in 1967 had been rejected at the auditions for The Monkees?

11. Which Everly Brothers song stayed seven weeks at UK number one in 1960?

12. Who was the lead singer with The Temperance Seven?

13. What was the title of White Town's 1997 UK number one?

14. Which were the only three Sixties singles to go straight into the UK chart at number one?

15. Which artist spent over half of 1953 in the UK number one spot?

16. What nationality was Glenn Medeiros who spent four weeks at UK number one in 1988 with 'Nothing's Gonna Change My Love For You'?

Answers to page 381
NAME CHANGES 14: 1. Yes 2. Chairmen Of The Board 3. Frankie Laine 4. Poly Styrene 5. Marilyn 6. Michael Bolton 7. The Alarm 8. Barclay James Harvest 9. Virginia Wynette Pugh 10. The Cars 11. Jet Black 12. Slik 13. Bauhaus 14. Patti Page 15. Badfinger 16. Mr Crowe's Garden